THE HIGH-SCHOOL STUDENT'S GUIDE TO STUDY, TRAVEL, AND ADVENTURE ABROAD

THE
HIGH-SCHOOL
STUDENT'S GUIDE
TO STUDY, TRAVEL,
AND
ADVENTURE
ABROAD

FIFTH EDITION

Council on International Educational Exchange

ST. MARTIN'S PRESS   NEW YORK

IMPORTANT NOTE

All information listed in this book, including prices, ex-change rates, and program fees, is subject to change. To the best of its ability CIEE verified the accuracy of information at the time *The High-School Student's Guide to Study, Travel, and Adventure Abroad* went to press. The most up-to-date travel information may be obtained from the latest issue of CIEE's *Student Travels* magazine or from any Council Travel office, and the most up-to-date information on the programs contained in this book can be obtained by contacting the organizations directly.

ISBN: 0-312-11822-8

First Edition: February 1995
10 9 8 7 6 5 4 3 2 1

CONTENTS

ACKNOWLEDGMENTS

*M*any people deserve credit for helping to put together the new edition of *The High-School Student's Guide to Study, Travel, and Adventure Abroad.* First and foremost is the project editor, Richard Christiano, who gathered and updated the information, rewrote much of the text, and organized the research carried out on programs available for high-school students. Thanks also to Matt Dougherty, who organized and compiled the program listings and assisted in many other aspects of this project. One other CIEE staff member, Jon Howard, who assisted in the research necessary for this book, merits recognition as well.

In addition to CIEE staff, a number of other people across the country also deserve thanks. First is Angene Wilson of the University of Kentucky, who contributed chapter 6 on the subject of reentry into one's own culture after an experience abroad. In addition, special recognition needs to be given to Marjorie Cohen, the person who first developed the concept of this book. Of course, Anne Savarese and all of the staff at St. Martin's Press who helped perfect the final product also deserve recognition and gratitude. Finally, I want to thank all of the organizations who cooperated with CIEE to provide the information in this book.

—Del Franz
Director, Information and Student Services
Council on International Educational Exchange

ABOUT CIEE

*T*he Council on International Educational Exchange (CIEE) is a nonprofit educational organization with offices in the United States, Europe, and Asia. In nearly fifty years of service to the educational community, CIEE—with its travel subsidiaries, Council Travel and Council Charter—has emerged as one of the foremost organizations concerned with international education and student travel.

CIEE was founded in 1947 to help reestablish student exchange after World War II. In its early days, CIEE chartered ocean liners for transatlantic student sailings, arranged group air travel, and organized orientation programs to prepare students and teachers for educational experiences abroad. Over the years, CIEE's mandate has broadened dramatically as the interests of its member institutions have spread beyond Europe to Africa, Asia, and Latin America. Today, CIEE's responsibilities include developing and administering study, work, voluntary service, and travel programs throughout the world; publishing books, academic papers, and informational material on international educational exchange; and facilitating inexpensive international travel for students, teachers, and other budget travelers.

Junior-High and High-School Programs

CIEE's Secondary Education Programs Department administers School Partners Abroad, a school-to-school partnership program which matches junior and senior high schools in the United States with counterpart schools in Costa Rica, France, Germany, Japan, Russia, and Spain. The program provides resources for the enhancement of foreign language and social studies curricula, as well as short-term reciprocal exchange opportunities for groups of students and teachers. Each exchange provides participants with the opportunity to live with local families and attend regular classes in the partner school. For more information, see page 126. CIEE also offers secondary students a summer study program in China with Chinese roommates. The program includes travel in China and a visit to Hong Kong.

Study Abroad for College and University Students

Among CIEE's most widely recognized educational services are the academic programs that it administers for college and university students in Argentina, Australia, Belgium, Brazil, Chile, China, Costa Rica, the Czech Republic, the Dominican Republic, France, Germany, Ghana, Hungary, Indonesia, Japan, the Netherlands, Poland, Russia, South Korea, Spain, Taiwan, Thailand, and Vietnam. These programs are administered by CIEE's University Programs Department on behalf of sponsoring colleges and universities that participate in policy and curriculum formation, ensure academic credibility and quality, and serve the particular academic field for which the program has been developed. Programs are available on the undergraduate and graduate levels and are open to all qualified students.

Adult/Professional Programs

CIEE's Professional and Continuing Education Programs Department designs and administers a wide variety of short-term seminars, study tours, and in-service training programs for groups of international professionals, including secondary-school teachers and administrators, university faculty, business managers, and other "adult learners." Among these programs is the International Faculty Development Seminar series, for faculty and administrators at two- and four-year institutions of higher education. These overseas seminars and professional interchange opportunities are designed to assist institutions with internationalizing home-campus curricula. At the K-12 level, CIEE arranges short-term "teaching visit" opportunities in overseas schools for U.S. teachers, with reciprocal opportunities in the United States for educators from abroad. The Professional and Continuing Education Programs Department is also active in placing English language teachers and teacher-trainers in host institutions abroad.

Work Exchanges

CIEE's Work Exchanges Department operates a series of work programs which enable college and university students from Australia, Britain, Canada, Costa Rica, the Dominican Republic, France, Germany, Ireland, Jamaica, New Zealand, and the United States to work in each others' countries.

Obtaining permission to work in another country is generally a very difficult and time-consuming procedure. However, because of the reciprocal nature of these programs, CIEE is able to quickly and easily secure permission for students to work in another country. CIEE then offers a variety of support services which guide students through the program and help them find work and accommodation.

In each country the program is offered in cooperation with a national student organization or CIEE office which provides an orientation on the country's culture and society, advises on seeking a job and accommodations, and serves as a sponsor during the participant's stay.

International Voluntary Service

CIEE's Voluntary Service Department operates an international work-camp program for young people interested in short-term voluntary service worldwide. Volunteers are placed with organizations conducting projects in Algeria, Belgium, Canada, the Czech Republic, Denmark, France, Germany, Ghana, Hungary, Japan, Lithuania, Morocco, the Netherlands, Poland, Slovenia, Spain, Russia, Tunisia, Turkey, Ukraine, the United Kingdom, and the United States. Projects include restoring historical sites, working with children or the elderly, constructing low-income housing, and taking part in nature conservation efforts. Work-camps bring young people from many different countries together to work in local communities. For more information, see page 219.

Student Services

CIEE's Information and Student Services Department answers thousands of inquiries on work, study, and travel abroad each year. In addition to the department's capacity as an information clearinghouse, it also administers the International Student Identity Card, the GO 25: International Youth Travel Card (for persons 25 years of age and under), and the International Teacher Identity Card in the United States. Over 200,000 identity cards are issued each year by CIEE's New York headquarters, its forty-one Council Travel offices, and more than 450 issuing offices at colleges and universities around the country. Cardholders receive travel-related discounts, basic accident/medical insurance coverage while traveling abroad, and access to a 24-hour toll-free emergency hotline. For more information, see page 56.

Publications

In addition to this guide, CIEE's Information and Student Services Department produces the following books for travelers:

- *Work, Study, Travel Abroad: The Whole World Handbook,* published biennially by St. Martin's Press. Divided by geographic region and country, this book contains essential information on work and study opportunities worldwide for travelers of college age. It also shows the traveler how to experience another country as an insider.
- *Volunteer! The Comprehensive Guide to Voluntary Service in the U.S. and Abroad,* published biennially in cooperation with the Council of Religious Volunteer Agencies. For anyone who wants to volunteer, this book describes more than 200 organizations that sponsor long- and short-term voluntary service opportunities for all age groups, both in the United States and abroad. Also included are a section on the basics of volunteering and essays written by former volunteers.

CIEE also publishes a wide range of informational materials that are available free of charge. Among these are:

- *Student Travels,* a 48-page travel magazine for students, which includes in-depth articles and travel tips, all from a student's perspective. Special sections contain information on the International Student Identity Card, the Work Abroad program, international workcamps, study-abroad programs, and updates on Council Travel's student airfares and services.
- *Basic Facts on Study Abroad,* a booklet compiled in cooperation with the Institute of International Education and NAFSA: Association of International Educators. This booklet provides general information for students interested in an educational experience abroad.
- *Travel Options,* a catalog of travel opportunities for educators. This catalog contains basic information on all of the programs and services that CIEE and Council Travel offer to educators at all levels, from elementary school teachers to university professors.
- *Update,* CIEE's bimonthly newsletter. *Update* keeps campus advisers and other professional educators informed about the latest developments in the fields of international educational exchange and travel.

Scholarships and Fellowships

CIEE provides financial assistance for U.S. students and professionals to participate in educational programs abroad. The following funds are available:

- *International Student Identity Card Fund.* This fund provides travel grants to enable full-time high-school or undergraduate students attending CIEE-member institutions, or participating in a program sponsored by a CIEE-member institution, to participate in study, work, voluntary service, internship, or homestay programs in the developing nations of the world. For more information, see page 56.
- *The Robert B. Bailey III Minority Scholarships.* These scholarships support members of minority groups who want to participate in any of CIEE's educational programs, including study, work, voluntary service, and internship opportunities. Funds are available for high-school, undergraduate, and graduate students who are United States citizens or permanent residents of the United States.

Travel Services

Council Travel, a subsidiary of CIEE, operates a network of 41 retail travel offices across the country that provide travel assistance to students, teachers, and other budget travelers. (See pages 7-11 for office locations.) Council Travel's services and products include:

- low-cost airfares (including special student airfares) between the United States and destinations all over the world.
- rail passes, including Eurail, BritRail, and French Rail passes
- The International Student Identity Card, International Teacher Identity Card, and GO 25: International Youth Travel Card, which entitle eligible bearers to discounts and services as they travel (for more information, see page 57)
- car-rental plans in Europe
- language courses in seventeen European cities and Japan
- travel insurance, guidebooks, and travel gear
- the New York Student Center, which offers low-cost accommodations and a travel advisory service for visitors to New York City

Travel Services for Groups

Council Travel's group departments specialize in negotiating low airfares for high-school, college, and special interest groups with international travel plans. Whether your plans involve flights, trains, and/or accommodations, Council Travel's group departments can help plan a worry-free international experience. These departments handle arrangements for thousands of students participating in programs all over the world.

Charter/Consolidator Flights

Another travel subsidiary of CIEE, Council Charter has been a reliable operator since 1947. It offers direct flights on scheduled and charter carriers between the United States and most major European cities, including Amsterdam, Brussels, London, Madrid, Milan, Paris, and Rome. Council Charter fares, which are open to students and nonstudents alike, have no hidden charges and require no minimum or maximum stay. Council Charter's flexible service provides travelers with a low-cost cancellation waiver allowing cancellation for any reason up to three hours prior to departure; the option of flying into one city and returning from another; continued assistance through its European offices; and frequent departures.

CIEE Membership

At present, 276 educational institutions and organizations in the United States and other countries are members of CIEE. As members, they take advantage of CIEE's information and publications services; become involved in CIEE's advocacy, evaluation, and consultation services; and participate in conferences and services organized by CIEE. Membership allows educational institutions and organizations to play a central role in the development and operation of exchanges at a national and international level. Members of the Council on International Educational Exchange are listed in the Appendix (see page 299).

COUNCIL TRAVEL OFFICES

U.S.A.

ARIZONA

- **Tempe**
  120 East University Drive,
    Suite E
  Tempe, AZ 85281
  (602) 966-3544

CALIFORNIA

- **Berkeley**
  2486 Channing Way
  Berkeley, CA 94704
  (510) 848-8604

- **Davis**
  University of California,
    Davis
  162 Memorial Union Bldg.
  Davis, CA 95616
  (916) 752-2285

- **La Jolla**
  UCSD Price Center
  9500 Gilman Drive
  La Jolla, CA 92093-0076
  (619) 452-0630

- **Long Beach**
  1818 Palo Verde Avenue,
    Suite E
  Long Beach, CA 90815
  (310) 598-3338
  (714) 527-7950

- **Los Angeles**
  1093 Broxton Avenue,
    Suite 220
  Los Angeles, CA 90024
  (310) 208-3551

- **Palo Alto**
  394 University Avenue,
    Suite 200
  Palo Alto, CA 94301
  (415) 325-3888

- **San Diego**
  953 Garnet Avenue
  San Diego, CA 92109
  (619) 270-6401

- **San Francisco**
  530 Bush Street,
    Ground Floor
  San Francisco, CA 94108
  (415) 421-3473

  919 Irving Street, Suite 102
  San Francisco, CA 94122
  (415) 566-6222

- **Santa Barbara**
  903 Embarcadero del Norte
  Santa Barbara, CA 93117
  (805) 562-8080

COLORADO

- **Boulder**
  1138 13th Street
  Boulder, CO 80302
  (303) 447-8101

- **Denver**
  900 Auraria Parkway
  Tivoli Building
  Denver, CO 80204
  (303) 571-0630

CONNECTICUT

- **New Haven**
  320 Elm Street
  New Haven, CT 06511
  (203) 562-5335

DISTRICT OF COLUMBIA

- **Washington**
  3300 M Street NW,
    2nd floor
  Washington, DC 20007
  (202) 337-6464

FLORIDA

- **Miami**
  One Datran Center,
    Suite 320
  9100 South Dadeland
    Boulevard
  Miami, FL 33156
  (305) 670-9261

GEORGIA

- **Atlanta**
  Emory Village
  1561 North Decatur Road
  Atlanta, GA 30307
  (404) 377-9997

ILLINOIS

- **Chicago**
  1153 North Dearborn Street,
    2nd floor
  Chicago, IL 60610
  (312) 951-0585

- **Evanston**
  1634 Orrington Avenue
  Evanston, IL 60201
  (708) 475-5070

INDIANA

Bloomington
  409 East 4th Street
  Bloomington, IN 47408
  (812) 330-1600

LOUISIANA

- **New Orleans**
  Joseph A. Danna Center
  Loyola University
  6363 St. Charles Avenue
  New Orleans, LA 70118
  (504) 866-1767

MASSACHUSETTS

- **Amherst**
  79 South Pleasant Street
  (2nd floor, rear)
  Amherst, MA 01002
  (413) 256-1261

- **Boston**
  729 Boylston Street,
  Suite 201
  Boston, MA 02116
  (617) 266-1926

- **Cambridge**
  1384 Massachusetts Avenue,
  Suite 201
  Cambridge, MA 02138
  (617) 497-1497

  Stratton Student Center
  MIT W20-024
  84 Massachusetts Avenue
  Cambridge, MA 02139
  (617) 225-2555

MICHIGAN

- **Ann Arbor**
  1220 South University
  Drive, #208
  Ann Arbor, MI 48104
  (313) 998-0200

MINNESOTA

- **Minneapolis**
  1501 University Avenue,
  SE, Room 300
  Minneapolis, MN 55414
  (612) 379-2323

NEW YORK

- **New York**
  205 East 42nd Street
  New York, NY 10017
  (212) 661-1450

  New York Student Center
  895 Amsterdam Avenue
  New York, NY 10025
  (212) 666-4177

  148 West 4th Street
  New York, NY 10011
  (212) 254-2525

NORTH CAROLINA

- **Chapel Hill**
  137 E. Franklin Street,
  Suite 106
  Chapel Hill, NC 27514
  (919) 942-2334

OHIO

- **Columbus**
  8 East 13th Avenue
  Columbus, OH 43201
  (614) 294-8696

OREGON

- **Portland**
  715 SW Morrison,
  Suite 600
  Portland, OR 97205
  (503) 228-1900

PENNSYLVANIA

- **Philadelphia**
  3606A Chestnut Street
  Philadelphia, PA 19104
  (215) 382-0343

- **Pittsburgh**
  118 Meyran Avenue
  Pittsburgh, PA 15213
  (412) 683-1881

RHODE ISLAND

- **Providence**
  171 Angell Street,
    Suite 212
  Providence, RI 02906
  (401) 331-5810

TEXAS

- **Austin**
  2000 Guadalupe Street
  Austin, TX 78705
  (512) 472-4931

- **Dallas**
  6715 Hillcrest
  Dallas, TX 75205
  (214) 363-9941

UTAH

- **Salt Lake City**
  1310 East 200 South
  Salt Lake City, UT 84102
  (801) 582-5840

WASHINGTON

- **Seattle**
  1314 Northeast 43rd Street,
    Suite 210
  Seattle, WA 98105
  (206) 632-2448

  219 Broadway Avenue East
  The Alley Building,
    Suite 17
  Seattle, WA 98102
  (206) 329-4567

OVERSEAS

FRANCE

- **Aix-en-Provence**
  12, rue Victor Leydet
  13100 Aix-en-Provence
  (33) 42-38-58-82

- **Lyon**
  36, quai Gailleton
  69002 Lyon
  (33) 78-37-09-56

- **Montpellier**
  20, rue de l'Université
  34000 Montpellier
  (33) 67-60-89-29

- **Nice**
  37 bis, rue d'Angleterre
  06000 Nice
  (33) 1-93-82-32-83

- **Paris**
  22, rue de Pyramides
  75001 Paris
  (33) 1-44-55-55-44

16, rue de Vaugirard
75006 Paris
(33) 1 46-34-02-90

GERMANY

* **Düsseldorf**
18, Graf-Adolf-Strasse
4000 Düsseldorf 1
(49) 211-32-90-88

* **Munich**
Adalbertstrasse 32
8000 Munich 40
(49) 89-39-50-22
(49) 89-39-61-27

JAPAN

* **Tokyo**
Sanno Grand Building,
   Room 102
14-2 Nagata-cho 2-chome
Chiyoda-ku, Tokyo 100
(81) 33-581-7581

SINGAPORE

* **Singapore**
CIEE Travel
110D Killiney Road
Tah Wah Building
Singapore 0923
(65) 7387-066

THAILAND

SYFS Company, Ltd.
108/12-13 Kaosan Road
Banglumpoo, Bangkok
   10200
(662) 282-0507

UNITED KINGDOM

* **London**
28A Poland Street
London W1V 3DB
England
(44) 71-437-77-67

PART ONE

AN OWNER'S MANUAL FOR YOUR TRAVEL DREAMS

Chapter 1

BEYOND THE BORDERS

*I*n an age when you can see, read, or hear all about what's happening in faraway places instantly, no matter where you are, why travel? You can watch 24-hour news reports on cable television, zap computer files across continents in minutes, and talk to anyone in any country, any time you please.

But even with the world so accessible from where you are, there is no substitute for actually going somewhere beyond this country's borders. From the moment you hop off that jumbo jet and feel the first breeze on your skin in another nation, you begin to experience how people in other nations think, feel, and live. No matter what you've seen in the movies about Argentina, France, Ghana, or Japan, nothing compares to the thrill and adventure of exploring these places and seeing for yourself what they're like. It's fun, but it's also a challenge: Once you've taken the giant step of learning and living another culture, you can never look at your own the same way again. You are wiser and more aware of yourself and others. In short, you are changed forever . . . and for the better.

You can do almost anything you can imagine. Picture yourself:

- Cutting a swath through the glassy waters of the Caribbean at the helm of a sailboat
- Bicycling across lonely, beautiful desert landscapes in Africa
- Unearthing long-forgotten artifacts on an archaeological dig in Israel
- Calling a Japanese family your own for a few months
- Using newly-learned survival skills while canoeing down a remote river in the wilderness of Canada
- Spending a summer learning French in the City of Light itself, Paris

You might be tempted to roll your eyes and think, "Sure, other people can do all that, but *me?*" It's a common response, but it's also a wimpy one. Try responding instead with a resounding "Well, why *not* me?" Remember, the list above is only a sample of the opportunities that await.

This book will let you know what's available and direct you to the people who can help make your trip abroad as exciting as it should be. The first step of your journey is to map out your territory and plan ahead, and you'll find vital information in the following pages to help you do just that. Part one starts out with the basics—vital things you need to know before you make your choices and pack your bags. The second part of the book describes the extraordinary array of available programs, one by one. The programs are grouped into general categories, but if you'd like to look for programs by location, focusing on a particular country or region, just flip to the index at the back of the book. Another index will help you find different types of programs, so if you're interested in bicycling tours, language study programs, summer camps, or voluntary service opportunities, you can find what you want by its category.

First, Some Useful Questions to Ask Yourself . . .

The temptation is often to get up and go without wasting another second, but if you're going to do it right, it takes a thorough search to find the program that suits you best. Chances are you'll find a number of programs that interest you; the hard part is finding the one that interests you the most and will bring the greatest benefits. The guidelines contained in the next few chapters should be useful in helping you sort out your options. Before you commit yourself to any particular plan of action—or even the idea of going at all—ask yourself the following questions. Once you're satisfied with the answers, discuss them with parents, counselors, and others whose opinions you respect.

Is now the best time for me to have an overseas experience? This is a tough one. There is no ideal age to go abroad, so it takes some serious reflection to decide if now is the time. If you and your parents agree that you should go now, great! If not, delaying your plans means you can use the time to learn as much as you can about the country you're interested in and work on developing more self-confidence and independence. Reading chapter 2 of this book will help you decide if you're ready to go—it contains some good advice about what to expect when you go abroad, some qualities you'll need, and many useful suggestions for getting yourself ready.

If you're ready for the experience now, there are several advantages to going abroad in high school, such as better preparation for college and a head start in pursuing your new career interests. But if you decide not to go for a while, the land of your dreams will still be there when you are ready.

What kind of program do I want? You can choose a program that emphasizes study, or one that involves travel, outdoor activities, the creative arts, voluntary service—the list goes on. You're at the helm of this adventure. Some of the more common types of programs appear below, but most programs aren't so neatly categorized. You might find that combining a travel tour with study, or a volunteer program and an outdoor expedition, makes for a more exciting, rewarding, and—believe it or not—a more educational experience.

- *Study Abroad:* You don't have to be a nerd or a grind to really enjoy spending time in a classroom learning another country's language, history, or culture. Study-abroad programs can be as brief as a few weeks in the summer to a semester or full academic year, and often involve staying with a family in the host country. In most countries, but especially in Mexico and Europe, you'll find many language schools established to serve foreign visitors—whether you know enough French to read today's issue of *Le Monde* or just enough to stutter through "Your mother eats crêpes on the Champs Elysèes." In the United States, a number of organizations specialize in placing high-school students overseas on academic exchange programs. In the program listings in part two of this book, you can find opportunities to study just about any subject area imaginable.
- *Study Tour:* A contradiction in terms? Not really. This category embraces a combination of study and travel in the same program, although the quality of study may vary greatly among programs. Some programs conduct actual classes with required coursework, while others consist of informal lectures that leave you a lot of time to roam around on your own. A number of U.S. universities offering summer study tours for credit accept high-school students. Many museums and other cultural organizations do, too.
- *Travel Tour:* While this category may seem self-explanatory, there actually are many options to choose from. If snapshots of you and your friends mugging in front of the Great Pyramid at Cheops are what you're after, most commercial tour organizers offer standard sightseeing trips to museums and monuments. Other organizations can put you in contact with the people of the country, allowing you to spend time and share experiences with

them. The difference between a bus tour of major European cities and a bicycle tour through China goes way beyond a few extra wheels and sore legs—the one you'll enjoy more depends on what you want from the experience. Who you go with also makes a difference: Most of the organized tour programs listed here cater exclusively to young people; a few others accept participants of all ages.

- *The Arts:* Do you create, or study the history of those who did? You can find all kinds of stimulating possibilities overseas, from fine arts institutes to ceramics workshops. Many art schools in the United States also sponsor their own programs abroad. Film-making and writing in England, weaving in Scotland, painting in France—it's all out there.

- *Camps:* A number of summer camps abroad bring together young people from all over the world. Why be satisfied with the usual routine of getting poison ivy and having your bed short-sheeted at good old Camp Mackawack every year when you can join new friends from other countries in windsurfing, sketching, playing tennis, or riding horses? Overseas camps let you make friends and enjoy cultures you never would have encountered otherwise.

- *Sports/Outdoor Adventure:* Don't be surprised when people in other countries show up in soccer gear when they ask you to meet them to play some football. Athletic competition and the outdoors are enjoyed the world over, but their sports can be very different, and slight variations in the rules for activities you thought you'd mastered can turn you into a novice again. In this book you'll find camps and programs that can give you the chance to ski down a snowy mountainside in the Alps or ride atop a horse through the Black Mountains of Wales. Other organizations specialize in wilderness expeditions such as hiking, mountain climbing, and sea kayaking. You'll be surprised how close perfect strangers can become when they learn to depend on each other and face a common challenge.

- *Voluntary Service:* People who want to give something back to the countries they enjoy visiting find volunteer programs the perfect solution—some of the most personally rewarding programs can be found in this category. Every country has some need for volunteers, and there are many organizations that gather young people from around the world to work together on special projects. The choices might involve maintaining scenic national parks, restoring historic landmarks, teaching English, or working on agricultural cooperatives.

Of course, organized programs aren't for everyone—sometimes the best way to explore is to travel on your own or with a friend. If you want to do it right, flip to chapter 4 for tips on taking advantage of student fares, youth hostels, and other privileges of your student status. Another option is to combine independent travel with a program—spend a few weeks at a voluntary service project or at a language institute, and then hitch up your saddle and go exploring. Even if you've traveled abroad before, you'll find that starting your trip with a structured program can help you get acquainted with the place before you light out on your own.

When do I want to go abroad? "Right now" may be the answer that gets your adrenaline going, but be realistic: on a hastily organized trip abroad you can find yourself stuck in a bad program or lost in some remote place where no one has seen an American since the Battle of the Bulge. It's best to make plans six months to a year in advance. Summer vacation is the time of choice for most students going abroad, but many organizations offer short-term opportunities during spring and winter vacations as well. In some cases, you can take a semester or even an academic year abroad. Consider, too, taking a year off between high school and college—many students find that the "in-between year" gives them the chance to reflect on their high-school experiences and make plans for their college years.

Do I want academic credit for my experience? It's possible, but not guaranteed. Some programs award high-school or college credits for participation, so even if credit isn't that important to you, it can't hurt to check with your guidance counselor and your prospective college choices to see if they'll accept these credits. Some language courses abroad, for example, will fulfill college language course requirements, saving you the bother of having to recite "Aunt Louise's hat is pink" ad nauseum at a language lab every week.

On the other hand, if you're planning on studying abroad for an entire year, you'd better make sure your home institution will accept the credit you'll earn abroad. If it's important to you, get it in writing before you go. For more information on credit, see page 44.

Where do I want to go? In the end, your decision will depend on many things: whether you want to practice a language you're studying now or acquire a new one, whether you want to explore your heritage or learn about a place whose name you can't even spell yet. Some students prefer to have their first experience abroad in an English-speaking country, while others thrive by immersing themselves in a culture that fascinates them. You may want to concentrate on one country, or cover more territory.

FINDING PEN PALS

One time-tested method of making friends abroad is by writing to a pen pal. There are many ways to go about finding a pen pal. Below are the names and addresses of four organizations that will help. Since some of these have limited budgets, you're more likely to receive a response by sending a stamped, self-addressed envelope with any requests in order to cover the cost of mailing.

- Afro-Asian Center, P.O. Box 337, Saugerties, NY 12477. Specializes in promoting correspondence between U.S. students and their peers in Africa, Asia, and the Middle East. Service fee: $2.
- International Pen Friends, P.O. Box 290065, Brooklyn, NY 11229-0001; (718) 769-1785
- Student Letter Exchange, 630 Third Avenue, New York, NY 10017; (212) 557-3312
- World Pen Pals, 1690 Como Avenue, St. Paul, MN 55108

How much am I able to spend? You knew it would come around to money sooner or later. Don't let this question scare you, though: While it's true that your choice of destination may depend on how you answer this question, the notion that an international experience is only possible for the rich and snooty is wrong. Many of the programs listed in this book cost no more than a similar-length stay at summer camp in your home state. And with help from your guidance counselor, you can find out about a wide range of full and partial scholarships offered by local and national organizations to help offset the cost. (See the Finding the Cash section in Chapter 4.)

A little ingenuity and entrepreneurial spirit can also go a long way toward raising the necessary funds; some creative suggestions appear on page 49. Of course, you'll have to work within a budget—that's part of life—but if you assume it's impossible without investigating the opportunities, you can miss out on the experience of a lifetime.

What do I want to get out of my experience? Here's where your answers begin dealing with the intangibles. It's good to set some goals before you go, but in some cases it's also normal to not know what you want at first; sometimes people discover only after they return that they found

A CONVERSATION WITH SUSAN

Susan spent the summer in Switzerland as a participant in a summer homestay program sponsored by AFS Intercultural Programs.

Q. Why did you choose this particular program?
A. The foreign students I met at my high school were really interesting. They were active and multitalented—it seemed like an excellent group of people to be with.

Q. What were some of the most difficult aspects of your experience?
A. Number one for me was frustration with the language. It took me three weeks before I started understanding Swiss German and being able to converse in High German, even though I had studied it for three years in school. Also, the family I lived with was large and noisy, and it overwhelmed me sometimes. My speaking became so much better, though, that I had my own Swiss friends by the time I left.

Q. Did your international experience change you?
A. Yes. It changed my life. It gave me a new perspective on my home community. I grew more independent and sure of myself. All the pressures in the high school scene didn't seem so important when I got back. I became close to fellow AFS participants from all over the U.S. and spent time at other high schools for AFS weekends my senior year. I understood my parents better after having had other "parents," and I became much more interested in politics, international affairs, and the rest of the world. The best part is having a second home and family abroad for life—an "AFS Mom and Dad," five "AFS brothers and sisters," in addition to my real family.

Q. Would you recommend this kind of experience to others?
A. Definitely. I wish I'd gone for a full year instead of just the summer. You have to be willing to get into every part of the life of your host family, though, to get the most out of it. If you just want to travel, a tour might be better.

A Conversation with Susan

Q. What advice do you have for someone about to do the same thing?

A. Expect highs and lows while you adjust to the new culture, family, and language. Be outgoing and inquisitive, and try to speak the language no matter what.

---

what they wanted. To help identify your own goals, try browsing through these and see if any strike a chord in you:

- Speaking a language more competently and with a "native" accent
- Learning a new language and putting it to immediate use
- Mastering a new skill for later career purposes or personal enrichment
- Reinforcing a sense of identity by exploring the place your family came from
- Finding the independent, self-sufficient qualities in yourself
- Experiencing life in another part of the world from an insider's perspective, and seeing the world from another culture's point of view
- Seeing how fantastic those historic and literary places you read about in school really are
- Meeting new and different people who will appreciate your efforts to understand their ways

Once you've decided what it is you want to gain from your trip abroad, you're in the best position to make a sound choice from the possibilities available to you. Your goals can be grandiose or modest, idealistic or practical. But once you've decided what they are, there are no limits to what you can do. So go for it!

Some Books That Can Help

For more program ideas, you might want to consult the following at your library or bookstore:

Summer Opportunities for Kids and Teenagers (1994). Peterson's Guides, P.O. Box 2123, Princeton, NJ 08543-2123 ($21.95 plus $6.75 postage). Scattered throughout this directory are some programs that take place outside the United States.

Adventure Holidays (1994). Also published by Peterson's, this guidebook gives details on hundreds of outdoor activities and vacation ideas in over 100 countries.

Vacation Study Abroad: The Complete Guide to Summer and Short-Term Study (1994). IIE Books, 809 U.N. Plaza, New York, NY 10017-3580 ($36.95 plus $4 postage). This publication, designed to inform U.S. students of summer study-abroad opportunities, lists programs offered by U.S. and foreign educational institutions in more than sixty countries. Not all programs described will accept high-school students, but many will.

Advisory List of International Educational Travel and Exchange Programs. Council on Standards for International Educational Travel (See page 299).

Chapter 2
EXPECTING THE UNEXPECTED

*C*oming to grips with life in a country with unfamiliar customs can be frustrating. "Culture shock" is the handy term for this process, but you'll more likely call it "that awkward first week" or "the time I insulted an entire restaurant with a single hand gesture." Spending time in another country will present you with some demanding emotional and intellectual challenges, but if you have the right attitude you'll come out of these just fine.

ANTICIPATING DIFFERENCES

Flexibility and adaptability are the key qualities you need to travel, and they're great for just about anything else in life as well. Your everyday rituals won't be the only things you'll have to change; sometimes everything you've taken for granted is suddenly turned upside down when you confront the unexpected. Here are some things you'll have to adapt to once you cross an international border:

Food. When you dine in another country, even familiar dishes and beverages may contain ingredients that make you balk. The trick is to not let the unfamiliar intimidate you; many interesting and delicious foods just aren't available in the United States.

Concepts of time. From country to country, people eat, work, and sleep at whatever times they consider normal. Some of your adjustments of this category can be downright pleasant: you may find yourself wolfing down huge breakfasts at the crack of dawn, for example, or taking a nap in the middle of the day. On the other hand, people in cultures with a different concept of punctuality may not understand your anger when they show up late for an appointment with you; indeed, they may think you're a little weird for loitering so long outside their door.

Sanitary facilities. How different can basic restrooms possibly be? Usually the answer is "Not very," although you might encounter anything from a gleaming, ultramodern apparatus to a hole in the floor. Bathing facilities may be different, too—there may be no choice between a shower and a bath, and in some countries a public bath is considered a social occasion. You'll probably want to wait for a private bath, however, to scrub behind the ears.

Dress. Students in some countries must don uniforms every morning, while others can wear whatever's on the bedroom floor when they wake up. Find out what's expected of you before you go. Colder climates may require some extra sweaters and coats. A little discretion may be required during visits to warmer countries—garments like shorts, miniskirts, and tank tops are comfortable and acceptable in the United States, but in some countries people who wear these items tend to leave a wake of raised eyebrows, slack jaws, and offended sensibilities wherever they go.

Etiquette. Unlike English, many other languages have different levels of politeness built into their grammar. This can go way beyond saying "please," "excuse me," or "thank you": How you talk to someone can vary greatly according to their age or social status. Your relationship with your teachers, for example, may be much more formal than at home. A good rule of thumb is to be overly polite until you get a feeling for where you stand.

Dating customs. Yes, young people in other countries do this too—in their own way. It's probably best to avoid dating until you're sure of what is acceptable. Dating may be pleasant in any country, but being ignored, reprimanded, or slapped certainly isn't. If you stay with a host family, you can probably expect your social life to be more closely supervised than at home. Try not to take this personally; they're only looking out for you and, in doing so, are living up to their responsibilities.

Numbers. For reasons that baffle the rest of the world, the United States is the only country that hasn't adopted the metric system officially. This means that if you use the words "inches," "miles," or "ounces," you'll get some pretty funny looks. You'll find life a lot easier when you can weigh and estimate in kilograms, meters, and centigrade. Different monetary denominations and currency exchange rates can also be a little mind-numbing at first: Keeping a small calculator on hand makes conversions easier.

Weather. Everybody talks about it, but we don't all talk about the same things because weather patterns differ all over the world. Unless you like squishy shoes and wet hair, it's a good idea to find out when the rainy season occurs in countries that have them (such as India and Japan), especially if you'll be spending a lot of time outdoors. Also, remember that winter occurs in Southern Hemisphere countries during summer in the North, and vice versa. You can be the first one on your block to wear a parka in July or a bathing suit outdoors in January.

Qualities You'll Need

A good sense of humor. This is invaluable. If you are able to laugh at yourself and your mistakes, people will laugh *with* you, and will probably be much more likely to help. Remember that everybody, everywhere, laughs, and that sharing a moment of amusement can bring people together.

Adaptability. Can you roll with the changes? Shrug off old habits and be open to new things? Show the world you can meet it on its own terms? If so, keep reading: you're on your way to being well prepared.

Patience. Don't expect to become an honorary citizen all at once. It takes time and determination. If the pace of your learning frustrates you, just remember that it's better to be proud of all you've learned so far than fearful of all you still don't know.

An open mind. In your travels, you'll find that the ideas and attitudes people have shape their lives. You will often find that these ideas differ greatly from your own, and it will be tempting to judge others' ways by your own standards. One people's way of life, however, is no less valid than another's. Nobody has the right to ask you, as an outsider, to accept their way of life, but you should make the effort to understand why their ways differ from yours.

Independence and self-reliance. Probably the most vital trait needed for a successful international experience is a sense of independence. After all, you will be the final authority on how to manage your time, stay healthy, and budget money to last the entire trip. Chances are, your living situation will be nothing like what you're used to at home—familiar faces won't be around when things get rough. But don't let it scare

WANT TO BE A HOST FAMILY?

All this talk about homestays abroad may start you thinking about the possibility of the other side of that experience—hosting a foreign student in your own home. Think of the benefits: you'll expose your family to a new culture, possibly a new language; you'll be able to introduce the U.S. to a stranger; and you'll establish a contact with another part of the world that can last forever and blossom into follow-up visits and lifelong friendships.

There are many U.S.-based organizations looking for host families. And don't think that only "nuclear families" are eligible— "families" take on many configurations these days, and a host family needn't be the old formula of mother, father, and 2.4 children.

An entire book has been written on the subject of being a host family. It's called *The Host Family Survival Kit: A Guide for American Host Families,* by Nancy King and Ken Huff (Intercultural Press, 1985). It's all here: arrivals and departures, cultural "baggage," host children's reactions, the adjustment cycle, communications. In an appendix, the authors give sound advice on how to determine the reliability and quality of the sponsoring organization you consider. Some of their points:

1. Find out whether the organization is known to your principal or guidance counselor.
2. Talk to families who have been hosts for this particular sponsor before.
3. Learn about how the organization works—how it screens students, how it "stays in touch."
4. Check into the emergency arrangements.
5. Meet with local representatives.
6. Find out if the program is designated by the U.S. Information Agency by writing to USIA, Exchange Visitor Program Services, Room 3030, 400 Sixth Street, SW, Washington, DC 20547. Request a copy of the list of designated teenage exchange organizations.
7. Look through the promotional materials and evaluate them.

Want to Be a Host Family?

8. Ask about special services to hosts—for example, counseling, orientation, and so on.

9. Ask about the costs to the students and to the host family.

10. Be sure your family is stable enough to take on another member, and avoid being pressured into any arrangement that might be too stressful.

The Host Family Survival Kit is available for $9.95 plus $1.50 postage from Intercultural Press, Inc., P.O. Box 700, Yarmouth, ME 04096.

---

you: It takes a bit of maturity to assert yourself without being afraid of failure, but the payoff is tremendous.

Above all, enjoy yourself. Periods of homesickness and confusion are normal and temporary. If you have one of those days where every possible misunderstanding happens and all seems lost, shrug it off and keep trying—it does get better. In fact, your international experience will probably be the best time you've ever had . . . but only if *you* make it so.

GETTING YOURSELF READY

Teenagers in other countries are often very politically conscious and historically aware. Sooner or later, you can count on your conversations with them in cafés and at parties to shift to politics—both the realities and the philosophies. Whether you want the job or not, you will be the closest thing to a U.S. ambassador these students can get. You can count on them to ask about your country's position on such issues as the Middle East, health care, the future of NATO, Big Macs versus Whoppers . . . and anything else they're curious about. You may even be thrust into the awkward position of explaining past actions of your country.

Of course, you can always shrug off questions about any of the above and proudly exclaim, "Don't worry, our president's taking care of it!"—but you're likely to be viewed as a moron if you do. So brush up on your U.S. history before you leave, paying particular attention to relations between the United States and the country you're going to visit. You and your new acquaintances may be surprised at how different stories of the

A WORD ABOUT THE THIRD WORLD

Undertaking a study program or voluntary service project in a Third World country means that you'll be meeting special challenges. These countries are so different from our own that you must be willing to make even more adjustments than you would for a stay in one of the industrialized nations. But if you believe you're up to the challenge, think seriously about it.

Three-quarters of the world's people live in the developing countries of the Third World. On a study program or service project in one of these nations you can experience a way of life that is truly different from your own. You come back with a better understanding of the people and the problems of the *whole* world—rather than just those of the industrialized nations. The experience is valuable preparation for life in a world that is growing increasingly interdependent.

The listings in part two of this book include programs that take place in Third World countries. If you choose to participate in a program sponsored by a CIEE member institution, you can also apply for the International Student Identity Card Travel Grants, which were designed especially for experiences in the Third World. (See page 64.)

same historical episodes have been taught in each country. As far as who got the "right" version, you'll have to iron that out for yourselves.

One good way to become familiar with recent issues is to read through *Great Decisions,* published annually by the Foreign Policy Association. Each year this book summarizes the background facts and examines different points of view on eight important foreign policy issues confronting Americans. *Great Decisions 1994* ($11, plus $3.00 for postage and handling) and other publications on U.S. foreign policy can be obtained from the Foreign Policy Association, Department SS, 729 Seventh Avenue, New York, NY 10019. Other good sources of both U.S. and international news include such newspapers as *The New York Times,* the *Christian Science Monitor, The Wall Street Journal,* and national news magazines such as *Time, Newsweek,* and *U.S. News & World Report.* Your local and school libraries can also be a big help, especially if they carry newspapers and magazines from the country you're interested in.

ESPECIALLY FOR PERSONS WITH DISABILITIES

An organization called Mobility International USA has devoted itself to making international travel accessible to the disabled. Besides publishing a quarterly newsletter called *Over the Rainbow,* MIUSA has published an excellent book called *A World of Options for the Nineties: A Guide to International Educational Exchange, Community Service and Travel for Persons with Disabilities.* Written and edited by Cindy Lewis and Susan Sygall, the book includes international educational exchange and work-camp programs that to accommodate the disabled. Also included are a special section on travel for the disabled, and first-person experiences of young people with disabilities who participated in a variety of travel adventures. As the authors state, "Their enthusiasm, sense of accomplishment, and matter-of-fact handling of the obstacles they faced are the essence of this book; their message is clear: 'I did it . . . you can, too.' " *A World of Options* is available by mail from MIUSA, P.O. Box 3551, Eugene, OR 97403, for $16, which includes postage and handling.

For information on the exchange programs sponsored by MIUSA, see their listing on page 234.

If all this sounds like studying for an exam, fear not: there are other ways to get vital information besides reading. If you know someone who has been to the country you're interested in, give them a call—especially if they've recently returned. They probably have their own opinions about issues in that country, and can describe them to you more directly and colorfully than a newspaper could. Find out if there are any foreign students from that country in your area, and look them up; many people who are far from home enjoy talking about where they're from, and they can give you that valuable "insider's view."

Of course, you don't have to become an expert on the country you are going to visit, but you should know enough when you arrive to show your hosts you're interested in them. For instance, before you go, listen to some popular or traditional music from that country. If it makes you want to smile, sing along, or dance, great! If it makes you shudder and reach for some aspirin, at least you'll have a common point of reference that can break the ice in a new situation (just be careful what you say about it!).

For non-English-speaking countries, picking up as much of the lan-

VOLUNTEER SERVICE PROJECTS: LEARNING BY HELPING

A wonderful way to get to know other people and their cultures is to join an international volunteer service project. These are groups of volunteers, usually from all over the world, who are brought together by a coordinating organization to gain a broader cultural and social awareness by working on a common project that benefits the surrounding community. Volunteers do things like restore medieval towers, clear streams, take care of the elderly, build schools in Third World countries, and remove refuse from forests. In their spare time, volunteers get to know each other by playing games, going on trips, cooking meals, and just hanging out together. Since in most cases volunteers must be at least 18, you might have to put this option off until the summer before college, but it's worth the wait.

Volunteers usually stay for two to three weeks and work in groups of 10 to 20. The work week is usually five days (40 hours) long; in exchange, volunteers receive room and board. Everyone lives together, sharing meals, group decisions, and chores. Some organizations charge a registration fee, but it's usually reasonable.

The word "luxurious" doesn't usually describe the accommodations at these projects, but volunteers have everything they need. Depending on the project, you may stay in a school, hostel, church, or tent. Leisure-time activities are organized by the group as a whole; weekends can be used for sightseeing, exploring local cities and towns, or playing a pickup game of soccer.

The work itself can be demanding manual labor or humanitarian social service work. No special skills are required, but at some projects you may be required to speak the local language. The emphasis of a volunteer service project is not on the work itself, but on how the group members form bonds with and learn from each other.

Some recent returnees from volunteer projects had this to say about their experience:

"I never imagined such a varied bunch of people getting along so well and learning so much from each other."

"By building something together, we formed some very close bonds—all working for the common goal."

"It's nice to know the work we did will be appreciated for a

Volunteer Service Projects: Learning by Helping

long time to come. If I ever go back and visit, I'll be reminded of the great time I had."

"It was a little awkward at first, but we all became friends and we're still keeping in touch today."

---

guage as you can before you go will do wonders. Check your library for language tapes. These will help you even if you don't learn a single useful phrase from them—getting used to the sound of a language will benefit you tremendously when it comes time to immerse yourself in it.

One often overlooked source of information on a country is that country's tourist office in the United States. When you contact one of these offices, be specific about what you want, whether it's information on study, camping, maps, or anything else. Most tourist offices have special information packets for young travelers—it can't hurt to ask, and you may find some great options you hadn't thought of before.

An excellent series of profiles on more than one hundred countries has been put together by Brigham Young University's David M. Kennedy Center for International Studies. Updated yearly, *Culturegrams* are four-page briefings containing information on customs and manners, useful words and phrases, socioeconomic statistics, history and government, travel tips, and maps. The cost is $2 for one *Culturegram,* $1 each for two to nine *Culturegrams,* and 75¢ each for ten to twenty-four. The entire set of 117 countries costs $50. These are available from Brigham Young University, David M. Kennedy Center for International Studies, Publications Services, 280 HRCB, Provo, UT 84602; (801) 378-6528.

Intercultural Press distributes a number of other books that deal with overcoming cultural differences, many of them country-specific. Among their titles are *With Respect to the Japanese: A Guide for Americans* ($12.95 plus $2 postage); *Good Neighbors: A Guide to Communicating with Mexicans* ($11.95 plus $2); and *Encountering the Chinese: A Guide for Americans* ($16.95 plus $2). Write to the address above for a catalog.

The works of anthropologist Edward T. Hall are recognized as classics in the field of cross-cultural communication. His four basic works are *The Silent Language,* which explores nonverbal communication; *The Hidden Dimension,* which studies the use of space in different cultures; *Beyond Culture,* which examines the way particular cultures bind humans to behavioral patterns; and *The Dance of Life,* which analyzes dif-

A Conversation with Sam

Sam spent six weeks on an island in the West Indies working on a voluntary service project sponsored by Operation Crossroads Africa.

Q. Why did you choose Operation Crossroads Africa?
A. I wanted to work to help others, not just myself. The setting sounded adventurous, too. I mean, how many people do you know who have gone to the West Indies?

Q. What expectations did you have before you went?
A. I thought that we would build a building or something concrete to "make our mark." In fact, the physical contribution we made was far less significant than the personal impressions we made on people—we showed them we cared about who they were and how they lived.

Q. What were some of the hardest parts of your six weeks?
A. Getting along with the seven other Americans in my group, being outgoing and meeting the people of the village, dealing with the poverty, and keeping up with the hard physical labor. It was tough, but rewarding.

Q. What advice would you give others about to undertake the same kind of experience?
A. Be outgoing and receptive to people of your host country. It's too easy to let your work group of Americans act as an insulation against experiencing a foreign culture. Don't be dainty—roll up your sleeves and get dirty.

ferences in the perception of time among cultures. You should be able to find these books in your library, or they can be purchased as a set for $32.80 (plus $2 postage) from Intercultural Press, P.O. Box 700, Yarmouth, ME 04096; (207) 846-5168.

Chapter 3

CHOOSING THE RIGHT PROGRAM

So you've breezed through the listings on pages 86-298 and found the program of your dreams. You've breezed through their brochure, and it sounds fantastic: It's in the country you want, the subject matter is interesting, and the duration of the program matches your summer vacation perfectly. Everything about it is irresistible. Could there really be a reason not to go on that program?

Better put the rose-colored glasses away: The answer is yes. No matter where you first hear of a program—in this or in some other publication, or from a friend or teacher—it should be examined carefully. Ask as many questions as you can think of and insist on answers. Ask questions of the program sponsors, past participants, and your guidance counselor. Ask questions about the larger aspects of the program, and about the smaller ones. Ask about the wallpaper and the paper cups, if that's what concerns you. Don't worry about being a nuisance: This is your future we're talking about! It's no fun wishing you'd never gone on a bad program while you're stuck right in the middle of it.

To help choose a good program that's right for you, ask yourself some of the following questions. Not every question relates to the kind of program you're considering, but they should help you start thinking in the right direction.

Who is the sponsor? As you will see, programs are offered by many different types of organizations: educational institutions such as high schools, colleges and universities, and language schools; private, non-profit agencies such as Youth For Understanding or World Learning Inc.; religious and fraternal organizations; commercial travel agencies; voluntary service organizations; and even individuals. Identify who is responsible for the program, and find out as much as you can about that person or group. Here are some things to consider:

- Is it a profit-making or a nonprofit organization? In this book we list both for-profit and nonprofit sponsors, and sometimes it's hard to tell the difference. Profit-making sponsors are commercial businesses owned by individuals or shareholders. Nonprofit companies generally provide services that are beneficial to society and are not established with the motive of making money. The U.S. government accords nonprofit organizations a special status that exempts them from corporate taxation. Although the primary concern of a profit-making business is making money, there is no guarantee that the services of a nonprofit organization are any better than those of a commercial one; indeed, some are not. But when choosing a program with an educational component, many people feel more assured of a certain earnestness of purpose with a nonprofit group.
- Is the stated sponsor fully responsible for the program? Determine whether the sponsor takes care of all aspects of the program or whether it hires other organizations to handle such things as travel arrangements and accommodations. This may sound like fussing over little details, but this information can be useful if you need to make special arrangements. While it's normal for programs that include travel to make group package deals through travel agencies, they should tell you exactly how these arrangements are made.
- Is the sponsor based in the United States, or elsewhere? This could matter if legal responsibility becomes an issue. If complications involving legal action were to occur, it might be difficult or even impossible to protect your rights as a U.S. citizen in a dispute involving a foreign organization. This is not meant to scare you off; rather, it is just to add a word of caution. If you need to check on the reliability of a foreign-based organization, contact that country's embassy or consulate.
- How is the sponsoring institution doing, financially? As a prospective participant, you have the right to know where an organization gets its money and how it spends that money. You should also know whether or not the organization expects you to do fund-raising as part of your participation. Ask how the organization finances itself and be sure you know it's financially sound before going. To get this kind of information, ask for the annual report of any organization you are seriously considering.

- What is the reputation of the sponsor? There are several ways to determine this. Your guidance counselor is a good starting point; see whether he or she has any information, or ask others around your school, especially foreign-language teachers. Checking with your state's department of education is also a good idea. To investigate commercial agencies, you can contact your local Better Business Bureau. The information you receive from the organization itself should be carefully scrutinized (see page 83). In the United States, any respectable organization should provide you, upon request, with the names of past participants you can contact by phone or letter. Ask them the kinds of questions the sponsor might not be able to answer; the day-to-day, nitty-gritty kinds of things. Your parents might want to talk to the parents of the past participants as well.

Who are the leaders? There's a category in each of this book's listings called "supervision," where some details about program leadership are provided. Some programs are not formally supervised, but if a program you're interested in has leaders, by all means check further into how these people are selected. Call the organization and ask how it selects its group leaders. If they are certified or accredited, ask for the name of the accrediting organization and contact it to verify this claim. Be especially wary when you're told they are "qualified" without any description of these "qualifications." Sometimes these people are chosen only for their ability to recruit participants—those who get a free trip or commission in return for registering a certain number of students, for example. A knowledgeable and capable leader is essential. Here are some good qualities to look for when checking them out:

- Maturity. Good leaders should be deserving of your respect. They should be wise and resourceful while still being able to identify with their younger companions.
- Knowledge. Leaders should be very familiar with the country or countries to be visited. They should have a first-rate command of the language, yet also be patient enough to help you with the most basic problem. They should also have a good understanding of the culture and customs.
- Dedication. Leaders should be ready and willing to devote almost 24 hours a day to the job. They are yours. Any leaders who are pursuing their own studies or interests should be suspect.
- Empathy. If, at any point, you find yourself confused, frustrated, or homesick, your leader should be understanding and constructive in giving advice.

How will you interact with the host culture? Believe it or not, home can seem like a foreign place after you've surrounded yourself with another country's culture (see chapter 5). This is a good thing: becoming a part of the surrounding culture and interacting with its people is the ultimate way to understand it. Academic types call this "immersion." Some programs in this guide will immerse you so far into the life of the host country that at times you'll forget you're a visitor. Others will let you observe the life of the country you visit from a distance. Semester-long study abroad and homestay programs provide more immersion than, say, a three-week tour of six countries, but short-term programs can be a valuable introduction to other countries for people who know nothing about them. But if a program claims to feature cultural immersion, the following questions should be asked:

- How much help will you get in developing cross-cultural understanding? Sometimes a study program will include courses that focus on the host culture, but others may expect you to discover this for yourself. Find out exactly how you will come into contact with local people and how you will be involved with the everyday life of the country or countries you visit. Some of the weakest programs erect invisible walls against the host culture— you could spend two weeks in France surrounded by a busload of squawking, camera-toting Americans and learn as much about French people as if you'd stayed home. If there's no true cross-cultural experience, and if you're living, studying, and spending leisure time only with other Americans, there isn't much point in going to the trouble and expense of studying abroad.
- Where will you be living? Youth hostels, family homes, dormitories, hotels, pensiones (the European term for guesthouses), tents, and even barns are some of the possibilities. You could wake up each morning swaddled in luxurious hotel bedcovers or stretched out on the shore of a river, enjoying the sunrise. Just be certain that you know before you go what to expect in the way of accommodations.
- Are living arrangements included in the cost of the program? As with everything else in life, read the fine print. It may state that you have to pay extra for accommodations. In some cases, the living situation isn't arranged at all, leaving you to fend for yourself. This isn't the kind of thing you want to discover after you get there.
- Will you be living alone or with a group? What you prefer may depend on how much privacy you want, how much time you like to spend alone, how you get along with other people in close quarters, and, of course, how much snoring you can tolerate.

- Will you live with Americans only, or with people from other countries? Some people like to retreat back to the familiarity of their own culture and language when they return home after a day of immersion. Others prefer to "go international" as completely as they can.
- If you're hoping to interact with young people your own age from the countries you visit, avoid deluxe hotels. Living with, or near, students in that country is your best bet. But if you're the kind who is miserable without your comforts, don't sign up for a workcamp where you have to sleep with four other people in a hastily converted village school.

Many of the programs listed in this book include a homestay as part of their experience. Nothing beats a homestay in offering an opportunity to share in the day-to-day life of a family in another country. However, this possibility has its own set of questions:

- *How are homestays arranged, and who selects the participating families?* Is it someone from the sponsoring organization, or is this task performed by another agency?
- *What criteria are used to select the families?*
- *Do program representatives visit with the families before they're accepted and during the participant's stay?* If not, how do program representatives check on the families to make sure everything is going well?
- *Are the families compensated in any way?* If so, are they paid by the participant or the sponsor?
- *Are you given the name and address of the family before you leave home?* This is a real plus; making a connection ahead of time, perhaps sending a picture of yourself and your family and a word or two about yourself, is an excellent way to begin.
- *What provisions have been made in case you do not get along with your family?* Be sure there's someone available to help if this happens. If you get into a spat with your host family, it will probably be due to a cultural difference and not a personal dislike. Having someone available to help work out small misunderstandings will prevent them from becoming big ones.
- *Will there be someone your age in the family?* This is not always possible. If there is no one of the same or nearly the same age, be ready to make friends outside of the family and realize that it will require resourcefulness and an outgoing personality.
- *Will you be expected to return your host family's hospitality?* Some of the best homestay experiences arise from reciprocal ex-

change programs, in which your own family agrees to invite a member of your host family abroad for a stay in the United States. Strong friendships between the two families often result from this sort of arrangement, but playing host requires much preparation.

What about money? Most programs in this book charge a fee for participation. The sponsoring organization's literature should clearly state what this fee includes, and representatives should be willing to supply this information. Be wary of organizations that refuse. Some tips about money:

- Find out whether international transportation is included, and if it is, whether it's from your hometown to the host country or, as is more likely, from one designated U.S. city (such as New York or Los Angeles) to the host country. If you choose to go with this kind of transportation package, don't forget to factor in the cost of transportation to the designated city.
- Compare the transportation costs cited by the organization with regularly scheduled fares. If they are much higher, ask why.
- Find out how much of your travel will be covered within the country. You may find that you're on your own after you leave the airport, which is fine if you can work out an in-country travel plan in advance. Sometimes there's a travel fee that includes ground transportation to your ultimate destination. Check to see if it also includes any daily transportation that might be necessary.
- Are all meals and lodging covered? Will you be expected to pay for any weekend or evening excursions on your own?
- Is there an application fee in addition to the program fee? Pay attention to disclaimers in small print about possible increases due to inflation or fluctuation in exchange rates. If airfares are hiked, will there be a surcharge?
- How much spending money will you need? Individual needs differ, but the sponsors should certainly be able to give you some idea of typical personal expenses, as well as advice on how far you can expect your dollar to go with the current rate of exchange. This is a good question to ask past participants, too.
- What, if any, insurance is provided? A responsible sponsor should be sure that all participants are covered by health and accident insurance. This does not mean that they must provide the coverage, although some do; they may simply provide informa-

HOW TO WRITE TO ORGANIZATIONS

When you write to any of the program sponsors listed in *The High-School Student's Guide to Study, Travel and Adventure Abroad,* or to any other sponsor, your letter should be specific about what you're interested in. Include the following:

- your age
- your grade in school
- how much time you want to spend abroad
- when you want to go
- what you want to do abroad
- what country or countries particularly interest you

Many of the sponsors you will be contacting have more than one program and staffs that are nowhere near large enough to draft individual replies. What you can expect in return is a number of printed materials from which you should be able to extract the information you need.

Remember, too, when writing to sponsors in other countries to include international postal reply coupons, available at the post office.

If you need some help putting a letter together, here's a sample you can follow:

Summer Study Abroad   36 Condurso Way
128 Main Street   Saddle Brook, NJ 07662
Chicago, IL 60616   October 2, 1995

Dear Friend:

I am a sixteen-year-old sophomore attending Millard Fillmore High School in Saddle Brook, New Jersey, and would like to spend the summer studying Spanish in Mexico. I noted in the book, *The High-School Student's Guide to Study, Travel, and Adventure Abroad* that you operate this type of program, and I'd like to find out more about it. Specifically, I'd like to spend the month of July in Mexico, and I am interested in living with a

How to Write to Organizations

family while I study. Please send me your organization's brochure and an application form.

Many thanks.

Sincerely,
Ellen Smith

---

tion about insurance and then require proof that you have insurance. *Don't leave the United States without full insurance coverage!*

- What if you cancel? Be sure to find out what the arrangements are for refunding your money in case of unavoidable cancellation or if an emergency forces you to come home before the program is completed.
- What about official papers? If a visa or other official government permit is necessary, are you responsible for securing it, or will your program sponsor do it for you?

How much contact will you have with other students or representatives of your program? Are you part of a group, or are you left to fend for yourself?

- How much of your time is scheduled? A good program will strike a comfortable balance between scheduled time and free time. Particularly in the case of travel tour programs, ask for itineraries. Free time is important, but unless you know exactly what you want to do, you may end up feeling you've wasted some of that time.
- What kind of support system will be available to you? This is a question parents will certainly want answered in detail. How much help will you get once you are thousands of miles from home? Is there someone available at all times in case of emergency? Whom can you go to if you're having trouble with your studies or having a hard time making friends? Is there someone you can talk to if and when you're feeling homesick? Independence is a wonderful quality, and one to be nurtured during an experience abroad, but there must be someone to turn to when help is needed.

QUESTIONS TO CONSIDER FOR STUDY PROGRAMS

Although travel tours of foreign countries, homestays, and voluntary-service participation can be educational, they are not, formally speaking, study programs. For you to receive academic credit from a study program, it must conform to the educational standards of your home school system. That means it should include graded coursework, tests, reports—in other words, all the fun evaluative devices that make something "educational." You'll have to make most of the arrangements for getting credit yourself: start by finding out out whether students who have gone before you on the program have received credit. Then check with your own counselors at your school to determine whether foreign credit will be accepted. Below are some specific questions to ask of study programs.

Where will you study? Will you be enrolling in a foreign high school? Will you be in classes with other Americans or with local students? Some programs may lead you to believe you're going to study in a foreign university, but if it's a summer program, beware. Make sure that country's academic calendar actually includes summer sessions. If not, you will probably be in a course designed for foreigners with little chance to interact with local young people.

What about the sponsor's academic reputation? How long has the sponsor been operating a study program? Does the sponsor oversee all aspects of the program (budget, staff appointments, curriculum planning, recruiting, and selection), or are some subcontracted? Beware of any so-called sponsor that is involved only in recruitment.

What are the admission requirements? Some programs are highly selective, but for some you need only to show some signs of life—and pay the fee—to be accepted. If you want a high-quality program, you are going to have to meet some specific standards. As part of the screening process, a sponsor should be doing whatever it can to determine your maturity, adaptability, and your earnestness of purpose as well as your ability to meet the more tangible application criteria such as grades or study prerequisites. In other words, ask yourself if the sponsors are as careful about choosing their participants as you are about choosing a sponsor.

What are the objectives of the program? The objectives of any valuable study program sponsor should be clearly stated in any printed materials it distributes. The description of the objective should be detailed and precise—not a meaningless list of clichés about international understanding. Look for the ways the sponsor plans to accomplish its goals. Do the curriculum, the place of study, and the extracurricular activities seem to fit in with the objectives, or are there inconsistencies? A good study program will balance academic learning with cultural contact. It will offer study opportunities you can't get at home.

What kind of preparation is provided? How well are participants prepared for the experience? Another sign of the sponsoring institution's seriousness is the type of orientation it offers. The best orientation materials do two things: (1) provide information and (2) guide the prospective participants toward finding their own information. (You'll find more about the specifics of getting ready in chapter 4.) Although it may be geographically impossible to spend a great deal of time with your group before you leave, there should be some kind of predeparture and postarrival orientation, certainly more than just a batch of materials sent by mail. There should also be some sort of prereturn orientation that addresses problems of coming home and suggests ways to use the international experience to best advantage once you've returned.

How good is the curriculum? Does the curriculum take advantage of the physical, human, and cultural resources of the host country, or will you spend all your time in a classroom? Have the sponsors been creative in their use of the foreign setting?

What size will classes be? This will give you an idea of the kind of individual attention you can expect. The larger the class, the more likely it is that you'll be just a number.

Are there adequate academic resources? Find out what the classroom activities are like, and what you'll need for them. You may be required to find and purchase your own materials, including books, notebooks, the A4-size paper commonly used in Europe, a blackboard tablet, and so on. The books specified in a program's curriculum may not be available on campus. A library and/or bookstore on site or nearby is always a plus. For language programs, labs should be conducted regularly to sharpen your abilities. If you're interested in a program involving fine or performing arts, check to see if studios or practice rooms will be made available to you.

What is the language of instruction? You'll need to speak the language well to be able to absorb regular subject matter. If you find this out too late, you may end up having to learn to say a lot more than "Oops."

GETTING CREDIT

Before you make any commitment to a particular program, decide whether or not you want to get academic credit for your international experience. Many of the programs in this book, including voluntary service and travel programs, can be converted to credit.

The best way to approach the topic of credit is to sit down with your guidance counselor long before your trip and discuss the possibilities. Some semester- and year-abroad program sponsors have had a great deal of experience in this area and can give you advice on how to go about it. Be sure to find out exactly what your school or district needs in order to accept credit. Some will accept a letter from the principal of the school you'll attend; others want a fully translated transcript. You must be sure to get clear guidelines on any necessary requirements from your counselor. If you're going to study for a semester in France, for instance, you should certainly be able to get credit for language, but getting credit for the math you may study while there might be trickier.

When you approach your guidance counselor about credit, emphasize the enrichment aspect of an international experience. In general, the school work abroad is more rigorous than that in the U.S.; most high-school classes are almost the equivalent of courses in our first and second years of college.

Some programs listed in this book have credit-granting arrangements with specific colleges and/or universities so that your experience can be translated into college credit. Ask whether this is a feature of the program you're considering.

Are the language requirements realistic? If a program in a non-English-speaking country admits beginners, language courses should be available. Likewise, if there's a library attached to the learning institution, it should have materials suited to your proficiency.

How are grades reported? Grades should be reported to students, and it should be possible to have transcripts sent to your own school. If the grade system at a host school is different from the one at home, which is almost always true, a table for converting the grades should be included.

What will the faculty be like? In the written materials the sponsors send you, the faculty members should be named, along with their academic

JOINING A DIG

Want to help? Grab a shovel! Virtually all archaeological digs around the world need the help of volunteers. Often, you must be 18 or over, but some digs accept younger participants. Here are some good sources of information on digs:

- Archaeological Institute of America (AIA), 675 Commonwealth Avenue, Boston, MA 02215. AIA publishes an annual *Archaeological Fieldwork Opportunities Bulletin,* which lists excavations all over the world. The booklet is published each January and costs $11.50 for AIA members and $13.50 for nonmembers, postage and handling included. Mail and telephone orders for the booklet are handled by the Kendall/Hunt Publishing Company, Order Department, 4050 Westmark Drive, Dubuque, IA 52002; (800) 228-0810.
- Archaeology Abroad, 31-34 Gordon Square, London WC1H 0PY, England. This London-based organization distributes information on digs outside the United Kingdom, in the form of an annual bulletin and two newsletters. The 1994 subscription price was $15. To receive these publications, write to the attention of the Secretary at the above address and enclose a self-addressed envelope, international postal reply coupon, and your check payable to University College London. (See page 40 for information about the international postal reply coupon.)
- Council for British Archaeology, 112 Kennington Road, London SE11 6RE, England, (44) 71-582-0494. This organization is solely concerned with archaeological projects in Great Britain. Its bimonthly newsletter, *British Archaeological News,* gives details of digs around the country that require volunteers. Most digs require participants to be at least 16. The subscription price from the United States is $25. Enclose a self-addressed envelope and international postal reply coupon with your request.

A CONVERSATION WITH MRS. FOSTER

Mrs. Foster is a German teacher who annually takes a group of students from her high school to Austria through CIEE's School Partners Abroad program.

Q. What can teenagers do to find out if they're ready for an experience abroad?
A. I think they need to know themselves pretty well; they need to ask themselves if they have the maturity and the flexibility needed to adapt to a totally new environment. But students should be aware that if they feel they're not ready for a semester- or year-long program, it doesn't mean all study-abroad programs are out of their reach. The School Partners Abroad program, for example, allows students to try a three- to four-week living experience abroad as part of a group from their own school. Since it's an on-going program at our school, interested students can speak with their peers who have already participated to get a better idea of what's involved and whether or not it's right for them.

Q. How do you help prepare teenagers for a trip abroad?
A. I meet with the students once a week beginning four months before the exchange takes place. We go over the language and culture of Austria—from its educational system, history, and politics, to religion and family life. We make plans both for the trip abroad and for hosting the Austrian students in our community.

Q. How does the experience affect those who decide to take part?
A. I'm always amazed at how much the students mature—emotionally and intellectually—as a result of even a brief experience abroad. They return to the U.S. with a much greater sense of themselves and the world around them. It's also interesting to see the impact that hosting foreign students from our partner school can have on the American students who, for whatever reason, do not travel abroad themselves. That's what's really exciting—the school partnership has an effect on the *entire* school.

affiliations, their degrees, and the subject areas in which they teach. This should give you an idea of how they were chosen. If you can get in touch with past participants, they should be able to tell you how approachable, enthusiastic, and involved the teachers are. Beware the ones who are aloof and pedantic. If they are not enthusiastic about their subject matter, you won't be enthusiastic about attending their classes.

What about the resident director? What kind of prior experience does he or she have? Is the resident director knowledgeable about the host country, fluent in the language, sensitive to students' needs? Does he or she understand the special needs and background of American students? Resident directors should have regular office hours and should be accessible when you need them.

Don't feel swamped by all these questions—not all of them apply to all programs. Use what's most helpful to you. For more on choosing a program, refer to a booklet put out by the Council on Standards for International Educational Travel, the *Advisory List of International Educational Travel and Exchange Programs.* Revised annually, the *Advisory List* lists programs that have earned what is essentially CSIET's "seal of approval." The book is available from CSIET, 3 Loudoun Street SE, Leesburg, VA 22075; (703) 771-2040. Call for the cost of the book.

Now that you have some guidelines for evaluating a program, use them to scrutinize every program you consider, whether it appears in this guide or not.

Chapter 4
THE LOGISTICS

*T*ake a deep breath and relax a moment: we've covered a lot of territory so far, and there isn't much more to talk about. Now that the program details are all laid out for you, it's time to take stock of all the practical matters that will make your trip possible—and as *cheap* as possible. An excellent source for this kind of information is another CIEE publication, *Student Travels*, a free 48-page travel magazine especially for high-school and college students. This magazine includes in-depth articles and travel tips, all from a student's perspective. It will also keep you up to date on the lowest student airfares and student services offered by Council Travel, CIEE's travel division.

THE ESSENTIALS

Your Passport

On your list of important things to get, this should be number one. United States citizens need a passport to enter just about any country other than Canada or Mexico, and for some countries, a visa is necessary too. Passports are issued by the U.S. Department of State as internationally recognized proof of who you are and what country you are from. A visa is an endorsement or stamp placed in your passport by a foreign government, giving you permission to visit the country for a specific purpose and a specific period of time.

Fortunately, the Department of State cuts young people a break on the fee it charges. Passports for U.S. citizens under 18 are valid for five years from date of issue and cost $30. For people 18 and over, passports valid for ten years cost $55. An execution fee of $10 is charged for both categories when you apply for the first time.

FINDING THE CASH

How are your entrepreneurial skills? With a little creativity and persistence, raising the money for your trip overseas can be an adventure in itself. The first thing to do in any strategy is find out who your allies are: people, organizations, religious groups, businesses, and charitable organizations have all been known to help defray the costs for students affiliated with them in some way—it can't hurt to ask. Religious organizations may be especially sympathetic to your cause if you're embarking on a voluntary service project. One good approach is to suggest doing a presentation on your trip after you return in exchange for whatever help they can give.

Community groups may also be willing to help; contact neighborhood associations, community newspapers, radio and TV stations, the Lions Club, Elks Club, Kiwanis Club, Rotary Club, and the local Chamber of Commerce. These groups, too, might like something in return—a slide presentation or an article for their newsletter, for example.

Support can also come from your fellow schoolmates. Organize your friends for some kind of fund-raiser—a bake sale, a car wash, a spaghetti dinner, or a dance.

Try putting up posters or putting an ad in the local newspaper offering to do odd jobs—car washing, baby-sitting, serving at parties, or dog walking.

If you're going on a study or service program in the Third World, remember the Council's ISIC Scholarship (see page 64). In addition, some of the programs included in this book offer scholarships. Be sure to ask about the possibilities.

Don't let the financial aspect of going abroad stand in your way. If you are determined to go and are resourceful, you will be able to raise the funds.

To get your first passport, you must apply in person at either (1) a U.S. post office authorized to accept passport applications; (2) a federal, state, or county courthouse; or (3) one of the passport agencies located in Boston, Chicago, Honolulu, Houston, Los Angeles, Miami, New Orleans, New York, Philadelphia, San Francisco, Seattle, Stamford, or Washington, D.C. If you apply between September and February, you'll most likely avoid the hordes of last-minute summer tourists whose applications choke the in-boxes at the State Department and make process-ing times seem more like life spans. In any case, apply several months before departure, as it generally takes at least three weeks to process a first-time passport application and even longer during the peak travel season. If you're going to need visas, allow yourself even more time. Some countries' consulates and embassies have last-minute visa ser-vices, but the fees they charge can thin your wallet pretty fast.

To apply, you'll need to bring proof of U.S. citizenship. This can be a certified copy of your birth certificate, naturalization certificate, or con-sular report of birth abroad. In addition, you must have proof of identity, such as a valid driver's license or student identification (not a Social Se-curity or credit card). You'll also need two recent, identical photographs two inches square (most vending machine photos are not acceptable), showing your entire face. The photos may be color or black and white, but must be taken against a plain white background. The distance in the photo between your chin and the top of your head may not exceed one and three-eighths inches. Most photo shops will know what you need. Finally, you must complete form DSP-11, "Passport Application."

You can apply by mail and avoid the $10 execution fee if (1) you have had a passport issued within 12 years of the new application; (2) you are able to submit your most recent passport with the application; and (3) your previous passport was not issued before your eighteenth birthday (that's the clause that eliminates most high-school students). In addition to sending your previous passport and two new passport-size photographs, you must complete form DSP-82, "Application for Pass-port by Mail."

You never know when you'll need to prove who you are, so when you get to your destination, carry your passport as if it were your only source of oxygen. If you lose it, however, you needn't choke. U.S. em-bassies and consulates in other countries can issue you a replacement. To make it easier for them to do so, make photocopies of the pages in your passport with your photo, identification number, and date and place of issue and take these copies with you to your destination. You should also have with you some other form of identification, such as a valid dri-ver's license or student identification. If you carry along two extra prints of your passport photo, it will speed up the replacement process faster.

Remember that a number of countries will not permit visitors to enter and will not place visas in passports that have a remaining validity of less than six months. If you return to the United States with an expired passport, you'll get a rude "welcome home" in the form of an $80 pass-port waiver fee.

Non-U.S. citizens who have permanent residency in the United States but do not have a valid passport from another country can apply for a U.S. travel permit. This permit functions much like a passport and can be obtained from the Immigration and Naturalization Service in the state where the applicant resides. Note, however, that requirements for obtaining visas with travel permits are usually different from those that apply to U.S. citizens. Non-U.S. citizens—whether traveling with a travel permit or a valid passport from another country—must consult the embassy or consulate of the country they want to visit to obtain the appropriate visa requirements.

If you have further questions about any of the above, write to Passport Services, Department of State, Washington, DC 20524 or call (202) 647-0518 for a recorded message on passport applications.

Visas

Visa requirements differ from country to country. To study in any foreign country for longer than a few months, you will most likely need a student visa. In most cases, a visa must be obtained before you leave the United States. Apply directly to the embassy or nearest consulate of the country you plan to visit. Travel agents sometimes help with visas; program sponsors may assist as well. One place *not* to look for help is the U.S. Department of State: they'll issue your passport, but the rest is up to you.

Most countries charge a visa processing fee, which usually isn't very much but can sometimes be expensive. Many also require proof that you will leave the country by a certain date (a round-trip air ticket usually suffices). Don't take this personally; they're just protecting their country from illegal immigration. *Foreign Visa Requirements,* a U.S. government publication, lists entry requirements for U.S. citizens in most countries. Single copies are available for 50 cents from the Consumer Information Center, Department 354A, Pueblo, CO 81009; (719) 948-3334. However, because entry requirements can change at a moment's notice, the best source of information is still a country's embassy or consulate.

Since visas are usually stamped onto one of the blank pages of your passport, you'll need to submit your passport along with a visa application form to the embassy or consulate of each country you plan to visit. Acquiring a visa may take several weeks, so it's wise to start the process early, especially if you need to get more than one.

Customs

You'll have to go through U.S. Customs on your return to the States. You can bring back $400 worth of goods free of duty, the tax usually charged for imported goods. However, the U.S. government prohibits the entry of certain articles and imposes import fees or duties on others.

For the lowdown on customs procedure, read *Know Before You Go,* a free pamphlet available from the U.S. Customs Service, P.O. Box 7407, Washington, DC 20044; (202) 927-6724. The list of prohibited items (birds, fruit, and soil, among other items) is seemingly random and rather amusing, but there are good environmental reasons why you can't bring home that toucan you won in a poker game. It's better to know what to avoid packing than to get caught with it (knowingly or unknowingly).

Health

Some countries require certificates of vaccination for inoculation against yellow fever and cholera. For others, certain inoculations are recommended even if not required. Check your medical records to make sure that your measles, mumps, rubella, polio, diphtheria, tetanus, and pertussis (whooping cough) immunizations are up to date. If not, go to your doctor's, grit your teeth, and hope for the best. The Centers for Disease Control has an International Traveler's Hotline to help you determine whether you need any special vaccinations to visit a country: (404) 332-4559.

The two greatest threats to travelers' health today are diseases against which you *can't* be inoculated: diarrhea and malaria. The most common causes of traveler's diarrhea and other gastrointestinal ailments are parasites and other organisms to which your body isn't accustomed, but which may be common to the water supply and certain foods, especially fresh produce, of the countries you're visiting. Malaria is spread by the bite of the female *Anopheles* mosquito—the bite itself doesn't hurt, but the consequences have a way of catching up with you. Some tourist bureaus won't tell you about the malaria risk in certain countries for fear that you'll spend your tourist dollars elsewhere. Most types of malaria can be prevented, but you must begin taking antimalarial drugs before you arrive in the infected area and continue taking them after you leave.

One group that works to alert travelers about the risks of malaria and other health problems worldwide is the International Association of Medical Assistance to Travellers (IAMAT), a nonprofit organization with centers in 450 cities in 120 countries. Members of IAMAT (there's no membership fee, but a donation is welcome) receive a pocket-size directory listing these centers, a world immunization chart, and various other publications that alert travelers to existing health problems throughout the world. Contact IAMAT at 417 Center Street, Lewiston, NY 14092; (716) 754-4883.

Whether or not you decide to go to another country, be aware of the risk of contracting AIDS (acquired immunodeficiency syndrome). Don't let exaggerated or distorted information alter your travel plans, but know the facts and prepare ahead. Some countries may require antibody tests

STAYING HEALTHY

You'll want to try to stay as healthy as you can while you're away. Even a head cold can be a real misery when you're far from home.
  A few things to remember on the subject:

1. Make sure your insurance covers medical care abroad.
2. If there are any prescription drugs that you use frequently, bring them with you in clearly marked bottles. It's wise to take along a copy of the prescription as well, in case a customs officer asks for it.
3. Go to the dentist before your trip—and try to eliminate any dental "surprises" while you're away.
4. If you wear glasses or contact lenses, bring an extra pair and a copy of your prescription.
5. Take a compact first-aid kit with you: bandages, aspirin or aspirin substitute, antiseptic, motion-sickness pills, and sunscreen should be the basics.
6. If you need an English-speaking doctor abroad, you can contact the American Embassy for names.
7. Eat well. The erratic hours and excitement of foreign travel make it even more important than ever to practice good nutrition.

for HIV (the human immunodeficiency virus, which causes AIDS) before they'll grant a visa for an extended period of time; tourists staying for 30 days or less are usually exempt. Some countries don't require testing for visitors below a minimum age, so you might try calling the country's embassy or consulate to find out if this concerns you. If you want to be tested before you depart, do so only at a center that offers pre- and post-test counseling and allow two weeks for the testing process. While traveling, remember: the best way to deal with AIDS is through knowledge, foresight, and action—not ignorance and fear.

  The Centers for Disease Control has issued the following advisory: "Because HIV and AIDS are globally distributed, the risk to international travelers is determined less by their geographic destination than by their individual behavior. HIV infection is preventable. There is no documented evidence of HIV transmission through casual contacts; air, food, or water routes; contact with inanimate objects; or through mosquitos or other arthropod (insect) vectors. HIV is transmitted through sexual intercourse, blood or blood components, and perinatally (at birth) from an infected mother. Travelers are at increased risk if they have sexual intercourse (homosexual or heterosexual) with an infected person; use or allow the use of contaminated, unsterilized syringes or needles for any injections, e.g. illicit drugs, tattooing, acupuncture, or medical/dental procedures; or use infected blood, blood components, or clotting factor concentrates."

There are several things that you can do to avoid contracting HIV. Abstinence is, of course, the most reliable means of avoiding infection. But if there's any chance you may have sex, bring condoms. You can't buy them in certain parts of the world, and the quality, manufacturing, and storage of condoms in some countries may be questionable. But even more important than bringing them is using them (if you choose to have sex, that is)—even if you are aware of the HIV status of your partner. Testing HIV negative doesn't necessarily mean that a person has not been in contact with the virus.

If you are concerned about needing a blood transfusion while abroad, contact others in your academic program or traveling group; you can arrange with those that have your blood type to be blood donors if necessary. It could be your life you gamble with, so play it safe and smart. For more information, write CIEE, 205 East 42nd Street, New York, NY 10017, for a free copy of Council Travel's brochure, *AIDS and International Travel,* which explains ways to avoid contracting the disease when you're abroad. Copies are also available free of charge from any Council Travel office. Another resource for information is the Centers for Disease Control AIDS Hotline: (800) 342-AIDS.

There are a number of helpful books written on the subject of staying well as you travel. The following books are recommended reading for overall health issues. You won't need to consult all of them, but it can't hurt to look through at least one:

- *The Pocket Doctor,* by Stephen Bezruchka, a doctor with extensive travel experience in Asia, is a slim, pocket-sized publication written especially for travelers. You can order it from The Mountaineers Books, 1011 S.W. Klickitat Way, Suite 107, Seattle, WA 98134, for $4.95 plus $2 postage and handling.
- *Staying Healthy in Asia, Africa, and Latin America,* by Dirk Schroeder, is basic enough for the short-term traveler yet complete enough for someone living or traveling off the beaten path. The book is also small in size, making it very portable. Order it from Moon Publications, P. O. Box 3040, Chico, CA 95927-3040, (800) 345-5473; $10.95 plus $3.50 postage (in California add 95¢ sales tax). Be sure to specify whether you prefer UPS delivery or first-class postage.

- *The International Travel HealthGuide,* by Stuart Rose, is updated annually and published by Travel Medicine, 351 Pleasant Street, Suite 312, Northampton, MA 01060; (413) 584-0381. Its 400 pages include country-by-country immunization, health, and safety listings. It also has chapters on AIDS, travel and pregnancy, traveling with disabilities, and a directory of clinics that offer pre- and post-travel medical services and consultation. The 1994 edition costs $17.95. You can find it in good bookstores or order it from the publisher (include $3.95 postage).

Taking along a compact first-aid kit designed for travelers can also be a good idea. Drug stores and outdoor-sports stores carry an assortment of these at varying prices, but the less expensive models usually contain everything you need and won't take up much room in your suitcase. An excellent first-aid kit designed with this in mind is the Micro-Doc Box, which is manufactured by Lee M.D. Ltd. The kit retails for $39.95, but holders of the International Student Identity Card can purchase it for $22.50 from Lee M.D. Ltd., 6700 Troost Street, Suite 500, Kansas City, MO 64131; (816) 361-8722.

Safety

Leaving the United States is not dangerous in and of itself; in fact, the crime rates in our country—particularly those for violent crime—tend to make other countries look like Disneyland. Before you start warbling about what a small world it is, however, remember one thing: while traveling, you will be recognized as a foreigner. To some this means you're a novelty; to others, a sucker. You must be aware and thoughtful at all times, because you can no longer rely on your instinctive knowledge of what may be considered unsafe, insulting, or provocative. This doesn't mean that you should not explore or stray off the tourist-beaten path. But it does mean that you should know where your passport and money are at all times, and take along a good guidebook that will give you a rough idea of the situations you will be getting yourself into. Ask a knowledgeable person which areas to avoid when alone or at night, and try to avoid arriving in strange cities late at night unless you have a confirmed place to stay and a secure means of getting there. You can't control everything that happens to you—at home or abroad—but you can sway the odds.

Women especially should be aware of situations in which they might be harassed, molested, or robbed. When traveling, there is not only the usual burden of sexism to deal with but also the fact that you will be treated according to stereotypes of Western women. American women, in particular, are thought in some parts of the world to be promiscuous, immodest, and wealthy.

If you're planning a trip to a spot where a political problem has existed for a while or just flared up, a reliable source of information is the Citizens Emergency Center (CEC) operated by the U.S. State Department in Washington, D.C. This center will inform you of any State Department travel advisories that warn travelers of danger and recommend taking special precautions, or, in more extreme cases, postponing travel to certain countries or regions. Recorded travel advisories can be obtained anytime from a push-button phone by calling (202) 647-5225. If you're using a dial phone, call between 8 A.M. and 10 P.M., Monday through Friday, or between 9 P.M. and 3 P.M. on Saturday.

Insurance

No matter how much of a crook you believe your local insurance salesman to be, never underestimate the importance of being insured when traveling abroad. Check to see whether your medical and accident insurance policies will cover you while you're traveling outside the United States. One benefit of purchasing an International Student Identity Card (see next section) is that you will automatically receive basic medical insurance for travel outside the United States, valid from the time of purchase until the card's expiration date. Also included is a toll-free emergency hotline number for travelers needing legal, financial, or medical assistance.

You should also investigate the various plans for baggage and flight insurance. Baggage or personal effects insurance covers damage to or loss of your personal belongings while traveling. Flight insurance covers the cost of your fare if you are unable to take a flight you have already paid for. One insurance package, Trip-Safe, provides a variety of options which may be purchased in any combination for any period from one month to one year. You can find details in *Student Travels,* available free from CIEE, 205 East 42nd Street, New York, NY 10017. Trip-Safe insurance can also be obtained at any Council Travel office.

International Student Identity Card

Each year, nearly two million student travelers obtain the International Student Identity Card. This card is internationally recognized as proof of student status, and it's your key to discounts and benefits in every part of the world. Any student—junior-high, high-school, college, university, or vocational-school—who is at least 12 years old and enrolled in a program of study leading to a diploma or degree is eligible. The card is issued by the International Student Travel Confederation (ISTC), made up of student travel organizations in 74 countries around the world. The Council on International Educational Exchange is the U.S. member of the ISTC.

Although the services of ISTC members vary from country to country, holders of the International Student Identity Card can usually expect to receive student discounts on transportation and accommodations, and reduced admission to museums, theaters, cultural events, and other attractions. Probably the best-known discounts are the student fares on international flights. Cardholders can save up to 50 percent over commercial fares on the same routes. For sample student fares, see "Student and Youth Airfares" (page 70).

Even in countries where there is no ISTC member, the card is often recognized as proof of student status. We advise following the "it can't hurt" theory: always show your International Student Identity Card and ask if there are any discounts available—whether it's for a trolley ride, entrance to a museum, or a night in a hotel.

Besides the student discounts, the International Student Identity Card provides basic medical insurance. All students who buy the card in the United States receive automatic coverage while they're abroad for as long as the card is valid. Also available to cardholders is a toll-free hotline to the Traveler's Assistance Center, whose multilingual staff offers worldwide assistance in medical, legal, and financial emergencies.

To obtain the International Student Identity Card, submit a passport-size photo and proof of student status. High-school students can prove student status with a photocopy of a report card or a letter from a principal or guidance counselor on school stationery. The card can be ordered through the mail from CIEE, 205 East 42nd Street, New York, NY 10017. You can also pick it up at any Council Travel office (see page 7) or any of over 450 U.S. issuing offices authorized by CIEE. (High schools are also eligible to issue the card. If a faculty member or administrator at your school is interested, have him or her write to CIEE's Information and Student Services Department at the address above.)

The 1995 card costs $16 and is valid for 16 months, from September 1, 1994, to December 31, 1995. For an application form, and more information, contact CIEE and ask for a free copy of *Student Travels.* Keep in mind that it takes two to three weeks (and longer in the peak seasons of December and April through June) to process a card through the mail.

Go 25: International Youth Travel Card

Nonstudents under the age of 26 are eligible for the Go 25 Card, a document sponsored by the Federation of International Youth Travel Organizations (FIYTO). Go 25 cardholders are entitled to similar benefits as holders of the International Student Identity Card receive, such as reduced airfares, but the discounts while traveling abroad with the Go 25 Card are more limited. Go 25 Cards issued in the United States through CIEE also carry the same insurance and traveler's assistance benefits as the International Student Identity Card described above. The Go 25 Card is valid for one year from the date of purchase and costs $16. For more information on the International Youth Card, contact CIEE or any Council Travel office (see page 7).

Youth Hostel Card

Staying at youth hostels is one of the best and least expensive ways to meet fellow travelers. In order to take advantage of the more than 5,000 hostels in 70 countries affiliated with Hostelling International—formerly the International Youth Hostel Federation—you must usually show a membership card. Some hostels, but not all, will accommodate nonmembers for a higher fee. Hostel membership cards are available in the United States from American Youth Hostels-Hostelling International offices and from Council Travel offices. If you're under 18, the membership fee is $10; for ages 18 to 54, it's $25. A family membership, which includes children under the age of 18, is $35. See page 74 for more on hostels.

For the full rundown on hostels, what they're like and where they're located, check Hostelling International's *Budget Accommodation You Can Trust.* This is a two-volume set: volume 1 covers Europe and the Mediterranean; volume 2 covers the rest of the world ($10.95 each plus $3 postage per book). You can purchase these from any Council Travel office (see page 7) or from American Youth Hostels-Hostelling International, 733 15th Street NW, Suite 840, Washington, DC 20005; (202) 783-6161.

Money

The best way to carry money abroad is in traveler's checks. The most common are American Express, Citicorp, Thomas Cook, and Visa. Most traveler's checks cost one percent of the total dollar amount you're buying; that is, you'll be charged one dollar extra for every hundred dollars you buy. Holders of the International Student Identity Card are eligible for a waiver of this service charge at participating dealers.

Most banks, except in the smallest towns and villages, will convert traveler's checks in dollars to local currency. Avoid changing money in hotels or restaurants; the rate won't be as favorable as at a bank or official exchange shop. For the latest conversion tables, simply consult the foreign exchange listings in any good financial paper, such as *The Wall Street Journal.*

You'll probably want to have some local currency with you when you first arrive in a country. Although there are exchange offices in most air, ship, or train terminals, it's a good idea to change some of your dollars before you leave the United States. You may want to buy a refreshment, make a phone call, or pay for transportation as soon as you arrive.

Carry your money and traveler's checks in a safe place, such as a money belt or neck pouch. But don't keep all your valuables in one place. Put your passport in an inside pocket, your traveler's checks in a money belt, and so on. Keep a separate list of the numbers of your credit cards and traveler's checks so that you can report them more easily if they're lost or stolen. You should also give a copy of that list to someone at home to put in a safe place.

If you need to have extra funds sent from home, your parents can use American Express or Western Union to wire you money. This takes only a few minutes but is relatively expensive: parents of students holding the 1995 International Student Identity Card can get a $10 rebate on American Express MoneyGrams. The handbook you get when you purchase this card contains more information on this.

If you have a credit card, you should be able to withdraw cash from automated teller machines (ATMs) around the world. Check with your local branch to see if this is possible in the country you're traveling to. You might need to change your PIN code, as most overseas ATMs accept only four-digit codes. Also check with your bank or credit card company to find out what fees you'll be charged; using an ATM overseas often gives you the best deal on currency exchange rates, since commissions are usually not charged.

Mail

While you're away, you'll certainly want to receive mail from home. If you're not sure what your exact address will be, have your mail addressed to Poste Restante (General Delivery) at the central post office of the cities you'll be visiting. American Express cardholders can have mail sent to local American Express offices overseas. For a list of offices abroad, call American Express at (800) 528-4800. Make up a list of mailing addresses before you go to tell your friends and family where and when they can reach you.

Packing

This might sound drastic, but the best packing method is to fill your backpack or suitcase with what you think you'll need, then dump it out and put only half of it back in. Forget the other half—it's just dead weight. If you're doubtful that this advice works, try packing everything and then walking a mile with your suitcases, backpack, and whatever else you'll be carrying. If you make it back, have a tall glass of cool water and eliminate whatever you can from the bags. You'll probably want to buy some souvenirs and other things once you're abroad, so you should leave some room for them, too. Some charter flights limit baggage to 44 pounds; you should certainly not exceed that amount. Your best bet is to keep it simple. Use this list as a guideline, and pick and choose what is essential for you:

Clothing

- one pair of walking shoes (light hiking boots are great; break them in before you go to avoid blisters)
- one pair of flip-flops (showers may not be the cleanest, and these will be easy to carry)
- three to five pairs of socks
- five to seven pairs of underwear
- one to two pairs of shorts
- one to two skirts/trousers
- two shirts
- one sweater/sweatshirt
- one poncho/rain jacket
- one light jacket
- one bathing suit
- one hat
- one semi-nice outfit (you never know when you might have to attend a function)

Medicine and Toiletries

- Prescription medicine (keep it in the bottle and carry a copy of the prescription)
- Toothbrush and toothpaste
- Soap and shampoo
- Comb and brush
- Sunscreen, moisturizers, cosmetics
- Deodorant
- First aid kit
- Contraceptives/condoms
- Aspirin
- Tissues
- Tampons
- Razor blades
- Eyeglasses, sunglasses, contact lenses, and cleaning solution

Miscellaneous

- Camera and film
- Swiss army knife
- Flashlight/batteries
- Address book
- Travel journal
- Change purse
- Pocket calculator (handy for currency conversions)
- Guidebooks and maps
- Day pack (if your stuff is safely stored, avoid dragging it all everywhere you go by carrying a small, compressible knapsack)
- Plastic storage bag (if two of your three pairs of socks are wet and smelly, don't contaminate everything before you get a chance to dry them)
- Laundry soap and line
- Sewing kit
- Hostel sleepsack (2 bedsheets sewn together on 3 sides)
- Umbrella
- Luggage lock and tags
- Battery alarm clock
- Batteries
- Moist towelettes
- Adapter and voltage converter

Documents, etc.

- Passport (and visa)
- Tickets/rail passes
- Student ID card
- Hostel membership card
- Money belt or neck wallet
- Cash, traveler's checks, credit cards
- Insurance information

Be sure that the clothes you take are easy to care for; dry cleaning is enormously expensive in most countries. Plan to dress comfortably, but be sensitive to the customs of the country you'll visit. For example, in most countries, don't wear shorts except when you're involved in sports, and always have proper coverings for visits to places of worship. Talk to someone who has recently returned for the best advice.

RECORDING THE MEMORIES

Don't let one of the best times of your life whiz past in a blur of fuzzy, happy memories—plan to keep a journal. Make a solemn vow to buy a notebook, take it along with you, and try to record your observations, activities, and feelings as regularly as possible. Don't worry about rivaling Shakespeare; if whatever you jot down means something to you now, it will be far more valuable to you in the future. Bring your camera and take some photographs, too—even that goofy photo of you checking your watch in front of Big Ben will bring back a flood of memories when you dig it out of the closet years later. If possible, take a small tape recorder along for interviews. (The tape recorder is also good for helping you keep in touch with the folks back home.)

In your journal, or in a separate book, record the names and addresses of the people you meet along the way. You'll want to contact them again or give their names to other friends who will be going in the same direction, and if you jot numbers and addresses on bits of napkins and corners of envelopes, most of them will end up in the trash before you realize what you've thrown away.

It might be fun to compile your own scrapbook-type record of your trip, mixing your own thoughts and impressions with ticket stubs, postcards, maybe even a pressed wildflower from an Alpine field. You're your own historian; preserve your story with whatever props you like.

Drugs

Many Americans traveling abroad assume that buying or carrying small amounts of drugs cannot result in arrest. This is simply *not true.* Americans have been jailed abroad for possessing as little as one-tenth of an ounce (three grams) of marijuana. Penalties for drug violations are severe in foreign countries, including pretrial detention for months or even years and lengthy prison sentences without parole. Many countries do not permit bail in drug-trafficking cases. Beware of the person who asks you to carry a package or drive a car across the border: you might unknowingly become a narcotics trafficker. Remember, when you are traveling abroad, you are not protected by U.S. law. You are subject to the laws of the country in which you are traveling.

To learn more about the facts, send for the brochure *Travel Warning on Drugs Abroad,* available free with a stamped, self-addressed envelope from the Bureau of Consular Affairs, Room 5807, Department of State, Washington, DC 20520.

Still More Books That Can Help

You'll probably need a good guidebook. The drawback of most guidebooks, of course, is that they're read by thousands of other travelers. There's always the danger that low-cost hotels, once listed, will suddenly raise their prices, or that those quaint local restaurants will be invaded by hordes of American travelers like yourself—just what you want to avoid! Don't depend on guidebooks every step of the way; after all, the fun of travel is exploring new things on your own. Still, a guidebook can help you get your bearings. When selecting a guide, it's important to look for one that doesn't just list the addresses of hotels and restaurants, but that attempts to give you a good feel for the territory and the people you'll be visiting.

The *Let's Go* series, produced by Harvard Student Agencies and published by St. Martin's Press, is written by students for students. Packed with budget travel information, there are *Let's Go* guidebooks for most European countries as well as Mexico, Israel, Egypt, and Thailand. They're available at Council Travel offices and most bookstores.

A series of books that competes with *Let's Go* is the Berkeley Guides, which are written by students at the University of California at Berkeley. Published by Random House, these guides feature budget-minded information and topics not found in conventional guidebooks, such as listings for hotels that have facilities for travelers with disabilities and tips on which activities to avoid because they may be harmful to the environment. Berkeley guides are available at Council Travel offices and most bookstores.

Prentice-Hall Travel publishes a good series called Real Guides. While they aren't always as budget-minded as the *Let's Go* and Berkeley guides, they offer a better historical and cultural introduction to the countries they cover and make more of an effort to understand contemporary attitudes. Real Guides also offer a wider array of titles, including countries in Asia, Africa, and South America.

If you really want to get off the beaten path and are on a tight budget, check out Lonely Planet Publications and Moon Publications. Lonely Planet's *Travel Survival Kits* cover countries throughout the Americas, Africa, Asia, and the South Pacific. Its *On a Shoestring* guides cover wider regions for those planning to visit several countries in a given area, such as Southeast Asia or West Africa. If you don't see these books in your local bookstores, ask for a catalog from Lonely Planet, Embarcadero West, 155 Filbert Street, Suite 251, Oakland, CA 94607-2538; (800) 275-8555. Moon Publications also covers many nontraditional

INTERNATIONAL STUDENT IDENTITY CARD TRAVEL GRANTS

The International Student Identity Card Fund provides travel grants to high-school and undergraduate students participating in educational programs in the developing nations of Africa, Asia, and Latin America. Students involved in any type of educational program including study, work, voluntary service, internship, and homestay programs are eligible for funding.

Established in 1981, the fund is supported by the sale of the International Student Identity Card in the United States as well as by private donations. Awards are made twice each year: in April for programs beginning between June 1 and December 31 and in November for programs beginning between January 1 and July 31 of the following year. Awards are for the minimum cost of transportation to and from the program site. Past recipients have undertaken such projects as the following:

- studying rural development in Zimbabwe
- teaching English in China
- working with a community health project in Jamaica
- studying social service agencies in Guatemala
- creating a photo essay on the black educational system of South Africa

Proposals are accepted only from students attending a CIEE member institution or participating in a program sponsored by CIEE or one of its members (see page 299). Awards are determined according to the educational merit of the proposal and the financial need of the applicant. Information and application forms are available from CIEE's Information and Student Services Department, 205 East 42nd Street, New York, NY 10017. Deadlines for applications are March 15 and October 15.

destinations with its *Moon Handbooks,* which are available at Council Travel offices or from Moon's catalog, which you can receive by writing to 722 Wall Street, Chico, CA 95928-5629, or by calling (800) 345-5473.

If you want a larger selection of titles, a number of travel bookstores

A CONVERSATION WITH SHERRIE

Just one month after her graduation from high school, Sherrie went off for a year to Tampere, Finland, as a participant in the International Christian Youth Exchange program.

Q. What did you expect to gain from your experience?
A. I didn't really *expect* anything in particular. I knew that this time was going to be one of intense self-awareness, and I looked forward to a period of personal growth. I hoped to gain more self-understanding and an ability to adapt, and possibly develop more defined goals for my future. But I wasn't sure how all of this was going to miraculously happen. I was also looking forward to learning the Finnish language—especially since I had heard many stories about how difficult it is, and the challenge of learning it intrigued me.

Q. What was the hardest part of your experience?
A. The language barrier was sometimes overwhelming. It was a chore every single morning to decide to continue to work on this impossible language and not just to give up. Another hard time that I experienced was the first time I caught a cold abroad. It seemed then that the distance between me and home grew greater than ever and problems loomed larger than ever. . . . Also difficult was that first month when I had to start from scratch and make friends in a foreign community in a foreign language. The final difficult time was coming home. I had adapted by the end of my year and came to feel such a part of my new situation that I did not want to leave.

Q. How did your experience change your perception of yourself and the U.S.?
A. I have become able to accept my personal shortcomings better, which I believe is the first step in overcoming them. It was also quite eye-opening to view my country from the outside instead of always from the inside out. I was able to see its role in the world today once I was able to get out and view it in a more detached way.

A Conversation with Sherrie

Q. What do you wish you had known before you went?
A. That makes me laugh! I wish I hadn't taken so many clothes. I also wish I had known what a profound difference the year would make in my life.

Q. Would you recommend that others do what you did?
A. One-hundred-and-ten percent yes! I feel that the experience of a year abroad is invaluable in today's world. I became so much more self-reliant, and I really have a better idea of who I am now. Before the exchange can have a positive effect on a person, though, that person must want to have a positive learning experience. You can't be pressured or forced into an undertaking such as this. It has to be *your* idea.

Q. What advice would you give someone about to embark on a similar experience?
A. I'd tell you then that an exchange experience is much like running. When you start, everything is awkward; muscles are tight and the body is uncoordinated. Soon, though, you get into your own pace, get warmed up and things go pretty well. Your ankle or your knee may ache a little, but the run is terribly satisfying. Toward the end, you become fatigued, but you know you can make it. At the finish line, you're proud of having finished but also have stronger muscles because of it. Like running, exchange has a long-term effect.

publish mail-order catalogs: Travel Bookcase, 8375 West 3rd Street, Los Angeles, CA 90048; Hippocrene Books, 171 Madison Avenue, New York, NY 10016; Forsyth Travel Library, 9154 West 57th Street, P.O. Box 2975, Shawnee Mission, KS 66201-1375; Wide World Bookshop, 1911 North 45th Street, Seattle, WA 98103; and Traveller's Bookstore, 22 West 52nd Street, New York, NY 10019.

An interesting magazine for travelers in search of a real cross-cultural experience, *Transitions Abroad* is geared primarily toward people looking for long-term employment or volunteer opportunities overseas, as well as university students who want to study abroad. However, each issue contains valuable information for anyone planning an experience abroad of any length. A yearly subscription of six issues costs $19.95. Write to Transitions Abroad Publishing, 18 Hulst Road, P.O. Box 344, Amherst, MA 01004.

One good source of general information on more than 90 different countries is *Work, Study, Travel Abroad: The Whole World Handbook,* compiled by CIEE and published by St. Martin's Press. The programs listed in the book are for university and college students, but it contains a wealth of general and cultural information on many countries, including suggested readings and films. The twelfth edition (1994-95) costs $13.95 and is available from Council Travel offices and bookstores, or by mail from CIEE (include $1.50 for book-rate postage or $3 for first class).

Chapter 5

How to Get There

*N*ow that you've begun the process of getting your passport, visas, and other necessary items, it's time to think about making your travel arrangements. Which airline will you fly? Where will you be staying? How much will you get around once you're abroad? You'll have many possibilities to choose from; to find the ones that are best for you, plan ahead. Good research and planning will help you make the most of the time you have and can make a big difference in keeping your costs low.

If you live near a Council Travel office, your research will be a bit easier. Council Travel is a full-service travel agency that specializes in providing services for students and other budget-minded travelers. There are 41 of them in the United States, as well as a number in Europe and Asia (see list on page 7). Most are located near university campuses. All are staffed by trained personnel who can answer your questions about student discount airfares, rail passes, and other ways to save money while traveling. CIEE's other travel subsidiary, Council Charter, is discussed later in this chapter.

Whether or not you live near a Council Travel office, your research should begin with a copy of *Student Travels,* available free of charge at Council Travel offices and at many study-abroad offices and international centers at colleges and universities, or by mail from CIEE. Besides the in-depth articles, its 48 pages are filled with information on travel basics, including airfares, car-rental options, and rail-pass plans. Take a look at it before going to a travel agency to make sure you're getting what you want at a reasonable price. Remember, research really is the only way to make your overseas experience an economical one.

The Art of Flying

Over the last several years, the airline industry has seen a number of changes—not uncommon in an industry that always seems to be in a state of flux. In general terms, international airfares remain highly competitive and prices for tickets to some international destinations are actually falling.

Before you begin researching fares, you'll need to make a few decisions about your trip. You should have a rough idea of your general itinerary, your travel budget, how many stopovers you plan to make, what time of year you plan to travel, and the length of time you plan on staying. Most people travel during the summer, but those who have more time on their hands should keep in mind that there are "low" and "high" seasons for travel, during which prices are accordingly lower and higher. The low season lasts roughly from January to March and the high season from June 15 to September 15. The period between April 1and June 15 is sometimes called the "shoulder" season, with prices somewhere between high- and low-season fares. Depending on the airline, you may find either low or shoulder fares from September 15 to January.

Remember that many bargain airfares are limited in availability and must be purchased far ahead of your departure date. Be aware, too, that although some advertised fares may be lower than others, there are usually certain restrictions attached that you'll learn about only by reading the fine print. As you do your research, keep in mind that inexpensive fares abound; they just require a certain amount of investigation, flexibility, and a good deal of creative planning. Let this be your guiding principle when it comes to airfares: the more conditions attached to a certain fare, the cheaper it's going to be.

If you use a travel agent, select one who is interested in selling budget travel. Many agents simply don't find it worthwhile to search through their computer databases on your behalf in return for the small commission a budget fare earns them. Those agents who don't normally devote a good deal of time to reading and studying bargain fares won't be of much help to you. To get an idea of available bargains, or to locate budget travel agents, check the Sunday travel sections of large metropolitan newspapers such as *The New York Times, The Chicago Tribune, The Los Angeles Times,* and *The Washington Post.* Usually, these are full of ads for competitive airfares and contain the latest travel information in columns or feature articles. Budget travel agents also advertise heavily in weekly papers such as the *Village Voice* and *L.A. Weekly.* You'll probably want to do some searching for airfare bargains. Here are the options you're most likely to encounter if you call an airline:

- *Economy Fares.* The term "economy," when applied to airfares, is always relative to first- and business-class seating. That is, it's a euphemism for a regular coach-class ticket. There's really nothing economical about it. You should be able to find less expensive fares, but if you are making reservations at the last minute, an economy fare may be your best—or only—option.

Some restrictions apply for the lowest fares on these seats, first and foremost of which is usually a two-week wait between the time you make your reservation and the time you board the plane.

- *Special Promotional Fares*. Promotional fares pop up sporadically, usually as part of a "quick sale" strategy that airlines use to fill seats during slow periods. One drawback to these fares is that they usually require the traveler to act immediately rather than plan an itinerary ahead of time. Many are also restricted to certain dates, usually in the low season. But if you have the luxury of flexibility, or if you find a deal on a flight that happens to fit your schedule, a promotional fare can be a dream come true.

- *Advance Purchase Excursion (APEX) Fares*. APEX fares are between 30 and 40 percent lower than regular economy class. Since low fares seem to go hand in hand with restrictions, however, beware of minimum and maximum stay requirements, cancellation and change penalties, and stopover restrictions. You must also purchase your ticket anytime from 7 to 30 days in advance. "Super" APEX fares are somewhat cheaper than regular APEX but are in effect on a limited number of routes.

- *"Last Minute" Youth Fares*. Almost every major carrier has replaced its old "standby" fares with what we call "last minute" youth fares. These are available usually to passengers 12 to 24 years of age on a one-way or round-trip basis, but must be booked within three days of departure.

Student and Youth Airfares While the least expensive airfares usually carry the most restrictions, special youth and student discounts are the exception to the rule. For those who are eligible, student/youth fares can cut as much as 50 percent off regular economy fares. Besides the low cost, student/youth fares have few of the restrictions that apply to most budget airfares, and are valid on regularly scheduled flights of a number of major airlines. In order to qualify for most student/youth airfares, you must have either the International Student Identity Card (see page 56) or the International Youth Card (see page 57).

Most student and youth fares are the result of special contracts made between student travel organizations (including CIEE) and the airlines, and are generally not sold directly by the airlines themselves. In fact, most airline ticketing offices will not have information about them. To find out about student/youth fares, check with Council Travel or any other agency that specializes in student and youth travel.

It's impossible to predict what prices will be at the time you read this book. To get current student/youth fares, check Council Travel's most recent edition of *Airfare Updates,* which provides the latest information on nearly every type of international airfare. Or, you can simply call your nearest Council Travel office (see list on page 7) for a fare quote.

Consolidator Tickets and Charter Flights A charter flight is one in which a tour operator reserves a plane to fly a specific route on certain dates. This arrangement allows charter companies to offer tickets at a discount. Consolidators offer a similar service. When airlines can't fill seats, consolidators buy extra tickets at a discount, then sell these discounted tickets to the public.

Keep in mind that consolidators and charter companies work with airlines. If you book with a charter company, be sure to find out what airline you'll be flying on. Also ascertain the exact arrangements that have been made between the airline and the company selling you the ticket. Before purchasing your ticket, ask for a copy of your contract; operators are by law required to supply you with one when you book a charter. Know your rights and responsibilities beforehand to avoid headaches later.

Consolidator and charter tickets are usually nonrefundable and cannot be changed. However, this isn't true for all companies, if you book with Council Charter, for example, tickets are at least partially refundable as long as you cancel before your scheduled departure from the United States. Council Charter return flights can be changed in Europe for a fee of $75. You can also purchase a trip cancellation waiver, which guarantees a full refund if you cancel anytime up to your scheduled check-in time. Another feature that makes Council Charter unique is its mix-and-match plan, which lets you fly into one city and return from another. Although the actual cities served vary slightly from year to year, Council Charter's destinations generally include Amsterdam, Brussels, London, Lyon, Madrid, Malaga, Nice, Paris, Rome, and other European cities. Council Charter flights depart from Boston and New York, with low-cost add-on fares from a variety of other U.S. cities.

For more information contact a Council Travel office (see page 7) or call Council Charter's toll-free number: (800) 800-8222.

Getting Around

Your international flight will only be the first step in your journey. If you plan to spend all of your time in just one city, you'll probably make use of local public transportation, such as subways, trams, or buses. But if you plan to travel more extensively, there's a wide variety of transportation options available to you, including planes, trains, buses, cars, boats, bicycles or—imagine this—walking.

Which of these options you choose will depend on things like geography, scenic interest, efficiency, and price. Taking an overnight ferry between two places, for example, may not get you there with the break-neck speed of a jet, but it's cheaper and often more scenic. In many countries, buses are faster and cheaper than trains, although they can be somewhat less comfortable and, if you get stuck sitting next to someone carrying a screaming infant, there may be no escape. Consult a good guidebook to get an idea of how you can get around. Also, try to pick up a good map of the country as well as detailed street plans of any cities you'll be visiting. If your local stores don't have any, contact the country's tourist board in the United States, or try bookstores that carry travel literature (see "Still More Books That Can Help" on page 63).

By Air Air travel to other continents usually isn't cheap, but there are special student/youth fares that are easier on the wallet. (Who says high school doesn't have its privileges?) To be eligible you need to have an International Student Identity Card or International Youth card (see pages 56 and 57). Student fares on many routes can be booked at any Council Travel office (see page 7). Popular routes like London-Paris, Rome–Athens, and Paris–Tel Aviv often fill up early, so do your planning, calling, and booking as soon as possible.

Foreign travelers in some countries can obtain special air passes that entitle them to a certain number of flights during a specified period of time. For example, in Brazil, a vast country with limited roads and railways, an air pass provides an economical and convenient way to get around. The Brazil Air Pass allows five stopovers within Brazil within 21 days for $440. It's smart to plan ahead if you're interested in these passes—for most countries they must be purchased before departure from the United States. To see if special air passes are available for a particular country, contact the country's tourist bureau or the office of its official airline.

By Train In the United States, we seem to have forgotten how useful railroads are; rail travel is much more common in many parts of the world than it is here. Trains give you the chance to talk to the locals at length and see some scenery as well. Fortunately, not only do many countries have excellent rail systems, but they offer special passes similar to air passes which can cut down your travel costs. If you're planning to cover a lot of territory by train, most national rail systems, such as BritRail and Japan Railways, offer passes good for travel over a certain period of time. Young people traveling to several countries in Europe may want to consider the following rail bargains:

- *Eurail Youthpass:* Anyone under 26 can purchase this pass for unlimited second-class travel in seventeen countries. One month is $578, two months is $768.

- *Eurail Youth Flexipass:* Also available to anyone under 26, this pass is good for 15 days of travel within two months and costs $540. Passes for 5 and 10 days of travel within two months cost $255 and $398, respectively.
- *Eurail Europass:* The basic pass is good for five days of unlimited travel within two months in three contiguous European countries, and costs $198. More days and countries can be added at extra cost.
- *BIJ Tickets:* Sold under the Transalpino, Eurotrain, and Twentours names, BIJ tickets (Billets Internationaux de Jeunesse) can save anyone under 26 up to 50 percent off second-class fares for international trips within Europe and Morocco. Tickets are valid for two months (six months for Turkey and Morocco), allowing free stopovers in other countries along a direct route. Tickets must be purchased from specified agents, usually student travel organizations, located throughout Europe.

Council Travel (see page 7) is an official distributor of Eurail passes. You can get Eurail passes, most other national rail passes, and BIJ tickets at any Council Travel office (see page 7). Eurail passes can also be purchased in the United States through Rail Europe, 226-230 Westchester Avenue, White Plains, NY 10604; (914) 682-5172.

By Bus Bus travel isn't as popular in Europe as it is here, but in other parts of the world—especially Latin America, Asia, and Africa—buses (and such variations on buses as minivans and flatbed trucks) are the most popular forms of transportation. In some areas, buses are virtually the only means of reaching reach certain destinations. While bus travel in most countries is already inexpensive, many countries also offer youth fares as well as passes good for travel over a certain period of time. Consult the national tourist office of the country you plan to visit.

By Boat Relax . . . you won't have to row anywhere unless you really want to. Water travel across lakes, rivers, and seas is still common—and necessary—in many parts of the world. Hovercraft skim the waves across the English Channel; hydrofoils connect the Mediterranean coasts of Europe and North Africa; steamers navigate the Amazon and the Nile; ferries link the East Asian countries of China, Korea, Taiwan, and Japan. If you're traveling with a Eurail pass, you're eligible for discounts on a number of European ferry routes. The International Student Identity Card (see page 56) is also good for special rates on English Channel and Mediterranean sailings. Contact a Council Travel office (see page 7) for details.

By Bicycle It's easy to take your bike along with you—the airline will tell you how to get it ready for the trip. You can also rent or buy one when you get there. In fact, many national rail systems offer their own special bike rental deals, allowing you to alternate travel by train and bike. Bicycle touring is a great way to see the country up close and at your own pace, stopping at will and choosing your own route. A number of organizations sponsor group tours abroad (see the Outdoor Activities section). If you want to go it alone, find out whether the country you're visiting has any cycling clubs; they should be happy to provide you with information.

Lodgings

If you're going abroad on an organized program, lodgings will probably be arranged for you. In the few programs that won't, looking for places to stay will be your own responsibility. With a little bit of resourcefulness, you won't have to put too big a dent in your budget. You can always consult one of the many guidebooks for budget travelers, but remember that even the most up-to-date guides usually reflect prices from at least the year before. Once you've arrived in a place, if it's a city of any size at all, the local tourist office can give you names and addresses of inexpensive hotels; some will even phone ahead to book your room. Local members of the International Student Travel Confederation (see page 56) should be able to offer some help; many, in fact, run their own student hotels.

Hostelling International and its network of hostels offer low-cost accommodations to members (for membership information, see page 58). Originally designed for hikers and cyclists, hostels now welcome all sorts of travelers. They can be found in major cities as well as in remote, scenic spots. Accommodations are usually dorm style, in which you share a room with fellow travelers. Many hostels, however, have a limited number of private rooms which couples or small groups can share at a slightly higher price. The hostel provides you with a bed, pillow, and blanket, and you provide your own sleep sack (a sheet folded over and sewn up on two sides) or rent one from the hostel. Sleeping bags are generally *not* allowed except in remote, rustic hostels that cater primarily to hikers. Many hostels have specific regulations. Almost all require that you help with a small domestic chore, such as sweeping out the bunk room. Most hostels have evening curfews and limit the length of stay to three consecutive days, unless you have made special arrangements ahead of time. Many also have a lockout system that requires all guests to stay out for most of the day, usually from 10 A.M. to 5 P.M. If you don't mind these restrictions, youth hostels are great places to meet fellow travelers, trade stories and information, and plan what's coming next.

A CONVERSATION WITH MRS. WHITE

Mrs. White's daughter spent two months in Chile as an AFS program participant. Here are some thoughts from a parent's point of view.

Q. Was the trip your idea or your daughter's?
A. It was entirely her idea. At first when she came to me and told me she was applying for a scholarship to go to Chile, I didn't think much about it, since I thought the possibility was remote. When she actually got it, though, I have to admit I got a bit nervous.

Q. What made you nervous?
A. I've never been anywhere out of the country, and the only time she'd spent away from home was a week at her aunt's house—even then I worried. She was going to a new country, to a place where she didn't know the language. I was nervous about the political aspect too.

Q. What convinced you to let her go?
A. The AFSers who came to my home for the family interview. They talked about their own experiences and turned my thinking around.

Q. What was the most difficult part for you while she was away?
A. I wasn't prepared for the fact that I wouldn't hear from her for such a long time. I didn't know that mail was so delayed in Chile—she was in a remote village—and it was five weeks before I got a letter. She seems to have done just fine, though, without needing me around every moment of the day.

Q. How did it all work out?
A. Very, very well. She definitely achieved a sense of independence. She felt she learned a lot, not only about Chile, but about her own country as well from the other AFSers from other parts of the United States. She had such a good time that she wants to go to Japan this year with the same program.

Pensiones (pronounced *pen-see-yo-nays*) are another option. These are guest houses in other countries which cater exclusively to foreign travelers. Rates and quality of accommodations vary greatly, but many aren't too expensive if you're only staying a few weeks. When you contact the country's tourist board for information about pensiones, be as specific as possible about where in the country you'd like to stay.

Meeting the People

Getting to know the local people should be one of your goals as a traveler. Probably the best way to accomplish this goal is to stay with a family. In the listings, you'll find a number of organizations that specialize in homestay experiences. Depending on the organization, the homestay may last anywhere from a week to a full year. One thing we must reiterate here: if you choose to participate in a homestay program, make sure to find out how the sponsoring organization selects host families. If you suspect that an organization's host families participate only to make some extra money, you'd do better to look elsewhere.

If you'd like to spend a short time with one or more families while you travel, you may want to become a member of SERVAS. This organization puts travelers in touch with host families who invite SERVAS members into their home for a two- to three-night stay. Applicants to SERVAS are interviewed by local area representatives and, if accepted, receive an introductory letter to families in the area they'll be visiting. The rest is up to the traveler and the family to arrange. The U.S. SERVAS Committee is located at 11 John Street, Room 706, New York, NY 10038; (212) 267-0252.

For those who want to visit local families without staying the night, most countries have organizations that specialize in short-term get-togethers. You may be invited to someone's home for dinner or just a few hours of conversation over tea. Contact the official tourism office of the country you plan to visit to see if such a service is offered.

Chapter 6
COMING HOME

*B*efore you go, you should think about one last thing: coming home. You probably feel there's no reason to worry about this, especially now, but there are adjustments to make when you come home as well as when you go abroad. Just as preparation helps make your trip easier, thinking ahead helps to ease the transition when you return home.

Returnees often report they feel strange coming home from abroad. You also may feel uneasy after you come home, and wonder why. After all, home is home, and you know how people act in your own culture. But remember, you have traveled or lived somewhere else for a while—several months, a year—and probably tried very hard to adapt to a different culture and to accept that culture's ways of doing things. When you come back, you may forget that you are seeing home a little differently from before. Your perspective now is not an exclusively American one, but the perspective of an American who has had a cross-cultural experience.

Not surprisingly, the person who becomes most comfortable in the new culture and has an intensely positive experience will probably have the hardest time coming home. If you have been speaking another language, your English may even be rusty. On the other hand, the person who travels with a group of American friends or eats mostly at McDonald's or Pizza Hut probably won't have a sufficiently different experience to find coming home very difficult.

Assuming that you *have* immersed yourself in another culture, at least in some small ways, you have to be ready to deal with not only some jet lag, but also some culture lag. Many returnees feel confused and disoriented, which is understandable if just yesterday they were in

This chapter was written by Angene H. Wilson, Professor, College of Education and Associate Director, International Affairs, University of Kentucky. Professor Wilson is also a volunteer for Youth for Understanding.

the cloud forest in Costa Rica or walking along the river Seine in Paris. But after a while they get back their rhythm and start to feel like they're back home again. Perhaps coming home was easier in the old days when people traveled slowly on ships!

Besides the culture lag, there are other reasons for feeling strange at home. Living or traveling in another country is a special experience, and you may feel like a special person as an exchange student or international workcamp volunteer. Being an American abroad is a novelty; it may be hard to readjust to ordinary life back home and also to being an ordinary person in the home culture.

Those who like adventure may adjust more easily overseas but less quickly at home. Abroad, there always seems to be a new place to explore or a new person to meet or a new challenge to overcome. At home, everything might seem just as it was when you left.

You might also find it frustrating to try to talk about your trip to people back home. Returnees say they get tired of the same old questions, such as "How was your trip?" or "Did you have fun?" You will probably be annoyed by what seem superficial questions, because the places you have been and people you have met are important to you and can't be described in just a few words. It's hard to remember that you once had to look on the world map to find the Caribbean island where you were going to take part in a workcamp. It's hard to remember that you knew little about Switzerland except that it was home of the Alps, before you spent the summer there as an exchange student. It's also discouraging if the places you lived in or traveled to overseas are rarely or never covered in your local newspaper, which makes it difficult to find news about them after you return.

Many returnees see educating others as part of their role. They have figured out ways to answer questions that challenge other people's stereotypes and to teach other people some of what they have learned. Some show pictures to help their friends visualize the country. Of course, it's still hard for people who have not had your experience to really understand what you're feeling inside, but you can help them see things in a different light.

Sometimes returnees have a slide party for family or friends and serve international dishes. Other ways to involve friends include inviting them to attend international activities at school or to see foreign films. You can also get to know new exchange students at your school and introduce them to your friends.

Of course, some people simply may not be interested in other cultures. In that case, there's not much you can do. You may want to tell everyone about what you've done, but it's important not to brag. Bring up your experience in a natural way when the opportunity arises in conversation.

Also remember to show interest in events that occurred while you were away; your younger brother's baseball team championship, your friends' beach party, and so on. If you show that you care about the activities of friends and family, they'll be more willing to share your experiences. (They may even stay awake during most of your slide show.)

What about your parents? One research study of high-school students returning from a homestay program abroad indicates that an experience abroad has a direct and usually positive impact on relationships with family. In communication with parents, returnees reported greater closeness, greater equality in the relationship, greater appreciation for parents, and a smoother and more open relationship.

What about school? Many schools have international clubs you can join to meet others who have traveled, as well as international students. Foreign-language clubs may offer a chance to keep up your new fluency in a second language. Sometimes these clubs sponsor international dinners, talent shows, or other activities. Members of these clubs can be helpful by organizing a buddy system for new international students.

Lots of returnees find they want to help build bridges between cultures as well as tell people about their experiences when they come home. Befriending a new international student who may be an immigrant, a refugee, or an exchange student is one way to do this. Since you're familiar with the nervous, confused feeling that foreign students have, go out of your way to talk to, eat with, or help students who are new.

Returnees may also find opportunities to be helpful in their wider communities. Many are inspired to act as tour guides for school groups visiting from other countries, to teach English to Spanish-speaking neighbors, and generally to provide assistance to new community members from outside the United States. Bridge-building doesn't have to be limited to people of the country you visited. You will probably feel generally more interested in people of other cultures and more understanding of what it is like to be a stranger in a new culture.

Here is a list of things you can do when you return from a trip abroad:

- Go to a reentry program after you get back if the organization you go overseas with has one. If not, get together with other students who have had similar experiences to talk. Remember that feeling strange is normal.
- Throw a party for your family and friends and share your pictures and international food.
- Tell people about other cultures from your own experience when they ask you questions. You can be a teacher!
- Keep in touch with new friends overseas.
- Make new international friends back home.

- Find international organizations to participate in, such as Amnesty International or Oxfam.
- Make presentations about your experience to a class at school, younger students in elementary school, and community groups.
- Invite an international student to your home for Thanksgiving or become a host family for an exchange student.
- Start a dream fund to save money for your next international experience.

With a little planning, you can feel enthusiastic not only about going abroad, but also about returning and using your newfound skills and knowledge at home. Don't make the mistake of thinking the experience is over when it's only beginning. Your adventure abroad doesn't have to end. If you maintain your new contacts, interests, and awareness, the experience can last a lifetime.

PART TWO
THE PROGRAMS

*I*n this book, you will find a wide range of program possibilities—programs based in the United States and overseas, programs run by nonprofit organizations and those run by profit-making firms, programs that emphasize study and others that offer touring, camping, sports, or voluntary service. To make your search for the one that's right for you easier, we've organized the program listings into seven sections:

- Study Abroad
- Language Study
- Creative Arts
- Organized Tours
- Work/Volunteer
- Outdoor Activities
- Homestay

Of course, some organizations do not fit neatly into a category; a number of them offer more than one type of program. In these cases, we've provided a complete description of the organization and its programs only in the section that reflects what seems to be the organization's main focus. For example, you'll find all the offerings of AFS Intercultural Programs—including volunteer, homestay, and outdoor activities programs—listed in the Study Abroad section, since most of its programs emphasize study. However, to make things easy for you, we have cross-referenced the organizations offering multiple programs in all the appropriate sections. Browsing through the Outdoor Activities section, for example, you'll come across references to organizations described in other sections of the book. You can also refer to the index, which lists programs both by location and by type.

The fact that an organization is listed here is no guarantee that its programs are flawless. You must be sure to apply the evaluation techniques we outlined in chapter 3 to the programs in this book, as well as to any others you encounter. There are, however, a few programs that we *can* vouch for—programs that are sponsored by members of the Council on International Educational Exchange. Check the description to see if the organization is a CIEE member. CIEE-member programs are all operated on a nonprofit basis; they include some of the largest and best-established international exchange programs available. As part of the membership review process, they have undergone the scrutiny of the CIEE Membership Committee, which has examined their programs and services as well as their organizational structure. As members of CIEE, they have demonstrated an interest in maintaining high standards and a willingness to contribute to the development of the field of international exchange.

Format for the Listings

We've tried to distill the material we received from each sponsor and present it in a format that will give you a feel for what each program is really about. Organizations are listed alphabetically in each section. Within each listing, the information is broken down in this way:

The sponsor: Some background about the organization that offers the program—when it was founded, what its stated goals are, what other organizatons it may be affiliated with.

The program: What the sponsor has to offer—the duration of the program, when and where it takes place, and what it involves.

Orientation: How the organization prepares participants for the experience.

Supervision: The type and amount of supervision offered by different organizations varies greatly. Some programs do not supervise participants outside the classroom or do much beyond handling program logistics. This does not mean that the program is better or worse than a more closely supervised one, but it should help tell you whether the program is the type you're looking for.

Services for persons with disabilities: Specific services for participants with disabilities. Some programs do not have any specific policy and simply consider applicants on a case-by-case basis.

Requirements: Age, academic, and language requirements, as well as other qualifications that the sponsors are seeking from applicants.

Living arrangements: Whether participants live in a tent, with a local family, or in a first-class hotel. Where room and board are included, we've sometimes distinguished between half-board and full board. Half-board includes breakfast only; full board includes breakfast and dinner.

Finances: How much the program will cost, what the fees include, and whether scholarship aid is available. For foreign-based organizations, we've converted local currency into U.S. dollars using exchange rates valid in 1994.

Deadline: The date by which applications must be received to be considered for the program.

Contact: Wherever possible, we give a specific name and that person's title, so that your letter of inquiry won't get lost in a pile of mail.

Not every listing has every heading; for some programs, a few of the items may not apply. Whenever information about the programs appears within quotation marks, it is a direct quote from the sponsor's promotional material.

Remember, we've only summarized the programs in this book; finding out all the information you need will be up to you.

STUDY ABROAD

*I*n this section, you'll find a wide range of study-abroad options, whether you want to study for an academic year, a semester, or just a few weeks during the school year. Most of the institutions or organizations in this section are based in the United States and offer programs especially designed for Americans.

Courses are usually taught in a classroom, and in some cases by a foreign instructor in the language of the country. Many of the programs, however, offer the option of courses taught in English. Students can learn about a variety of topics, including the country's history, culture, and language.

Many of the study-abroad programs also involve homestays or organized tours before, during, or after the study experience. Individual students can enroll in most of the study programs described, but a few involve school-to-school exchanges—a group of students (and teachers) from one school exchanges with a group from a school abroad.

ACADEMIC STUDY ASSOCIATES
355 Main Street
P.O. Box 38
Armonk, NY 10504
Telephone: (914) 273-2250

The sponsor: Academic Study Associates (ASA) is a commercial agency that was founded in 1982.

The program: ASA offers study programs in Narbonne, France; Andalusia, Spain; and Oxford, England.

Supervision: ASA representatives, who must be at least 21 years old and have foreign language fluency, provide general supervision and emergency assistance.

Services for persons with disabilities: Every provision possible has been made to enable participation by disabled persons. Everyone is invited to participate.

Requirements: Participants should be between 13 and 18 years old and in the ninth through twelfth grades. One year of language instruction in the foreign language is also required.

Living arrangements: Accommodations are provided in homestays or in the Residential Language Center, where all rooms have a private bath.

Finances: Prices range from $3,695 to $3,895 which includes room and board, instruction, and all other activities.

Deadline: There is no set deadline.

Contact: Will Thompson (above address).

ACADEMIC TRAVEL LOWESTOFT LTD.
at the Briar School of English
8 Gunton Cliff
Lowestoft
Suffolk NR32 4PE
England
Telephone: (44) 502-589150

The sponsor: Established in 1958, Academic Travel has many years of experience in educating youth from all over the world in English language courses.

The program: Subject to yearly review, courses are offered in literature, drama, the environment, travel, and tourism. The school is located near the beach, which allows for water sports such as sailing, canoeing, and kayaking in addition to other land-based ones like tennis and horseback riding.

Orientation: There is an orientation at the beginning of the program at the Briar School in England.

Supervision: Group leaders provide supervision while keeping daily contact with the directors and managerial staff, who take care of any possible emergency situations.

Requirements: Students must be at least 10 years old.

Living arrangements: Students are placed in homestays with host families with up to three students to a family. Single beds and full board are provided.

Finances: For a three-week course, the fee is 635 British pounds (approximately $978 dollars), which includes full board, lodging, tuition, sports, cultural visits, social activities, and transportation to and from the airport.

Deadline: Two weeks before the course starts.

Contact: Mr. Neville J. Doe, Office Manager (address above).

ACADEMIC YEAR IN AMERICA/AMERICAN INSTITUTE FOR FOREIGN STUDY FOUNDATION
140 Greenwich Avenue
Greenwich, CT 06830
Telephone: (800) 322-4678

The sponsor: Academic Year in America (AYA) has nonprofit, tax-exempt status through its affiliation with the American Institute for Foreign Study Foundation. Since 1984, AYA has conducted study abroad programs for high-school students.

The program: AYA offers two programs, the Academic Year in Germany program and the Summer in Chile program. The Academic Year in Germany program places the American student in a German high school and in a homestay with a German family for either a semester or the full academic year. The month-long Summer in Chile program is possible because the month of July is wintertime in Chile, which means the Chilean secondary students are still in school. This program also includes a homestay with a Chilean family.

Orientation: There is a two- or three-day orientation session either in New York or Miami before departure.

Supervision: Local coordinators supervise the students.

Services for persons with disabilities: Applications from persons with disabilities are considered on a case-by-case basis.

Requirements: Students must be between the ages of 15 and 18 with an overall C average. For the Germany program, students need to have 2 years of German. For the Chile program, students need to have 1 to 2 years of Spanish.

Living arrangements: Both programs feature homestays with local families. Host families, who are not paid, are selected through a referral system which includes reference checks and interviews.

Finances: The Academic Year in Germany price range is from $4,595 to $5,200, including transportation. For the most recent Summer in Chile price, contact AYA.

Deadline: Rolling admissions.

Contact: Kimberly Martin, Director of Marketing (address above).

ACCENT
425 Market Street, 2nd Floor
San Francisco, CA 94105
Telephone: (415) 904-7756

The sponsor: ACCENT is a commercial agency which plans and coordinates academic programs in conjunction with U.S. colleges and universities.

The program: ACCENT offers summer and semester programs in Florence, Italy and Paris, France.

Orientation: Predeparture orientations and intensive on-site orientations are provided.

Supervision: The student-teacher ratio is usually ten to one.

Services for persons with disabilities: Accent encourages participation by persons with disabilities to the extent that host institutions can accommodate their needs.

Requirements: Students should be at least 17 and have completed their junior year in high school.

Living arrangements: Students generally have a choice between residence halls, homestays with local families, or private apartments.

Finances: Costs for summer programs range from $2,100 to $2,600; semester programs from $3,600 to $4,900. The fee includes instruction, housing, orientation, excursions, and partial board.

Deadline: Varies according to program.

AFS INTERCULTURAL PROGRAMS
220 East 42nd Street, Third Floor
New York, NY 10017
Telephone: (212) 949-4242 or (800) AFS-INFO

The sponsor: The AFS idea originated with volunteer ambulance drivers who served in World War I and World War II and then established an international exchange program for secondary-school students in 1947. Originally called the American Field Service, the mission of AFS is education that reaches beyond the classroom to promote intercultural learning and understanding that contributes to a more peaceful world. It offers a broad range of international exchanges including homestays for secondary-school students and special programs for teachers. This nonprofit organization is a member of CIEE.

The program: AFS offers choices in more than 50 countries:

- *Semester Program*: Young people may spend five months attending local secondary schools in any of 12 countries. (Departures in January/February and July/August.)
- *Year Program*: Students spend a year attending local secondary schools in any of 42 countries. (Several departures in January–March and July–September.)
- *Summer Programs*: AFS offers summer placements in 30 countries (Departures in June/July and January for the Southern Hemisphere). These include the following:
    Summer Homestay: Students immerse themselves in the local culture by living with a host family.
    Language Study/Homestay: Choose among Spanish, French, German, Japanese, or Russian. In Latin America and Japan, participants live with host families while attending classes during the day. Participants in Europe receive two to three weeks of language training at a university campus or in a youth hostel preceded or followed by a homestay.
    Outdoor Education/Homestay: This program in Australia, New Zealand, and Switzerland includes a five-week homestay with school attendance. In a two- to three-week group experi-

ence, students participate in such activities as map reading, outdoor skills, rock climbing, canoeing, and camping.

Environmental Studies in Brazil: This program gives participants a chance to learn about environmental issues facing Brazil and the rest of the world. Students live with a host family and study a variety of ecological habitats in one of four areas throughout Brazil. Activities include hiking, canoeing, caving, and camping.

Team Missions: Summer programs of three to four weeks for groups of high-school age students and their leaders age 25 or over. Team Missions typically involve not only homestays but also intensive examination of important global issues, such as emerging democracy in Russia, environment in Costa Rica, and economics in Hong Kong and China.

Orientation: AFS provides orientations on a local and national level before departure, as well as an orientation once the participants have arrived. For semester and year programs, additional orientations are held periodically throughout the stay.

Supervision: AFS works with partner AFS offices in each country. Local staff and volunteers provide support for the participant and the host family. Travel and orientation periods are conducted by staff and trained AFS volunteers. Each student has a local volunteer contact who is available at all times.

Services for persons with disabilities: AFS welcomes disabled candidates. Participants are placed in appropriate accommodations.

Requirements: Although specific requirements vary, AFS programs generally are open only to high-school students ages 15 to 18, who have not yet graduated. Most programs require at least a 2.7 grade point average.

Living arrangements: The homestay is integral to the AFS experience. Host families are carefully screened and receive no payment.

Finances: The fees vary from program to program. Costs range from $2,395 to $6,875 (for the year University Program). The fee includes international transportation, secondary medical insurance, and living expenses. Scholarship assistance is available for most programs.

For returnees: More than 25 United States colleges and universities offer scholarships and financial aid for returnees of exchange programs. A list of schools giving preference to AFS experience for admission called *AFS: The College Connection* is available from the AFS New York headquarters.

Deadline: Rolling admissions.

Contact: AFS (address above). Be sure to indicate any special interests you may have; new programs are being developed all the time.

ALEXANDER MUSS HIGH SCHOOL IN ISRAEL (AM/HSI)
3950 Biscayne Boulevard
Miami, FL 33137
Telephone: (305) 576-3286; (800) 327-5980

The sponsor: Established in 1972, AM/HSI sponsors short-term academic programs in Hod Ha'Sharon, Israel. AM/HSI works in cooperation with public and private schools in the United States, the Israeli Ministry of Education, and the Mosenson Regional High School in Israel.

The program: There are five sessions. Four sessions are eight weeks long and occur during the school year, beginning in September, November, February, and April. The fifth session is a seven-week summer session starting in late June. The curriculum concentrates on the history of Israel from ancient to modern times, using the historical sites in Israel as living classrooms. The basic disciplines of mathematics, science, and foreign language are also taught. Classes are conducted on campus and at the related historical sites.

Supervision: The full-time staff, consisting of Americans who are permanent residents of Israel, provides student supervision. There is one teacher for every eighteen students.

Services for persons with disabilities: Because more than 50 percent of the program involves strenuous hiking to ancient sites, the program does not often accommodate persons with physical disabilities.

Requirements: Students must be high-school juniors or seniors, have a minimum 2.5 GPA, and be recommended by their home school.

Living arrangements: Students stay in coed dormitories.

Finances: The fee ranges from $3,625 to $4,700, depending upon session dates. Included are tuition, room and board, international airfare, and ground transportation in Israel.

Deadline: Applications should be sent in at least two months prior to departure. Classes are often booked to capacity two to four months prior to departure.

Contact: Admissions Department (address above).

AMERICAN ASSOCIATION OF TEACHERS OF GERMAN
  (AATG)
112 Haddontown Court 104
Cherry Hill, NJ 08034
Telephone: (609) 795-5553

The sponsor: AATG is a nonprofit professional association of teachers of German in the United States from the elementary to college level.

The program: Each summer AATG sponsors a four-week travel/study program to Germany in cooperation with the Pedagogical Exchange Service, a German government agency. Participants live with German families and attend *Gymnasium* classes (*Gymnasium* is the German equivalent of American high school). Organized field trips are included and often the host families plan excursions as well.

Supervision: An American teacher of German is available to help with trips, act as a liaison with German school authorities, and provide personal counseling.

Services for persons with disabilities: Provisions may be made according to the disability involved.

Requirements: Applicants must be high-school students at least 15 years old with at least two years of German and the recommendation of a German teacher.

Living arrangements: The families chosen to host the students have a son or daughter about the same age as the American visitor. The entire four weeks is spent with the host family.

Finances: The fee of approximately $1,995 includes round-trip airfare, room and board, excursions, insurance, and classes.

Deadline: April 1.

Contact: Helene Zimmer-Loew (address above).

AMERICAN COLLEGE OF SWITZERLAND
1854 Leysin
Switzerland
Telephone: (41) 25-342223
Fax: (41) 25-341346

The sponsor: Founded in 1963, the American College of Switzerland is a division of Schiller International University.

The program: The Preparatory Program for University Entrance was created for high-school students who wish to finish their senior year in a university setting. The academic program entails small tutorial courses in social studies, science, English, foreign languages, art, and mathematics. Students reside on the campus of the American College of Switzerland, which offers a full range of college services such as a computer laboratory, a language laboratory, a 50,000-volume library, and university staff and instructors. Extracurricular and cultural activities fortify the academic program by taking advantage of the college's central European setting as well as the Swiss Alps.

Orientation: There is an orientation for students upon arrival.

Supervision: The Administrative Director provides assistance in the event of an emergency.

Requirements: Students must be at least 16 years old and going into the twelfth grade.

Living arrangements: Students live in dormitories at the American College of Switzerland.

Finances: The fee is 23,575 Swiss francs (approximately $18,000 dollars), which includes room and board. Some scholarships and grants are available upon application.

Deadline: Rolling admissions.

Contact: Cindy Frith, Administrative Director (address above).

AMERICAN FRIENDS OF THE COLLÈGE LYCÉE CÉVENOL INTERNATIONAL
c/o Moses Brown School
250 Lloyd Avenue
Providence, RI 02906
Telephone: (401) 272-5158

The sponsor: The College Lycée Cévenol International is a boarding school located in the village of Chambon-sur-Lignon, in France. It was founded in 1938 by two pacifists, pastors from the local parish. The goal of the College Lycée Cévenol International is still "to foster world peace and global understanding by bringing together students from many different places and cultures." The American Friends of the College Lycée Cévenol International is a nonprofit organization made up of former students, workcamp participants, and ministers. It was founded in 1946 and is staffed by volunteers.

The program: Situated on a 30-acre campus that was once a family farm, the college offers an academic year program, a summer school, and a workcamp. The school year runs from September to June. The student body and faculty is international and the curriculum is that of the standard French *lycée*. Fifteen to twenty countries are usually represented. The summer school combines language study with tennis, horseback riding, swimming, team sports, workshops (woodwork and drawing), performing arts (music, drama, film), and excursions to the surrounding countryside. The workcamp takes place in July, and participants from all over the world work together on a project that might involve remodeling building interiors, painting the outside of a building, landscaping or doing farm or forestry work. Each day includes time set aside for a language course; evenings are reserved for group activities.

Supervision: During the summer and academic year programs, there is one teacher for every 10 students, and resident counselors live in the student dorms. The workcamp has one or two group leaders responsible for limited supervision of twenty volunteers.

Requirements: For the school year program, students should be 13 to 18 years old with two years of French. The summer school, which has two sessions, one in July and one in August, accepts students from 12 to 18 with some French-language background; for the workcamp, a minimum age of 18 and some knowledge of French is required. International Baccalaureate preparation is available (some courses in English).

Living arrangements: Students live together in dormitories with two or three students per room. There are resident counselors in each dorm. "The College Cévenol seeks to promote a simple life, where students learn the importance of helping one another, of working together with shared responsibilities. All students are expected to help with campus chores in the dorms or dining hall."

Finances: The school year program costs approximately $2,500 per trimester, with travel and vacation expenses extra. The summer school requires payment in francs (approximately $1,140, depending on the length of the session). The fee for the workcamp is $150 plus $35 for insurance.

Deadline: May 15 for school year and summer program, May 1 for workcamp.

Contact: Anne W. Burnham (address above).

AMERICAN HERITAGE ASSOCIATION
P.O. Box 425
Lake Oswego, OR 97036
Telephone: (503) 635-3703

The sponsor: American Heritage Association is a nonprofit organization which, since 1957, has provided intercultural and experiential educational programs. The organization is a member of CIEE.

The program: American Heritage Association offers programs for Pacific Northwest secondary-school students that include international homestay/travel programs and school-to-school exchanges. Groups of students travel to Europe, Asia, and Mexico on programs custom-designed to suit their needs. The emphasis in all programs is on education, using travel as a tool. Students and their adviser are required to participate in a training course during the academic year preceding travel.

Orientation: An orientation at a weekend camp is held six weeks prior to departure. In addition, students must participate in a series of pre-departure meetings required of each group.

Supervision: An adviser stays with the group during the program. The student-teacher ratio is 10 to 1.

Services for persons with disabilities: Each participant with a disability is handled individually.

Requirements: Participants usually are between 13 and 18 years old. Students are accepted based on personal and educational motivation, participation in group preparation including orientation, satisfactory medical examination, attention to program deadlines, satisfactory transcript, and references.

Living arrangements: For most of the time, participants stay in local homes but might also be housed in hotels or youth hostels.

Finances: Program costs vary depending on itinerary and activities. The average cost for a 30-day program in Europe is $2,700, which includes round-trip airfare, all meals, and lodging.

Deadline: For spring programs, applications should be submitted by December 31; for summer programs, the deadline is February 15.

Contact: Eloise Mark, Director, Secondary Programs (address above).

**AMERICAN INTERNATIONAL YOUTH STUDENT
  EXCHANGE PROGRAM**
200 Round Hill Road
Tiburon, CA 94920
Telephone: (800) 347-7575

The sponsor: Founded in 1980, American International Youth Student Exchange Program is a nonprofit educational organization accredited by the California Exchange Network, CSIET, and USIA.

The program: AIYSEP offers summer, semester, and year-long study programs in Australia, Austria, Belgium, Canada, Denmark, England, France, Germany, Ireland, Italy, Japan, New Zealand, the Netherlands, Spain, Sweden, and Switzerland. The summer programs begin at the end of June and last four, six, or eight weeks. The semester programs last from August to January and January to June. The year program runs from August to June.

Orientation: All students are given orientations before departure and upon arrival.

Supervision: Local counselors are on site.

Services for persons with disabilities: Persons with disabilities are accepted for the summer programs only.

Requirements: Participants must be between the ages of 15 and 18 with three years of foreign language study for the programs in non-English speaking countries.

Living arrangements: Participants stay with host families which are selected, screened, and interviewed by counselors in the area.

Finances: The fees for the programs range from $1,800 to 4,800, depending on duration and location of the program. This fee includes room and board, medical insurance, airline tickets, counselor fees, and homestay. Some scholarships are available.

Deadline: April 1, but there is a rolling intake of applications.

Contact: Francella T. Hall, Executive Director (address above).

THE AMERICAN SCHOOL IN SWITZERLAND
CH 6926 Montagnola-Lugano
Switzerland

The sponsor: The American School in Switzerland (TASIS) was founded in 1955 to educate American students in an international environment. It is accredited by the European Council of International Schools.

The program: TASIS administers an American college preparatory curriculum during the school year as well as in the summer. TASIS is a coed boarding school, with 250 students, half of whom are American and half are from the rest of the world. Summer programs offered are in England, French-speaking Switzerland, Spain, and Greece. The summer programs specialize in languages, travel, and cultural immersion.

Supervision: The faculty is responsible for daily supervision of the students. There is a resident nurse in case of emergencies.

Requirements: Students must be between the ages of 13 and 18 and grades 7 and 12 in school. No foreign language experience is necessary.

Living arrangements: Students share a room with one or two others.

Finances: The yearly fee of $16,250 covers tuition, room, and board. Applications for financial aid are available from the Director of Admissions.

Contact: David Damico, U.S. Director of Admissions, TASIS Schools, 326 East 69th Street, New York, NY 10021; (212) 570-1066.

ASPECT FOUNDATION
26 Third Street
San Francisco, CA 94103
Telephone: (800) 879-6884
Fax: (415) 777-0907

The sponsor: ASPECT Foundation is a nonprofit educational foundation established in 1985 to pioneer a variety of opportunities to bridge cultures and build bonds of international friendships.

The program: The ASPECT Foundation's Outbound division offers academic year, semester, and short-term programs. Academic year and semester programs are available in France, Germany, Japan, Brazil, Spain, Argentina, and Uruguay. Participants stay with host families and attend the local high school. Short term homestay programs to Australia and Japan are also available.

Orientation: Participants receive a predeparture orientation as well as a welcome orientation upon arrival in their host country.

Supervision: Each student is supervised on an individual basis by an appointed counselor. Professional staff in the host country and the United States are available for support or emergency assistance.

Services for persons with disabilities: Each case is handled individually.

Requirements: Students must be between the ages of 15 and 18 and be sophomores, juniors, or seniors in high school. Participants must have had two years of any foreign language and a 2.5 minimum GPA. Students participating in the Japan program will need to pass a Japanese proficiency test.

Living arrangements: Students live with host families for their entire stay.

Finances: The program cost for European destinations is presently $3500 for an academic year and $3,200 for a semester. The program cost for Japan and South American destinations is $4,300 for an academic year and $3,950 for a semester. The short-term program cost for the Japan program is $1,950. The cost includes individual host family selection and high school placement, staff support, and orientations. The cost of the short-term program to Australia is $3,100 and includes airfare from Los Angeles and an adventure travel tour.

Deadline: Rolling admissions.

Contact: Marilyn Jackson, Outbound Program Director (address above).

ASSE INTERNATIONAL STUDENT EXCHANGE PROGRAMS
228 North Coast Highway
Laguna Beach, CA 92651
Telephone: (800) 333-3802

The sponsor: Affiliated with the Swedish and Finnish ministries of education, ASSE was founded in 1976 to provide student exchange between Sweden and the United States. In the last decade it has expanded to include exchanges with Australia, Canada, the Czech Republic, Denmark, Finland, France, Germany, Great Britain, Iceland, Italy, Japan, Malta, Mexico, the Netherlands, New Zealand, Norway, Poland, Portugal, Slovakia, Spain, and Switzerland. ASSE believes that "through cultural exchange programs and homestay programs a greater international understanding is achieved among people and countries."

The program: There are three choices for U.S. students going abroad with ASSE:

- *The Academic Year Abroad*: This program consists of ten months in Australia, Canada, Czech Republic, Denmark, Finland, France, Germany, Great Britain, Iceland, Italy, Mexico, the Netherlands, New Zealand, Norway, Portugal, Spain, Sweden, or Switzerland. Participants leave home in August (for Northern Hemisphere destinations) or February (for Southern Hemisphere destinations) and attend school for the academic year.
- *Summer Abroad*: If you can't get away for a full year, ASSE sponsors a summer program for either four or eight weeks from early July through August in all European countries. Students live with a host family in which at least one member speaks English.
- *Language Adventure*: Another summer possibility, this 28-day program takes place in France (the Riviera), Germany (Berlin), or Spain (Costa del Sol), and combines a homestay, intensive language and culture study, and excursions for sight-seeing, shopping, or recreation.

Orientation: All three programs include orientation—a half day for the summer programs, a full day for the year-long program—prior to departure. For students going to a non-English-speaking country for the academic year, an intensive 8- to 10-day language training and culture orientation is included.

Supervision: Students receive supervision from a volunteer community representative.

Services for persons with disabilities: ASSE will accommodate students with disabilities on an individual basis.

Requirements: Students must be 15 to 18 years old. Applicants for the year program must have at least a B average; summer applicants must have a C+ average. The organization looks for participants with emotional maturity, intellectual curiosity, and an outgoing disposition, among other characteristics. All participants must be interviewed and must supply letters of recommendation, an autobiographical essay, transcripts, and a health form. There is no language requirement.

Living arrangements: Each program provides a homestay experience.

Finances: The Year Abroad program costs $2,950 to $6,500 and includes round-trip airfare (excluding Canada and Mexico programs), insurance, accommodations, school placement, and supervision. The Summer Abroad program ranges from $2,200 to $2,600. Scholarships are available.

Deadline: April 1 for Northern Hemisphere destinations. August 1 for Southern Hemisphere destinations.

Contact: William J. Gustafson, President (address above).

BRILLANTMONT INTERNATIONAL SCHOOL
Av. Secretan 16
Lausanne CH 1005
Switzerland
Telephone: (41) 21-3124741
Fax: (41) 21-3208417

The sponsor: Brillantmont, founded in 1882, is accredited by the European Council of International Schools and the New England Association of Schools and Colleges and is a member of the Swiss Federation of Private Schools. It offers two curricula—one prepares students for entrance to an American or European university, and the other teaches languages. The school is coeducational, both boarding and day. Situated in the center of Lausanne, Brillantmont overlooks Lake Geneva and the Swiss Alps.

The program: Students can attend the year-long program from mid-September to the end of June or the summer program in July and August. The school offers programs at the 9th- through 12th-grade levels. Five programs are offered:

- *The American High School Program*, which is the equivalent of ninth through twelfth grades in the U.S. educational system
- *Cultural Experience and Enrichment*, for high-school graduates, a precollege course with advanced placement classes
- *The British Section*, which prepares students for the IGCSE (International General Certificate of Secondary Education) and Advanced (A) Level of the Cambridge Board Examinations
- *The Language Program*, which includes English, French, German, Italian, or Spanish
- *The Commercial Program,* in French, with emphasis on languages

Classes have an average enrollment of 15 students and are in session from 8 A.M. to 4 P.M., five days a week. The school also offers instruction in the following subjects at an additional cost: art, art history, music history, current affairs, mass media, photography, modern or classical ballet, cooking, drama, piano, guitar, flute, horseback riding, and tennis. A variety of sports activities is available. Optional excursions are organized for weekends and school breaks. The summer program includes French language study, a variety of sports and cultural activities, and optional sewing and cooking courses.

Supervision: Supervision is provided by the instructors during the day and by house mistresses and resident teachers at night.

Requirements: Brillantmont accepts girls and boys between the ages of 13 and 18.

Living arrangements: Students live in the five main buildings, which are divided according to age groups. Two students are housed in each room. Students are encouraged to speak French.

Finances: One year of schooling and boarding costs 40,000 Swiss francs (approximately $32,150). A deposit of 6,000 Swiss francs (approximately $4,590) is required to cover extra expenses such as private or extra lessons, clubs, students' supplies, excursions, pocket money, health insurance, and laundry. The summer program costs 990 Swiss francs (approximately $750) per week and includes all required and optional classes, excursions, cultural activities, and room and board, but does not include pocket money. The application fee is 30 percent of tuition, which is deducted from the final account when full payment is made.

Deadline: By May 31 for the year program. There is no deadline for the summer program.

Contact: Mrs. F. Frei-Huguenin, Principal (address above).

CENTER FOR CULTURAL INTERCHANGE
42W273 Retreat Court, Dept. CS
St. Charles, IL 60175
Telephone: (708) 377-2272
Fax: (708) 377-2307

The sponsor: Center for Cultural Interchange was founded by writer and teacher Emanuel Kuntzelman to promote cultural understanding, academic development, and world peace.

The program: Center for Cultural Interchange conducts summer and academic year programs in Spain. In the ten-month academic year program, the students live with host families and enroll full-time at private or public schools. The summer program is a study and excursion trip which encompasses homestays, activities, and classes in language, Spanish history, and culture.

Orientation: There is a predeparture orientation as well as an orientation upon arrival in Spain.

Supervision: Local representatives and regional directors provide supervision and assistance to participants.

Requirements: Participants must be between the ages of 15 and 18 and in grades 10 through 12. It is suggested that participants have two years of Spanish language instruction.

Living arrangements: Students live with host families who are chosen through interviews, home visits, amount of interest in the program, and confirmed references.

Finances: $2,650 includes insurance, homestay, orientation, and supervision by local representatives. Scholarships are available on a limited basis depending on a student's financial situation and academic ability.

Deadline: April 15.

Contact: Stephen Foust, U.S. Programs Director (address above).

COLLEGIUM AUSTRIACUM
Gebhard-Strasse 4
A-5020 Salzburg
Austria
Telephone and fax: 43-662-849611

The sponsor: The Collegium Austriacum has conducted summer curriculums for young people from all over the world since 1990.

The program: In the summer, German language courses are offered with 18 sessions per week. Courses make every effort to incorporate elements of Salzburg in the instruction including its history and environment. For student groups, there are the year-round Salzburg Project Weeks, which teach German and provide social contacts with Austrian students of the same age. Leisure options include theater, concerts, painting, chess, tennis, hiking, swimming, and biking.

Requirements: The minimum age for the program is 10.

Living arrangements: Students live in a country house at a lake nearby Salzburg.

Finances: Fees are 5,500 Austrian Schillings (approx. $505 dollars) a week which include tuition, excursions, guided activities, lodging, and full board.

Deadline: For summer courses, May 1. Contact the Collegium Austriacum for dates and deadlines for week-long courses.

COOPERATIVE CENTER FOR STUDY IN BRITAIN
Northern Kentucky University
BEP 301
Highland Heights, KY 41099
Telephone: (606) 572-6512

The sponsor: The Cooperative Center for Study in Britain, founded in 1981, is accredited by the Southern Association of Schools and Colleges.

The program: The Center offers three programs:

- The *Ireland Program* is a two-week program in May in Dublin, Ireland.

- The *Celtic Program* goes from June 8 to July 4 in Dublin, Ireland and Glasgow, Scotland.
- The *London Summer Program* goes from July 4 to August 8, which features optional sidetrips to Edinburgh and Paris.

Orientation: There is an orientation for participants before they begin the program.

Supervision: Faculty members and program directors from consortium member institutions, although responsible for the general well-being of students, do not rigidly supervise the participants. Program directors generally have prior experience in the host country and are selected by the CCSB Board.

Services for persons with disabilities: Individuals with disabilities are accepted but "they must keep in mind that the countries in the British Isles have not yet adopted our American Disabilities Act rules." Individuals in wheelchairs have been accommodated in the past.

Requirements: Participants must be 18 or older and a high school graduate. College credit can be earned.

Living arrangements: Students reside in double rooms of a college campus in the British Isles.

Finances: The fees are $1,850 for the Ireland Program; $2,995 for the Celtic Program; and $3,295 for the London Summer Program. Fees include round-trip air transportation from select U.S. cities, accommodations, breakfasts, and some additional meals and some excursions.

Deadline: March 1 for the Ireland Program; March 23 for the Celtic Program and the London Summer Program.

Contact: Dr. Michael A. Klembara, Executive Director, CCSB (address above).

EF FOUNDATION
1 Memorial Drive
Cambridge, MA 02142
Telephone: (800) 447-4273

The sponsor: EF (Education First) Foundation is a nonprofit organization dedicated to promoting intercultural understanding through student exchanges. Since 1979, over 20,000 high-school students from thirty countries have participated in the organization's academic homestay programs around the world.

The program: EF Foundation participants can spend an academic year or semester in France, Germany, England, Australia, or New Zealand. In each country, participants attend a local school and live with local families. EF Foundation also offers short-term, one-month programs in Salzburg, Austria; Cannes, France; and Salamanca, Spain.

Orientation: The programs have an optional, introductory component— a language and culture camp—held in each of the host countries. At the camps, students receive instruction in the language and culture of the country.

Supervision: Each exchange student is assigned to one of EF Foundation's local area representatives abroad. These representatives serve as a liaison between the students and the families and schools and are available to offer advice and encouragement.

Services for persons with disabilities: EF Foundation will attempt to accommodate most persons with disabilities by handling cases individually, placing disabled participants in appropriate programs.

Requirements: Applicants should be between the ages of 14 and 18 and have a minimum GPA of 2.7. The program in France requires two previous years of language study.

Living arrangements: EF Foundation students live with families that have been selected by area representatives. Families choose the student that best suits their interests, personalities, and lifestyle.

Finances: For the full-year program, the fee is approximately $4,500 for the European countries, and $5,200 for a year in Australia or New Zealand. The semester program costs $4,200 for Europe, and $4,900 for Australia or New Zealand. The one-month programs cost between $2,000 and $2,500. Fees include round-trip airfare, ground transportation to the host family, orientation materials, family placement, school placement, tuition, school books for compulsory subjects, orientation meetings before departure and in the host country, supervision, a certificate of completion, and a subscription to *The Exchange* newsletter. Scholarships are also available.

Deadline: April 1 for programs beginning in the fall; August 1 for programs beginning in January.

Contact: Outbound Program Director (address above).

EUROPEAN STUDIES ASSOCIATION
424 Dorado Terrace
San Francisco, CA 94112-1753
Telephone: (415) 334-4222

The sponsor: The European Studies Association is a tax-exempt, non-profit organization which has been sending American students abroad since 1978.

The program: The European Studies Association conducts a program called Summer Study in Paris for the entire month of July. This summer program entails French language instruction, conversation courses, and civilization classes as well trips around Paris.

Orientation: There is a half-day orientation before departure.

Supervision: Faculty leaders accompany the group on all activities and provide daily supervision.

Services for persons with disabilities: The European Studies Association is careful to advise applicants with mobility impairments that France is not equipped for them. Some students with modest mobility impairments have participated in the past.

Requirements: Participants must be at least 16 years old and a junior in high school. All levels of language ability are accommodated.

Living arrangements: Options include university dormitory rooms, apartments, and family homestays, where the families are matched with applicants.

Finances: The program costs $2,400, which includes tuition, lodging, breakfast, the civilization program, and activities.

Deadline: June 1.

Contact: Dr. Blair, Director (above address).

EUROVACANCES YOUTH EXCHANGE, INC.
P.O. Box 715
Brockport, NY 14420
Telephone: (716) 392-8941
Fax: (716) 392-8999

The sponsor: Eurovacances USA is a nonprofit educational organization formed in 1989 to encourage the development of mutual respect, concern, and trust among young people from different nations. Eurovacances, Germany, its parent organization, was formed in 1979; other partner organizations presently exist in Australia, Colombia, and Denmark.

The Program: Eurovacances offers both semester and academic year programs in Germany, Denmark, and Australia (from August through January or June of the following year.) Students are expected to become fully integrated family members. An all-expense-paid excursion to Berlin is included in the full-year program.

Supervision: There is a regional representative and school official in the area.

Requirements: Participants must be at least 15 years old. The maximum age is 18. At least two years of foreign language study is recommended.

Living arrangements: Participants live with German host families in many different areas of the country.

Finances: Fees are $4,250 for the full-year German or Danish program; $3,250 for the one-semester stay. The Australian program costs $4,690 for a full year, $3,690 for one semester. This includes room and board with selected host family, round-trip transportation, insurance, counseling, meetings, Berlin excursion (full year in Germany). Field trips may be available (e.g., Ayers Rock camping trip in Australia). A $60 nonrefundable application fee is required. Partial scholarships may be available based on merit and need.

Deadline: May 15 for first-semester and full-year programs. December 1 for second semester.

Contact: Margaret L. Johnson, Executive Director, Eurovacances Youth Exchange (address above).

FSL
Outbound Programs
P.O. Box 400
Douglassville, PA 19518
Telephone: (800) USA-4FSL
Fax: (410) 820-8057

The sponsor: FSL was founded to allow students to strengthen intercultural bonds through firsthand experience and personal understanding while learning another language and living in the country where it is spoken.

The program: FSL Outbound is designed for American students to experience the cultures of France, Germany, Ireland, Mexico, or Spain. Homestays are available for students between ages 14 and 18 for a summer, a semester, or an academic year, including high-school enrollment in the host country. Some flexibility in length of stay is possible.

Orientation: Orientation material is mailed several weeks before departure.

Supervision: A representative from the overseas partner organization, a local coordinator, is available at all times and the affiliate offices are open during business hours. Fax lines are open 24 hours a day to FSL in the United States. Participants are covered by full accident, illness, and third-party liability insurance.

Services for persons with disabilities: EFL is open to the enrollment of students with disablilities depending on individual needs and the ability of the host family overseas to accommodate any special conditions.

Requirements: Participants must be between the ages of 14 and 25, have studied the language for at least two years, and be in good health. Also required are a good academic record, a teacher recommendation, and interview.

Living arrangements: Participants stay with host families who are screened by FSL representatives. Host family information is sent to the participant before departure to the host country.

Finances: Prices vary depending on the program and length of stay. For example, the Mexico City/Merida three-week program costs $1,200 and the Spain ten-month program costs $9,800.

Deadline: For summer programs, April 1; academic year programs, May 1; second semester, October 1.

Contact: Robert Nobel, Outbound Director, FSL, P.O. Box 1996, Easton, MD 21601; (410) 822-0636.

GORDONSTOUN INTERNATIONAL SUMMER SCHOOL
Elgin
Moray IV30 2RF
Scotland
Telephone: (44) 343-830798
Fax: (44) 343-830241

The sponsor: In 1993, 250 students from 27 countries participated in Gordonstoun, an international summer school founded in 1934 that offers a program involving academics and recreation.

The program: The 24-day program offers courses in July and August in computer studies, British history, and French language. Courses are interspersed with recreational activities including sailing, sports, and a six-day adventure program based at an old Highlands shooting lodge.

Orientation: All students take course tests in their chosen subject so that they can be assigned to an appropriate student group.

Supervision: Staff members supervise students. There is one instructor for every two students.

Requirements: Students must be 8 to 16 years old.

Living arrangements: Students stay in dormitory houses at the school and are carefully supervised throughout. There is a hosting service at the London and Scottish airports.

Finances: The fee is 2,200 British pounds (approximately $3,388) for the all-inclusive 24-day course, not including travel expenses.

IBEROAMERICAN CULTURAL EXCHANGE PROGRAM (ICEP)
13920 93rd Avenue NE
Kirkland, WA 98034
Telephone: (206) 821-1463

The sponsor: This nonprofit organization was founded in 1970 with two objectives: to enhance foreign-language teaching and study programs and to foster mutual international and intercultural understanding and respect. To meet these broad objectives, ICEP sponsors homestay programs in Bolivia, Costa Rica, Guatemala, and Mexico.

The program: Program choices include homestay programs lasting six weeks, three months, a semester, or an academic year. Each program consists of three basic parts: an orientation, a homestay, and a reentry orientation. The first orientation, held in Mexico City or Miami, involves two days of training in intercultural communication and preparation for the family homestay. From the orientation session participants travel to their homestay—"host families consist of educated, cultured people who are interested in young people and the promotion of good will between their country and the U.S." At the end of the homestay, participants return to Mexico City or Miami before returning to the United States. Programs coinciding with the academic calendar in the foreign country include a school experience. "In an ICEP school experience, you are likely to be the only American student, or one of very few, in a foreign school in a Spanish-speaking, culturally authentic environment." Participants are often asked to help teach English in the schools they attend and are often expected to tutor members of the host family or their friends as well.

Supervision: There are program coordinators and local representatives in each participating city.

Services for persons with disabilities: ICEP accepts participants with disabilities, provided they submit verification from a physician that the disability would not preclude successful participation in the program.

Requirements: Programs are open to 15- to 18-year-olds. Participants must have two years or the equivalent of Spanish, the recommendation of a Spanish teacher, and have "demonstrated responsibility, maturity, good character, and academic ability."

Living arrangements: "The families selected are as representative of the middle class as possible. Within the middle class, though, there is a very wide range. Some houses are rather humble by most U.S. standards, and some are luxurious." Participants are accepted as a family member and are expected to do their share of the household chores.

Finances: Fees range from $725 for six weeks to $2,500 for a full year. This includes orientation, ground transportation to the homestay, and homestay arrangements. Airfare is not included.

Deadline: Three to four months before start of the program.

Contact: Bonnie P. Mortell, President/Executive Director (address above).

INTERNATIONAL COUNCIL FOR CULTURAL EXCHANGE
1559 Rockville Pike
Rockville, MD 20852
Telephone: (301) 983-9479

The sponsor: The International Council for Cultural Exchange (ICCE) is a nonprofit, tax-exempt educational organization conceived in 1982.

The program: There are three summer programs, the French Language and Culture program at the French Riviera; the Spanish Language and Culture program at Costa del Sol; and the Italian Language and Culture program which includes a painting option, held at Riviera della Versilia. Courses can be taken for two, three, four, or more weeks and feature excursions and sight-seeing trips in addition to classroom instruction.

Orientation: Printed material with maps is sent to applicants who enroll.

Supervision: University staff, the ICCE representative, and the home-stay host cooperate to provide guidance for the students.

Requirements: Applicants must be at least 16 years old.

Living arrangements: Accommodations are in university dormitories, homestays, or hotels. Homestays are referred through the university abroad.

Finances: One-month programs cost from $2,499 to $2,999. This fee includes round-trip airfare, registration, tuition, transfers, room and board, excursions, sightseeing, and use of university facilities.

Deadline: February 15. Applications that arrive after this date require a late fee.

Contact: Dr. Stanley I. Gochman (address above).

INTERNATIONAL STUDENT EXCHANGE
P.O. Box 840
Fort Jones, CA 96032
Telephone: (916) 468-2264

The sponsor: International Student Exchange (ISE), founded in 1982, is committed to furthering international harmony through student exchange, allowing students to become a part of a community by attending school and living with a family.

The program: ISE arranges a School Year Abroad program for American students to attend high school and live with a host family in Italy, Germany, Mexico, or Spain. The program encourages the students to absorb the culture through language instruction and local family life.

Orientation: There is an orientation in the United States and in the host country so the student understands the obligations and objectives of the program.

Supervision: The local representative of the program supplies assistance and supervision for the students.

Requirements: The age range is from 14 to 18. It is preferred that the student have some experience with the language of the country of study.

Living arrangements: All students stay with local families.

Finances: Fees vary depending on the country, but range from $3,000 to $4,400.

Contact: International Student Exchange (address above).

INTERNATIONAL SUMMER INSTITUTE
P.O. Box 843
Bowling Green Station
New York, NY 10274
Telephone: (800) 292-4452

The sponsor: The International Summer Institute is a nonprofit organization founded in 1984 by parents and faculty of three New York City high schools for the academically talented: Stuyvesant, Bronx Science, and Brooklyn Tech.

The program: From July through August, the International Summer Institute brings academically talented students together from around the world. Programs are held in the United States (Long Island) as well as in Australia, China, England, France, and Russia. Students participate in sports, academic programs, science research such as the Westinghouse Science Talent Search, and travel tours to places of historic interest. Under the leadership of world-class scientists, students participate in independent research projects with opportunities available in biology, medical science, chemistry, engineering, mathematics, and social science. Students are assisted in writing their research paper and Science

Talent Search application. Research is conducted at national laboratories and university research centers.

Orientation: Students participate in an orientation seminar in New York City prior to departure.

Supervision: There is one group leader for every ten students.

Services for persons with disabilities: The International Summer Institute has accommodated participants in wheelchairs and students with impaired eyesight in the past.

Requirements: Students must be between 10 and 18 with high academic standing.

Living arrangements: Students live in dormitories, hotels, and with host families. Families are selected through the faculty of the university in the host country.

Finances: The Europe, Russia, and United States programs each cost $2,995; the Australia and China programs each cost $3,695. Fees include airfare, tuition, and room and board. Partial scholarships are also available.

Deadline: June 1.

Contact: Dr. Carl Berkowitz, Executive Director (address above).

IRISH AMERICAN CULTURAL INSTITUTE
3 Elm Street, Suite 204
Morristown, NJ 07960
Telephone: (201) 605-1991

The sponsor: The Irish American Cultural Institute, a nonprofit foundation with members throughout the United States and twenty-six countries, is dedicated to "preserving and promoting Irish culture. It is nonpolitical, nonreligious, and nonsectarian."

The program: Now in its twentieth year with more than 2,000 alumni, the Irish Way program offers American teenagers the opportunity to live and learn Irish culture for five weeks each summer. Students divide their time in Ireland between St. Brendan's College in Killarney, County

Kerry, and Wesley College in Dublin, with a 10-day homestay with an Irish family in between. Classes cover Irish literature, history, language, creative writing, dance, music, and drama. Special elective workshops are also offered in such areas as Celtic jewelry making, Irish current events, Irish sports, and intensive Irish language. Field trips include attending a production at the Abbey Theater in Dublin, touring the Ring of Kerry, and visiting numerous other historical sites across Ireland, tying them into the subjects that the students have studied in class. Students are offered a wide variety of free time activities on each campus such as swimming, sports, movies, group talent shows, and discos. The program ends with a four-day tour of the country. The Irish Way staff is made up of certified Irish secondary school teachers who are supported by counselors, American college graduates who are also Irish Way alumni.

Orientation: Predeparture information is provided by mail. Orientation sessions are held in some cities before departure.

Supervision: Certified secondary-school teachers form the core of the Irish Way staff. The teachers live on campus with the students, lead the tours, and accompany the students on all Irish Way activities. They are supported by counselors, American college graduates who are also Irish Way alumni. The counselors also stay with the students in the dormitories. The staff is supervised by the Irish Way administrator.

Requirements: Applicants should be in ninth through twelfth grade, have "reasonable grades and a good recommendation from a counselor and a teacher."

Living arrangements: Students live on the St. Brendan's and Wesley campuses in large European-style dormitories; boys and girls live in separate dorms. For the homestay part of the trip, students are placed with carefully selected families throughout Ireland. During the four-day tour, students and staff stay in upscale Irish hotels.

Finances: The cost of the program is $2,150, which covers books, tuition, travel within Ireland, some entertainment, room and board, and laundry expenses. Transatlantic and domestic airfare is not included. Limited financial assistance is available.

Deadline: May 15, but earlier application is recommended.

Contact: Irish Way (address above).

IRISH INTERNATIONAL CAMP
Castleknock College
Dublin
Ireland
Telephone: (353)1-2895240

The sponsor: The Irish International Camp has conducted summer camps since 1965.

The program: The program takes place at Castleknock College in Dublin from June to August. Offerings include Irish language studies (Gaelic), tennis, and golf.

Supervision: Directors and staff, chosen by leadership qualities and foreign language experience, live on campus to provide supervision.

Requirements: Participants must be from 10 to 18 years old.

Living arrangements: Accommodations are provided at the college in dormitory rooms. Homestays are also available.

Finances: The program costs $400 per week which includes courses and use of all facilities.

Deadline: The middle of May.

Contact: Tom Fitzsimons, Director (address above).

KW INTERNATIONAL
159 Ralph McGill Boulevard NE, Room 408
Atlanta, GA 30308
Telephone: (404) 524-0988
Fax: (404) 525-5420

The sponsor: Founded in 1972, this nonprofit organization encourages and supports international Christian education at two college-preparatory schools in India.

The program: KW International offers a year-long program called SAGE (Studies Abroad for Global Education) at the following schools:

- *The Woodstock School:* A boarding school that offers teenagers the chance to take courses in Indian culture, history, music, art, and literature; to take part in an extracurricular program which includes music, hiking, field trips, drama, sports, and social service; and to join the school's five-week winter tour of India. The school is located on a steep hillside on the outskirts of Mussoorie, a city of 10,000 that grows to 80,000 in summertime.

- *Kodaikanal International School Study Program:* This school is located in the southern Indian hill station of Kodaikanal, three hours from Madurai. Courses include an intensive academic program, including the International Baccalaureate, combined with courses on Indian life and culture, extracurricular activities as above, and the chance to live with a host family during winter vacation.

Supervision: All school events and field trips are chaperoned.

Services for persons with disabilities: KW International does not discriminate against disabled persons; however, it advises that mobility within the schools and travel throughout India may be difficult for a physically disabled participant.

Requirements: Both programs are suited to high-school students in the tenth and eleventh grades. There is no language requirement.

Living arrangements: Students are housed in a dormitory that is rustic but comfortable. Two to four students share a room and all students eat in a central dining room.

Finances: The fee of $8,500 includes tuition for two semesters, room and board, field trips, vacation hospitality, and a winter tour of India. Airfare is not included. Scholarships are available based on need.

Deadline: April 15.

Contact: Jane Cummings, Executive Director (address above).

MORRISSEY LANGUAGE & ACTIVITY INSTITUTE LTD.
St. Mary's House, St. Mary's Place
Athlone
Ireland
(353) 902-74780

The sponsor: Morrissey Language & Activity Institute Limited, accredited by the Irish Department of Education, was founded over 22 years ago.

The program: The program consists of language courses in the months of July and August in the Athlone Community College in the heartland of Ireland. The school's facilities include an indoor swimming pool, tennis and basketball courts, and a fully equipped gymnasium. The Institute also directs classes in golf, horseback riding, sailing, and can arrange homestays.

Orientation: There is an orientation to inform participants of culture, rules, and what resources are available to them.

Supervision: During the program, there is always a representative present to assist participants and provide supervision.

Requirements: Participants must be between 6 and 20 years old.

Living arrangements: Housing is provided in guest houses or with Irish families.

Finances: Costs range from 160 to 185 Irish pounds ($243 to $281 dollars).

Deadline: Two weeks before arrival.

Contact: Mrs. G. Morrissey, Director (address above).

NORTH CAROLINA STATE UNIVERSITY STUDY ABROAD
2118 Pullen Hall, Box 7344
Raleigh, NC 27695
Telephone: (919) 515-2087

The sponsor: North Carolina State University is a state-supported, coeducational, four-year liberal arts, sciences, and professional studies college.

The program: NC State has three summer programs for high-school students: The London Experience in London and surrounding areas; Summer in Moscow in Moscow, St. Petersburg, and Novogorad; and Summer in Vienna in Vienna, Austria, and Prague in the Czech Republic.

Orientation: There is an information session before the program begins.

Supervision: Group leaders are responsible for daily supervision of students as well as handling emergencies.

Requirements: Participants must be at least 17 years old and entering their senior year in high school. For the Summer in Vienna program, students must have had some prior experience with German.

Living arrangements: Students live in dorms for the London and Vienna programs; for the Moscow program, students stay in apartments with English-speaking families.

Finances: Fees are $2,100 for The London Experience which includes tuition, a single room, breakfast and dinner, theater tickets, and day trips; $1,850 for Summer in Vienna, which covers tuition, room and board, and excursions such as a banquet in a castle and parties with Austrian students; and $1,499 for Summer in Moscow which encompasses excursions and room and board.

Deadline: For the London program, April 1; for the Vienna program, March 1; for the Moscow program, April 30.

Contact: Michael Ciriello, Study Abroad Office (address above).

NORTHFIELD MOUNT HERMON SCHOOL
206 Main Street
Northfield, MA 01360

The sponsor: Northfield Mount Hermon School is an independent boarding school founded in 1879. The school is a member of CIEE.

The program: Northfield Mount Hermon offers summer study-travel programs in France, Spain, and China, as well as a marine biology course in the Caribbean.

- *French Language and Culture:* This program begins with an intensive orientation and a tour along the southern coast of France. The heart of the program is a three and one-half week homestay in Arcachon, on the Bay of Biscay. The schedule includes morning classes and afternoon excursions. There is a trip through the Loire Valley, and a final week in Paris.
- *Spanish Language and Culture:* The program begins with an intensive orientation, followed by a three and one-half week homestay with Spanish families in Valladolid. The schedule includes classes, excursions, and family activities. There is a five-day trip through Spain, and a final week in Madrid.
- *Spanish Intensive Language Study (SILS):* Students are exposed

to the maximum number of hours of direct language experience. During the first week, six to eight hours each day are spent in class on the NMH campus. The next four weeks are spent in Burgos, where students live with families and continue with intensive morning classes. The program includes excursions, and a final few days in Madrid.

- *Chinese Language and Culture:* The program begins with an intensive three-day orientation in Hong Kong. The group then flies to Beijing for a four-week stay at Beijing No. 4 High School. The academic focus is on proficiency in Mandarin, and cultural appreciation. The schedule includes morning classes and afternoon excursions. There is a train trip to the south of China, and a final few days in Shanghai.
- *Marine Biology Course:* The course takes place on Grand Cayman Island in the Caribbean. The course starts with a 12-day period of orientation at the school and continues with four weeks of diving and marine biology explorations on Grand Cayman Island. The diving program leads to scuba certification.

Orientation: Students spend two to three days at the Northfield Mount Hermon campus for "intensive predeparture preparation." Both the Spanish and French programs include several days of language instruction in the host country before the homestay begins. The China program includes an orientation in Hong Kong before departure to Beijing.

Supervision: Group leaders are responsible for daily supervision of students, including "teaching, advising, counseling, and disciplining." There is one group leader for every ten students.

Requirements: Students in the French, Spanish, and Chinese programs must be entering at least eleventh grade. Participants must have a minimum of two years of language instruction for the programs in France and Spain. At least one year of language instruction is required for the China program. For the marine biology course, applicants must have completed the tenth grade and at least one year of high-school biology.

Living arrangements: Students live with local families in France and Spain. At Fudan University, students live at No. 4 High School in Beijing.

Finances: Cost for the French Language and Culture is $4,400; Spanish Language and Culture is $4,000; Spanish Intensive Language Study (SILS) is $3,980; and Chinese Language and Culture is $4,300, which includes transatlantic airfare, room and full board, tuition, and excursions. The Marine Biology Course and scuba program costs $4,400, which includes round-trip airfare, room and board, and textbooks; equipment rental is not included. Financial aid is available.

Deadline: For China program, March 18; for other programs, rolling admissions.

Contact: For language programs: Eleanor D. Johnson, Director of International Programs, (413) 498-3251. For marine biology program: James B. Ward, Director, Summer School, (413) 498-3290 (address above).

OXBRIDGE ACADEMIC PROGRAMS
Box 250328
Columbia University Station
New York, NY 10025-1535
Telephone: (212) 932-3049

The sponsor: OxBridge Academic Programs, founded in 1985, is a commercial agency emphasizing "imaginative teaching, active learning, and cultural enrichment" in the intellectually stimulating environments of Oxford University in England and the Académie de Paris in France.

The program: Oxbridge Academic Programs offers the following summer programs:

- *The Oxford Tradition:* This is designed to immerse students in an academic subject or creative art, while taking advantage of the enormous cultural resources of Oxford. Previous course offerings have allowed students to learn in and out of the classroom with such examples as the drama class's presentation of Shakespeare's *Twelfth Night* and the archeology class's dig on the site of a Roman villa.
- *Académie de Paris:* "Designed to introduce students to French culture and Parisian life regardless of the particular subjects they select," the courses range from art history, literature, and philosophy to international law and business. While French language is offered at every level, it is not required, which permits all students, even those with no French language background, to fully experience French history and culture.

Supervision: Program supervision is performed by the full-time staff and faculty. Group leaders, who must have teaching backgrounds as well as prior experience in the host country, are selected by the program director and founder.

Services for persons with disabilities: Although there are no specific provisions because the number of handicapped applicants is low, every effort is made to accommodate them.

Requirements: Students must be between the ages of 15 and 18 and in grades 9 through 12 with no prior foreign language experience necessary.

Living arrangements: Students live in dormitories at the academic institutions.

Finances: The Oxford Tradition costs $3,975; the Académie de Paris program costs $3,895. This fee includes tuition, room and board, local transportation, and field trips but does not include airfare. A limited number of scholarships are available.

Deadline: January 15, but flexible.

Contact: Kimberly C. Warner, Associate Director (address above).

PARSONS SCHOOL OF DESIGN
66 Fifth Avenue
New York, NY 10011
Telephone: (212) 229-8910

The sponsor: Founded in 1896, Parsons School of Design is a four-year private art college.

The program: The Parsons Summer Program is held at the Parsons campus in Paris, France, for four weeks in July. The art and design classes offered take advantage of the famous museums and art community of Paris.

Orientation: There is an orientation session upon arrival where "survival" French is taught.

Supervision: Parsons has resident advisors on duty in the housing at the Paris campus.

Requirements: Students must be at least 16 years old.

Living arrangements: Accommodations are in school dorms.

Finances: Fees are $2,418 for tuition; $150 for orientation; $40 for health insurance; and $800 for room and board.

Deadline: May 1.

Contact: Office of Admissions (address above).

PARTNERSHIP INTERNATIONAL e.V.
  (formerly Fulbright Gesellschaft)
Frankstrasse 26
50676 Cologne
Germany
Telephone: (49) 221-210411
Fax: (49) 221-212930

The sponsor: Partnership International was founded in 1967 by former Fulbright grantees and scholars to promote high-school student exchanges. PI is a nonprofit association offering programs in Germany for students as well as study missions for administrators and educational leaders.

The program: PI offers academic-year programs for individuals and summer programs for student groups. The academic-year program, which PI arranges, is the official Congress-Bundestag Youth Exchange program which offers a full scholarship for highly motivated U.S. high-school students. This program begins with a special summer language class to acclimate students and is followed by regular high-school attendance with special German language classes. The summer program groups, chaperoned by an American teacher, are hosted by German families for three to four weeks. The summer programs can be customized to meet the group's needs with study options including government, world history, music, drama, sports, and German language. School partnership programs also exist for interested institutions.

Orientation: Preparatory seminars are held for the exchange groups.

Supervision: Participants are expected to "integrate into the families and to accept family rules like members." Group leaders are responsible "at all times for the welfare and discipline of their students." There is a program representative available in case of emergency. Students are supervised by Partnership International personnel and teachers.

Services for persons with disabilities: Partnership International places no limitations on disabled students who can fully participate in the program.

Requirements: Participants must be between the ages of 14 and 18. German is not required. A summer compact course in Germany is compulsory for longer programs.

Living arrangements: Participants live with families in Germany.

Finances: Costs vary according to the program. One special program, the academic-year-long Congress-Bundestag Youth Exchange Program, provides scholarships to all of its selected participants.

Contact: The Parrish Foundation, 109 Oakmont Court NE, Vienna, VA 22180.

RAMAPO COLLEGE OF NEW JERSEY
505 Ramapo Valley Road
Mahwah, NJ 07417
Telephone: (201) 529-7463

The sponsor: Established in 1969, Ramapo College of New Jersey is a state-supported, coeducational, four-year college of liberal arts, sciences, and professional studies. It is a member of CIEE.

The program: Ramapo College offers a number of summer study-abroad programs, some of which are open to high-school juniors and seniors. Among these programs are an Italian language and culture course in Urbino, Italy, a studio art program in London, a summer study program in Kenya, and an archaeological dig at Tel Hadar, Israel.

Supervision: Courses are taught by Ramapo College professors and local faculty.

Services for persons with disabilities: Ramapo College accepts persons with disabilities.

Requirements: Requirements vary from program to program.

Living arrangements: Accommodations vary from university dormitories to hotels to kibbutz housing.

Finances: Costs for most programs range from $2,000 to $3,000. Prices usually include round-trip airfare, room and board, local transportation, and excursions.

Contact: Summer Study Abroad Programs, Study Abroad Office (address above).

ROTARY INTERNATIONAL
1560 Sherman Avenue
Evanston, IL 60201-3698
Telephone: (708) 866-3000

The sponsor: Rotary Clubs exist worldwide and are dedicated to an ideal of service. The first Rotary Club was established in 1905; today there are more than 26,000 clubs in 149 countries.

The program: The Youth Exchange program offers two types of exchanges: a full academic year and a short-term stay of several days to several weeks. The full-year program includes a stay with three to four families and attendance at a school in the host country. The short-term programs usually take place during vacation periods and are sometimes arranged as international youth camps. Both short- and long-term exchanges can be arranged for disabled students. Programs are sponsored by individual Rotary Clubs and districts.

Supervision: Each student on the long-term program has a Rotarian counselor from the local host Rotary Club. Short-term programs are led by volunteers who are appointed by the Rotary Clubs or districts involved.

Services for persons with disabilities: Persons with disabilities are encouraged to participate.

Requirements: Participants must be 15 to 19 years old, but their parents need not be Rotarians. Applicants are chosen by a sponsoring club on the basis of a written application and a personal interview.

Living arrangements: These vary for short-term programs; long-term students live with their host families.

Finances: Arrangements vary. Participants pay their own travel, insurance, and other costs. For long-term exchanges, the host Rotary Club provides a small monthly allowance and usually pays tuition fees for required academic programs. The host families provide room and board.

Contact: For information on opportunities in your area, contact your local Rotary Club.

SCHOOL PARTNERS ABROAD
Council on International Educational Exchange
205 East 42nd Street
New York, NY 10017
Telephone: (212) 661-1414, ext. 1234

The sponsor: School Partners Abroad is administered by the Council on International Educational Exchange, which has been involved in secondary-school partnerships for 20 years. Approximately 3,000 students participate in inbound and outbound exchanges each year.

The program: School Partners Abroad matches American secondary schools with counterpart schools in Costa Rica, France, Germany, Japan, and Spain. The program is designed as a curricular resource to complement foreign language and social studies classwork. Linked schools are encouraged to communicate frequently; to exchange letters, photos, slides, videos, and curricular materials; and to plan for the program highlight, a three- to four-week annual reciprocal exchange of students and teachers. During each short-term exchange, American students and teachers participate fully in the life of the host school abroad, attending regular classes, joining in extracurricular activities, and living with the families of local students. Similarly, through the experience of hosting overseas students and faculty, U.S. schools benefit from a rich variety of formal and informal encounters in the classroom, local homes, and the surrounding community.

Orientation: Group leaders attend an orientation session once a year. In addition, extensive written materials are sent to group leaders and participating students throughout the year in preparation for both the hosting and sending programs.

Supervision: Group leaders are designated by the participating schools; they are full-time teachers or administrators, with foreign language ability and experience in international education. The average ratio of students to leaders is ten to one.

Services for persons with disabilities: Every effort will be made to accommodate students with disabilities.

Requirements: Applicants must come from participating schools. They should be 15 to 17 years old, high-school sophomores to seniors (although mature freshmen are eligible), with two years of language study for French- and Spanish-speaking countries. A junior-high-school program is also available for seventh- and eighth-graders.

Living arrangements: Participants live with local families for the duration of the school hosting program (one student per family). While on field trips, participants are accommodated in student hotels.

Finances: Costs varies from $600 to $2,000, depending upon the destination. The fee includes international airfare, domestic transportation in the host country, full room and board, insurance, International Student Identity Card, group leader's fee, excursions (where applicable), and program materials. A grant from the German government's Foreign Office is available to students of German.

SCHOOL YEAR ABROAD
Phillips Academy
Andover, MA 01810
Telephone: (508) 749-4420
Fax: (508) 749-4425

The sponsor: This program, founded in 1964, is sponsored by Phillips Academy, Phillips Exeter Academy, and St. Paul's School. Faculty from these schools supervise the program; the headmasters form the Board of Trustees. School Year Abroad is a member of CIEE.

The program: School Year Abroad offers a year-long academic program in Barcelona, Spain, or Rennes, France, and a one-semester experience in Beijing, China, that gives students the advantage of living in a foreign culture "without sacrificing progress in their schools at home or strong preparation for college." Every year, 55 students go to Spain, 60 go to France, and 15 to 20 go to China. Each student lives with a host family and participates fully in the life of the family and the community. Students take five courses. Classes are taught in both English and French, Spanish, or Mandarin Chinese by American and native teachers. The sponsors emphasize that "School Year Abroad is not just travel abroad, it is not 'the grand tour.' It is a year of serious academic study in an unfamiliar environment." School Year Abroad organizes school trips during the year. Those in France travel to Normandy, Paris, and Provence; in Spain, students go to Toledo, Segovia, and Madrid as well as to several important cities near Barcelona. From Beijing, the group travels to the Great Wall, to Southwest China, and to Hanoi.

Orientation: During the summer before the school year starts, orientation begins with information packets sent by mail and continues after the students arrive in the country. The first week abroad is devoted to orientation.

Supervision: Resident directors are selected by a committee of representatives from the sponsoring school. They act as teachers and counselors and are responsible for daily supervision.

Services for persons with disabilities: School Year Abroad treats each case individually. It has accommodated participants with extremely poor eyesight and other physical disabilities in the past.

Requirements: Participants may come from any secondary school. They must be entering the eleventh or twelfth grades and must have a minimum of two years' language training and a good academic record. Among the less tangible requirements are "a concern for others and demonstrated maturity." Admission is very competitive.

Living arrangements: Homestays are an integral part of the School Year Abroad. According to sponsors, "Students live with butchers, shopkeepers, and postal employees as well as doctors, lawyers, and landed gentry." Most but not all host families have children; more than half have a child the same age as the School Year Abroad student.

Finances: The 1994–95 fee, $18,100 for France and Spain and approximately $9,000 for China, includes room and board, instruction, 14 to 19 days of group travel within the host country, and counseling. Although students must pay their own airfare, School Year Abroad arranges group travel, and 96 percent of the students choose to go with the group. Scholarships are available; one-third of the students receive financial aid up to full tuition.

Deadline: March 1, but flexible.

Contact: Woodruff W. Halsey III, Executive Director (address above).

SEVEN CONTINENTS' EXCHANGE PROGRAMS
P.O. Box 8163
Paramus, NJ 07653-8163
Telephone: (201) 444-8687

The sponsor: Seven Continents' Exchange Programs blends university studies, homestays, and excursions to some of Spain's greatest cultural treasures to provide a unique international experience in preparation for life in a global community.

The program: The program includes 80 hours of intensive Spanish language, culture, and civilization courses at the University of Granada in Granada, Spain. Upon completion of the coursework, the University of Granada issues a diploma. Cultural excursions in Granada and to either Cordoba or Sevilla are also conducted to round out the classroom learning.

Orientation: Information packets are mailed to participants and there is a predeparture orientation in the United States. Another orientation session and a guided walking tour take place after the participants' arrival in Spain.

Supervision: Dominick M. Vene, the Director, personally supervises each group.

Services for persons with disabilities: Persons with disabilities are encouraged to apply. Special arrangements can be made for persons with disabilities after discussion with the director.

Requirements: The minimum age is 17. No previous Spanish knowledge is necessary.

Living arrangements: There are three housing options for students. One is a private apartment with kitchen facilities where meals and laundry are not included. The second option is living with a Spanish family with full room and board and laundry service included. The third choice is living with a Spanish family with housing and laundry included, but without meals.

Finances: The prices, which include tuition, housing, and cultural excursion charges, range from $2,000 to $2,200 per month, depending on which housing option is chosen. Each additional month costs from $1,800 to $2,000. Scholarships will be offered beginning in the 1995–96 school year.

Deadline: 40 days before the commencement of each session.

Contact: Dominick M. Vene, Director (address above).

STUYVESANT CENTER FOR INTERNATIONAL EDUCATION
P.O. Box 843
Bowling Green Station
New York, NY 10274
Telephone: (212) 747-1755

The sponsor: Founded in 1984, the Stuyvesant Center for International Education is a nonprofit group sponsored by the Academically Talented Youth (ATY) association.

The program: The Stuyvesant Center for International Education (SCIE) administers three-week programs in July and August to Australia, China, and Russia. Curriculum choices consist of foreign language study, culture studies, history, research projects, and visits to places of cultural and historic interest. Excursions include Brisbane, Ayers Rock, Sydney, Alice Springs, and Melbourne in Australia; Beijing, Shanghai, Hangzhou, Xian, Guilin, and Hong Kong in China; and Moscow, St. Petersburg, and Central Asia in Russia. Courses are conducted at Shandong University in China; Moscow State University in Russia; and Queensland University in Australia.

Supervision: Stuyvesant High School teachers serve as group leaders and provide assistance.

Requirements: Students must be between the ages of 14 and 18 and in the eighth through twelfth grades. No foreign language experience is required.

Living arrangements: Homestays are arranged with university families.

Finances: The fee is $1,995 for the Russia program and $2,695 for the Australia and China programs. The fee covers all expenses, including airfare and transportation.

Deadline: June 1.

Contact: Mr. Jack Scheckner (address above); (800) 292-4452.

SUMMER DISCOVERY EDUCATIONAL PROGRAMS
1326 Old Northern Boulevard
Roslyn, NY 11576
Telephone: (800) 645-6611, (516) 621-3939 in NY State
Fax: (516) 625-3438

The sponsor: Musiker Student Tours and Summer Discovery is a family-owned company that has been educating students for over 28 years.

The program: Summer Discovery at Cambridge University, in England, is a summer precollege program for high-school students. Students can study and earn college credit, take enrichment or SAT preparation classes, perform community service, and participate in athletic, recreational, and cultural activities. Numerous workshops, trips, and excursions (London, Stratford-upon-Avon, concerts, theater, ancient cathedrals, and castles) are included as well.

Supervision: Most staff members (resident counselors) are program alumni who have trained for five years. The student/leader ratio is eight to one. Leaders are on duty at all times and responsible for everything.

Services for persons with disabilities: Students with disabilities are invited to inquire. Students in wheelchairs may have a difficult time traveling.

Requirements: Students need to apply for admission and must be a current sophomore (tenth grade) to current senior (twelfth grade) in high school.

Living arrangements: Students stay at Cambridge University's New Hall College.

Finances: Summer Discovery at Cambridge costs approximately $4,000 and includes tuition, breakfast and dinner, daily activities, excursions, and admissions. Airfare is additional.

Deadline: Applicants accepted on a rolling admissions basis.

UNIVERSITY OF NEW ORLEANS
Lakefront
New Orleans, LA 70148
Telephone: (504) 286-7455

The sponsor: The University of New Orleans, through the Office of International Study Programs in cooperation with the Honors Program, operates The Glories of France, a credit program for qualified high-school students, including graduating seniors. The school is a member of CIEE.

The program: The Glories of France is an intensive language program that also includes study of French culture and civilization. Students may travel to Avignon, Albi, Paris, and many other cities. During a four-week summer school in Montpellier, France, students may earn up to twelve hours of credit in language, based on an advanced standing exam.

Orientation: Orientation for Glories of France is upon arrival at Montpellier.

Supervision: Faculty and staff members from the university accompany each program and are responsible for its operation.

Requirements: Two years of French, with a 3.25 average; higher than B average in high-school courses, letter of recommendation from a French teacher.

Living arrangements: Participants live in university dormitories, with faculty and/or staff members housed in the same facility.

Finances: The approximate cost, not including airfare, is $2,195 for The Glories of France. Fee includes travel in Europe, tuition, room, and most meals.

Deadline: April 15. Late applications are accepted if space is available.

Contact: Marie Kaposchyn, P.O. Box 569, International Study Programs, Division of International Education (address above).

UNIVERSITY OF PENNSYLVANIA
  PENN SUMMER ABROAD
3440 Market Street
Suite 100
Philadelphia, PA 19104-3335
Telephone: (215) 898-5738

The sponsor: The University of Pennsylvania/Penn Summer Abroad has one of the most extensive listings of study abroad programs.

The program: Summer programs for high-school students are currently offered in the Czech Republic, England, France, Germany, India, Italy, Korea, Poland, and Spain. These summer programs provide an introduction to the language, culture, politics, and individual histories of each country and region of the world.

Orientation: There are informational meetings at the University of Pennsylvania campus, and materials are also mailed out to participants.

Supervision: University of Pennsylvania and local faculty provide guidance and assistance in the event of an emergency.

Services for persons with disabilities: Every effort is made to accommodate persons with disabilities when possible. Visually impaired students have participted in the past.

Requirements: Graduation from high school and acceptance to or enrollment in an accredited college are required.

Living arrangements: Accommodations can be youth hostels, dormitories, or homestays with local families.

Finances: Including tuition and housing, costs range from $1,000 to $4,000, depending on the program.

Deadline: Depending on the program, the deadline is either March 1 or April 1.

Contact: Penn Summer Abroad, University of Pennsylvania (address above).

WO INTERNATIONAL CENTER
1601 Punahou Street
Honolulu, HI 96822
Telephone: (808) 944-5871

The sponsor: The Wo International Center is a nonprofit educational foundation that administers cultural and study programs to promote international awareness among high-school students.

The program: The Wo International Center features outbound programs to China, Germany, Japan, and Tahiti.

- *Summer in China*: A six-week program including intensive Chinese language and culture studies as well as outside activities and day-trips. The program, which is conducted at Capital Normal University in Beijing, concludes with a two-week exploration of China and Hong Kong.
- *Summer in Japan*: This four-week term features classes in Japan-

ese language and society with additional outings and activities to pursue.

- *Summer in Tahiti*: A five-week seminar involving French language and culture study, activities, local exploration, and trips to neighboring islands. Students with previous exposure to French culture are given preference.

Orientation: There is a required week-long orientation in Honolulu before departure which includes an introduction to the culture, language, and geography of the destination.

Supervision: The host institution staff supervises the program participants. The group leaders are selected through a questionnaire and interview process which evaluates their teaching experience, counseling skill, and flexibility.

Requirements: Participants must be between the ages of 15 and 18 and in grades 9 through 12. Previous foreign language study is not required but is helpful.

Living arrangements: Homestays are arranged with a host family which are selected through interviews and questionnaires. For the Summer in China program, participants live in the guest house on the campus of the Capital Normal University in Beijing.

Finances: The Summer programs range in cost from $2,500 to $3,000 which includes room, board, tuition, excursions, and extracurricular activities. The fee does not include airfare. Financial aid is available to some students from the state of Hawaii.

Deadline: February 15.

Contact: Siegfried Ramler, Director (address above).

WORLD EXPERIENCE (WE)
2440 South Hacienda Boulevard
Suite 116, Department EE
Hacienda Heights, CA 91745
Telephone: (800) 633-6653

The sponsor: "Founded in 1977, World Experience strives to forge links of friendship, support, and understanding among students, families, and communities through a personally guided program of sharing. WE believes that the sensitive awareness of cultural differences, developed when students and families live together, results in mutual respect for each culture."

The program: WE offers one- and two-semester study programs in Australia, Brazil, Bulgaria, Colombia, Czech Republic, Denmark, Ecuador, Estonia, Finland, France, Germany, Hungary, Japan, Mexico, New Zealand, Panama, Poland, Russia, Slovakia, Spain, Thailand, Uruguay, and Venezuela. Homestays are an option in many of these programs. WE also offers homestay-language programs in Japan, Russia, and Spain.

Orientation: All students attend an orientation before departure and after arrival in the host country.

Supervision: Directors and representatives in each host country are available to offer assistance. Many are volunteers who have sent their own children abroad and/or have hosted students in their families.

Services for persons with disabilities: Homes are sought with medically educated parents. In the past, persons with chronic illnesses such as diabetes, asthma, and allergies have been accommodated.

Requirements: Participants must be from 15 to 18 years old. Programs in France, Germany, and Japan require two years of language with above average grades. All students should have above average academic ability.

Living arrangements: Participants live with host families. They have their own bed, but may share a room with a family member of the same sex. They are expected to abide by the same rules as other teenagers in the family, and share the same responsibilities.

Finances: Costs for the one-semester program range from $2,500 to $3,600; for the two-semester program, $2,550 to $4,400; for the summer program, $1,215 to $2,585. Variations in price depend on the destination. Transportation and visa costs are extra, and in some cases there are additional private-school fees on the one- and two-semester programs. Insurance is provided, and financial aid is available if need is proven.

Deadline: Deadlines vary by country and range from March 1 to April 1 for programs in the Northern Hemisphere; October 1 to December 15 for programs in the Southern Hemisphere; May 1 for the summer language program.

Contact: Bobby J. Fraker, President/CEO (address above).

YOUTH EXCHANGE SERVICE (YES)
4675 MacArthur Court, Suite 830
Newport Beach, CA 92660
Telephone: (714) 955-2030 or (800) 848-2121

The sponsor: Founded in 1974, YES is a nonprofit organization that organizes international student-exchange programs for teens.

The program: YES operates a homestay exchange program in which students can spend the academic year or second semester in countries of Asia, Europe, or Latin America. The program offers the opportunity to live with local families and attend local schools. YES also seeks families and schools to serve as hosts for students visiting the United States.

Orientation: Orientation sessions are provided before departure and after arrival.

Supervision: Local representatives are available for counseling, orientation, and supervision.

Services for persons with disabilities: Students with disabilities are accepted provided YES can find "the right host family."

Requirements: Students must be 15 to 18 years old.

Living arrangements: Students live with host families.

Finances: Academic-year programs cost $4,000; second-semester programs cost $3,100. Fees do not include transportation.

Deadline: May for academic-year programs, October for second semester.

YOUTH FOR UNDERSTANDING (YFU) INTERNATIONAL
    EXCHANGE
3501 Newark Street NW
Washington, DC 20016
Telephone: (202) 966-6800 or (800) 424-3691

The sponsor: YFU began as a post–World War II effort to reestablish ties between the United States and Germany. It is dedicated to promoting international understanding and world peace through the exchange of young people in thirty countries around the world. Since 1951, YFU has placed more than 150,000 high-school students. The organization is a member of CIEE.

The program: YFU offers programs that last a full year, a semester, a summer, or one month.

- *Overseas Year Program:* Participants spend an academic year in Argentina, Australia, Belgium, Brazil, Chile, Denmark, Ecuador, Finland, France, Germany, Italy, Japan, Mexico, the Netherlands, New Zealand, Norway, Paraguay, Spain, Sweden, Switzerland, the United Kingdom, Uruguay, or Venezuela. During their stay, they live with host families and attend school. High-school or college credit may be arranged.
- *Overseas Semester Program:* Students live with families and attend school from July to January in Argentina, Brazil, Denmark, Finland, France, Mexico, Russia, Spain, the United Kingdom, or Uruguay; or January to July in Argentina, Australia, Brazil, Chile, Denmark, Finland, Japan, and New Zealand.
- *Overseas Summer Program:* This homestay program involves all the countries listed under the year-long and semester programs plus China, Greece, and Poland. Participants live with host families and participate in a variety of YFU-sponsored activities.
- *Sport for Understanding (SFU):* This exchange is built "around the excitement and camaraderie of sport." Participants choose any of 30 sports, including swimming, basketball, field hockey, gymnastics, and tennis. The group forms a team, usually 12 to 16 students, that travels to a host country for a stay of about four weeks. They are hosted by a sport club and its coaches. Choices of location vary.

Orientation: Cross-cultural orientations are provided on a regional basis, and orientation materials are periodically mailed to YFUers before they leave.

Supervision: YFU has area representatives wherever there are participants backed up by a support/counseling system coordinated through regional, national, and overseas offices. Sport for Understanding participants are accompanied by leaders who are experienced in coaching and education and have had international experience. There is one coach for every ten to twelve students.

Services for persons with disabilities: YFU consults its contacts in the applicant's preferred country to make sure they will be able to deal with the particular disability.

Requirements: YFU programs are open to students 14 to 18 years of age. Language proficiency is required for some of the year and semester programs and for the summer program in French-speaking countries. There is no language requirement for the one-month tour program or for Sport for Understanding.

Living arrangements: The heart of YFU's summer, semester, and school-year programs is the host family living experience. As a family member the student learns firsthand about the host country and culture in a way not afforded the average tourist. In many cases a member of the host family has participated in a YFU exchange to the United States.

Finances: Fees include international travel, room and board but do not include travel to the point of departure. Participants are responsible for their own insurance. The cost of the year program is $4,640 to $4,980; the semester program, approximately $4,380 to $4,980; the summer program, $2,080 to $3,590; and the Sport for Understanding program, $2,350 and up. Scholarship aid is available.

Deadline: Varies with program.

LANGUAGE STUDY

*M*ost study-abroad programs include an element of language study, but some programs concentrate primarily on languages. Some U.S. organizations, colleges, and universities sponsor language programs abroad, but the majority of available opportunities are offered by language institutes that specialize in the instruction of foreign students.

Language institutes generally offer instruction at all levels, from beginning to advanced. Most of the programs involve "intensive" instruction of at least three to four hours daily. Many offer a homestay option so that students will be immersed in the language outside the classroom.

Most courses operate on a weekly schedule, allowing students to enroll for as many weeks as they want. Some language institutes offer a broader curriculum involving courses on the country's history and culture, as well as recreational activities and excursions.

While language institutes generally welcome teenagers, you'll need to be fairly independent and have a relatively high level of maturity to get the most out of this type of program. Your teachers, classmates, and roommates are not likely to be from the United States, so you may not be able to slip back into English when you tire of using the language you're studying. It's good to keep in mind that most language institutes are privately owned operations and that many high schools and colleges will not readily give you academic credit for institute courses. If you need academic credit, be sure to check with your school before enrolling in a language institute abroad.

ACADEMIA HISPANO AMERICANA
Mesones #4
San Miguel de Allende
Guanajuato 37700
Mexico
Telephone: (52) 465-20349 or (52) 465-24349

The sponsor: Founded in 1959, Academia Hispano Americana (AHA) aims to provide students with enough knowledge of the Spanish language and culture to become a part of the societies of Latin America.

The program: Enrollment is open to students of all abilities and experience with classes offered year-round for two- to four-week terms. Emphasis is placed on actually speaking the language, and living with a Mexican family is recommended. In addition to language study, topics such as Mexican history, literature, folklore, and cuisine are explored.

Orientation: All printed information is mailed prior to arrival and an orientation meeting is held on registration day.

Supervision: The director of AHA is available in the event of an emergency.

Requirements: Students must be at least 14 years old.

Living arrangements: Although homestays are encouraged because they provide the most immediate contact with the language and culture of Mexico, lists of hotels and boarding houses are also available.

Finances: For a shared room, the cost is $474 for two weeks and $724 for four weeks. Costs are higher for a private room, $516 for two weeks, and $904 for four weeks. Fees include instruction, room, and three meals a day. Through an application process, two tuition scholarships are offered for each session.

Contact: Registrar, Academia Hispano Americana (address above).

AMERISPAN UNLIMITED
P.O. Box 40513
Philadelphia, PA 19106
Telephone: (800) 879-6640

The sponsor: AmeriSpan is a commercial agency founded in 1992 by experienced language travelers functioning primarily as an agent for selected Spanish schools in Latin America. A portion of their programs are conducted in conjunction with the University of Southern Mississippi.

The program: Although AmeriSpan works with nearly 40 schools in some 21 different cities throughout Latin America, only five are suitable for high school students who are traveling without a group leader:

- *Heredia, Costa Rica.* Heredia is a quiet city only seven miles from San Jose. The program includes airport greeting, four hours of language instruction per day, homestay (breakfast, dinner, and laundry service), daily dance classes, a weekly music hour, and Costa Rican cooking classes. Additional afternoon activities and weekend excursions are available at an extra charge.
- *Escazu, Costa Rica.* Escazu is an affluent suburb of San Jose with many restaurants and shops. The program includes airport greeting, four hours of language instruction per day, homestay (breakfast, dinner, and laundry service), weekly dance classes, and afternoon lectures and discussions. Additional afternoon activities and weekend excursions are available at an extra charge. Many families travel together to this program because the school offers many options for children under 10, including lessons and child care.
- *Alajuela, Costa Rica.* Alajuela is a city of about 80,000 located about 15 miles west of San Jose. The program includes airport greeting and return, four hours of language instruction per day, homestay (breakfast, dinner, and laundry service), daily afternoon activities, weekly dance classes, and an excursion program (at an extra cost of $275). This program is approved for academic credit by the University of Southern Mississippi.
- *Antigua, Guatemala.* This program is the most intensive, with four hours daily of individual instruction (within a school setting), airport greeting, orientation tour, homestay (breakfast, lunch, and dinner), afternoon activities, and weekend excursions available for a fee. Antigua is known around the world as the place to learn Spanish, attracting more than 10,000 students annually. The local AmeriSpan office offers constant support and service to every AmeriSpan student.
- *Cuernavaca, Mexico.* AmeriSpan cooperates with Cemanahuac, one of the oldest schools in Cuernavaca, Mexico. Cemanahuac has earned its reputation as one of the best schools in Cuernavaca over the years. The program consists of four hours of group instruction a day, a daily one-hour grammar workshop, afternoon Latin American studies classes, homestay (three meals a day), and optional weekend or afternoon field study trips. The school's program has been approved for academic credit by the University of Southern Mississippi.

Orientation: Most of the programs have an orientation on the first day of classes, but some, including the program in Guatemala, provide a more formal orientation tour. The programs in Costa Rica send out comprehensive factsheets with details students need to know.

Supervision: Supervision varies from program to program. AmeriSpan, because it has an office in Antigua, provides daily supervision and assistance in Guatemala. For the other programs, supervision is provided by the partner schools and the homestay families.

Services for persons with disabilities: Minor disabilities can be accommodated in certain programs.

Requirements: While the program in Guatemala accepts students as young as 14, the minimum age for most of the others is 16; some accept 15-year-olds. All levels of Spanish are taught, so no previous study of Spanish is required.

Living arrangements: All living arrangements are homestays with local families.

Finances: Contact AmeriSpan for an up-to-date price sheet.

Deadline: Four weeks before the first class. A late fee will be charged for applications received after the deadline.

Contact: AmeriSpan (address above).

ANGLO-GERMAN INSTITUTE (AGI)
Christophstrasse 4
D-70178 Stuttgart
Germany
Telephone: (49) 711-603858

The sponsor: The Anglo-German Institute is a nonprofit organization established in 1972 as a branch of Pitman Training of London to teach English to Germans. In 1985, its German Language Centre began to offer German language instruction in Stuttgart.

The program: AGI offers German language courses throughout the year. Special summer courses (twenty lessons plus extracurricular activities) are offered in July and August.

Supervision: There is one teacher for every 6 to 10 students.

Services for persons with disabilities: AGI will accept students with disabilities depending on the seriousness of the disability. At least eight weeks' advance notice is required.

Requirements: Students must be at least 16 years of age. There is no language requirement.

Living arrangements: Students live with local host families in their own room.

Finances: Summer courses cost 1,490 deutsche marks (approximately $957) for two weeks. Courses at other times of the year cost 2,090 deutsche marks (approximately $1,342) for four weeks. Program fee includes tuition, accommodation with family, breakfast and evening meals, and full board at weekends. Summer course fees also include materials and guided activity program.

Deadline: Rolling admissions.

ATHENS CENTRE
48 Archimidous Street
11636 Athens
Greece
Telephone: (30) 1-701-2268
Fax: (30) 1-701-8603

The sponsor: Founded in 1969, the Centre is an educational organization that sponsors study and travel as well as year-round modern Greek language classes for foreigners in Greece.

The program: Classes in all levels of modern Greek are available throughout the year at the Centre. Courses consist of 60 hours of instruction; class size varies from 8 to 15 students. All courses include information about films, plays, and lectures as a way of enhancing classroom language study. Each summer, the Centre sponsors three- and four-week travel programs entitled Classical, Byzantine, and Modern Greece, which include time in Athens and field trips to Santorini, Crete, Delphi, Olympia, Mycenae, Epidaurus, and Turkey. Lectures and workshops are incorporated into the programs.

Supervision: Bilingual instructors and counselors accompany the groups on all field trips.

Requirements: Participants must be at least 16 years of age and entering their senior year in high school. Maturity, the ability to be on your own, and the ability to relate to adults as well as your peer group are necessary.

Living arrangements: Travel program participants stay in hotels. Those who study at the Centre have access to a file of apartment sublets, hotels, and pensiones nearby.

Finances: The language courses at the Centre cost approximately $260; fees for the tours range from $1,800 to $2,500, which includes accommodations, breakfast, field trips, and transportation within Greece.

Deadline: May 30.

Contact: Rosemary Donnelly, Program Director (address above).

BABEL
22 ter, rue de France
06000 Nice
France
Telephone: (33) 93-822744
Fax: (33) 93-882130

The sponsor: Founded in 1977, this school teaches French through the use of audio and videotape in the language laboratory facilities.

The program: Classes are taught at all levels and are arranged in two-week sessions from June through August. The school is located in the heart of Nice, one block from the beach. People enroll individually or in groups with their own leaders.

Supervision: The teacher-student ratio is 1 to 12.

Requirements: The minimum age is 16.

Living arrangements: The school arranges living accommodations and will help students find a place in a hotel, with a family, or in a university residence.

Finances: The 1995 fee for the two-week course is 2,600 French francs (approximately $488); the four-week course costs 5,800 French francs (approximately $1,088). This covers tuition and use of textbooks and equipment only. Side trips and accommodations can be arranged for an additional fee.

Deadline: Five weeks before the start of the course.

Contact: Monique Broch, Director of Studies (address above). To ensure a response, include two international reply coupons with your letter.

THE BRITISH INSTITUTE OF FLORENCE
Lungarno Guicciardini, 9
50125 Firenze
Italy
Telephone: (39) 552-84031
Fax: (39) 552-89557

The sponsor: The British Institute of Florence (BIF) is a nonprofit cultural organization established in 1917 to provide a center of Anglo-Italian cultural cooperation in Florence.

The program: Courses in Italian language are offered throughout the year and at all levels. Most of these courses are on four-week schedules but some flexibility is possible, depending on your experience. The Institute also provides for language study to be combined with courses in art history, drawing, opera, photography, and Italian cooking. Two week summer courses are held in Massa Marittima, a medieval hill town that hosts an opera festival, and in Lido di Camaiore, which many young people prefer due to its beach resort location.

Orientation: An orientation session is held at the beginning of each new course.

Supervision: The entire BIF staff, including the director and the school supervisor, is available to help students.

Services for persons with disabilities: The school is accessible by elevator and has accommodated persons with physical disabilities in the past.

Requirements: The minimum age is 16. No previous knowledge of Italian is necessary.

Living arrangements: Pensiones (small hotels) and homestays are available. Students interested in homestays have the option to eat breakfast and dinner with the family.

Finances: Prices range from $350 to $600 depending on length of stay and language level. The homestay fee scale is $25 a day for full board and $15 a day for half-board. The pensione rate starts at $30 a day.

Deadline: Two weeks before the course starts.

Contact: Victoria Stockton (address above).

CASA DE ESPAÑOL XELAJU
1022 St. Paul Avenue
St. Paul, MN 55116
Telephone: (612) 690-9471

The sponsor: Centro de Español Xelaju offers Spanish-language courses in Quezaltenango, Guatemala. Its Yum Kax division caters especially to the needs of high-school students.

The program: Students study Spanish while living with a Guatemalan family in Quezaltenango. Courses last five hours per day. Daily social and cultural activities, such as movies, lectures, and field trips, are also included. Cooking and weaving courses are offered at additional cost for materials.

Supervision: Students study one-on-one with an instructor.

Requirements: None, other than the desire to learn Spanish.

Living arrangements: Students stay with host families. Meals and laundry services are included.

Finances: The basic cost is $155 per week plus a $30 registration fee, which includes language classes, activities, homestay, in-country transportation, and health insurance.

Deadline: Four weeks before classes start. Classes are held throughout the year.

Contact: Julio E. Batres, General Director (address above).

CEI-CLUB DES 4 VENTS
104, Rue de Vaugirard
75006 Paris
France
Telephone: (33) 1-44393222
Fax: (33) 1-45449156

The sponsor: This organization offers a variety of language programs and holiday camps for French-language students.

The program: French classes are offered in July and August. Courses provide 15 hours of classwork per week and are offered at several locations around France, including Brittany, the Atlantic coast, and the Mediterranean coast. All include outings to nearby places of interest. Sports holidays, international music workshops, farmstays, and other holiday programs are also offered.

Supervision: For language classes, the student-teacher ratio is 12 to 1.

Requirements: Minimum age varies according to the program. Most programs require at least one year of previous French-language study.

Living arrangements: Language students have a choice of homestays or dormitory accommodations.

Finances: The Atlantic coast two-week homestay language program costs 4,350 French francs (approximately $815); the Mediterranean coast three-week course costs 6,020 French francs (approximately $1130). The Brittany two-week residential language program costs 4,600 French francs (approximately $860); the Mediterranean coast three-week residential program costs 7,500 French francs (approximately $1425). For other program costs, contact the organization.

CENTRAL AMERICAN INSTITUTE FOR INTERNATIONAL AFFAIRS (ICAI)
P.O. Box 10302-1000
San Jose
Costa Rica
Telephone: (506) 338571
Fax: (506) 215238

The sponsor: The Central American Institute for International Affairs (ICAI) has offered Spanish-language courses since 1984, in addition to other programs on Central American politics and culture.

The program: Language courses begin every Monday of the year. Students have four hours of instruction daily and live with Costa Rican families. Additional programs include tours of all seven states and principal cities.

Orientation: Students participate in a general orientation upon arrival.

Supervision: The student-teacher ratio is 6 to 1.

Requirements: The minimum age is 15.

Living arrangements: Students live with Costa Rican families.

Finances: A two-week program of only language study only costs $575; the same program with cultural tours to areas beyond San Jose costs $740. Fees include homestay with two meals per day and airport pickup. Scholarships are available.

Contact: Write to the address above or contact the U.S. office at the Language Studies Enrollment Center, P.O. Box 5095, Anaheim, CA 92814; (714) 527-2918.

CENTRE INTERNATIONAL D'ANTIBES
19 Reichert Circle
Westport, CT 06880
Telephone: (203) 226-0405

The sponsor: Since 1985, this organization has offered a chance to "learn French under the Riviera sun" at a school a few minutes from the beach.

The program: Courses on all levels are offered year-round, from two to eight weeks. Each class has a maximum of 14 students for regular classes and six students for intensive classes. For beginners, the sponsor claims that "in one day you'll be familiar with a number of common phrases; in a week you'll be able to manage by yourself in a store; in two weeks you'll know enough to explain your last weekend." Excursions are offered weekly to nearby destinations such as Nice, Monaco, the Lérins Islands, and St-Jean-Cap-Ferrat.

Supervision: Students staying with host families are supervised by the Centre during classes and excursions and by their host family in the remaining time.

Requirements: Minimum age is 14.

Living arrangements: Students stay in a one- or two-room apartment in a high-standard resort complex, or live with a French family.

Finances: Tuition costs begin at $1,000, which includes instruction, homestay, meals, excursions, and materials.

Deadline: Rolling admissions.

Contact: Renée Chenette, Côte d'Azur Langues (address above).

CENTRO DE ARTES Y LENGUAS (CALE)
Calle Nueva Tabachin 22-B
Cuernavaca 062170 Morelos
Mexico
Telephone: (52) 73-130603
Fax: (52) 73-184405

The sponsor: CALE is a Spanish-language institution in operation since 1969.

The program: CALE combines language learning with the study of Mexico's culture. Classroom learning is supplemented by outside social and cultural activities. Courses are offered at all levels, and instructors are native speakers. Classes last five hours daily, for a minimum of one week. Additional evening courses focusing on Mexican history and contemporary society are available at extra cost to groups at the Mexican Institute of Latin American Studies.

 CALE also organizes additional cultural activities and excursions, most of which are free to its students.

Supervision: There is a maximum of four students per instructor.

Requirements: Students must be at least 13 years of age.

Living arrangements: CALE has its own dormitory; if students prefer, the staff will help them find alternative accommodations. CALE particularly recommends living with a Mexican family, which can be arranged.

Finances: A one-time registration fee of $125 is required to reserve a space. This fee is not refundable, but is deducted from the cost of a second visit. Tuition is $150 per week. For $300 total (plus the $125 registration fee), students receive one week of classes, lodging with a local family, and meals. Transportation from the airport in Mexico City to the program site is provided at a cost of $60.

Contact: Xavier Sotelo, President (address above).

CENTRO DE ESTUDIOS DE CASTELLANO
Avenida Juan Sebastian Elcano, 120
29017 Malaga
Spain
Telephone and fax: (34) 52-290551

The sponsor: This language school, founded in 1960, is located in a mansion in a quiet residential section of Malaga, "surrounded by gardens with tropical flowers and palm, orange, and banana trees." It is 70 meters from the beach and a 30-minute walk from the town center.

The program: Spanish courses at beginner and advanced levels start the first of each month. All teachers are Spanish, and classes are never larger than eight students. Lessons last from 9 A.M. to 1 P.M.; homework requires 10 to 15 hours per week. Three to four months is the suggested course length for beginners, but students can enroll for a stay of as short as one month.

Supervision: The student-teacher ratio is 8 to 1.

Requirements: The minimum age is 16.

Living arrangements: If they wish, students can be placed with Spanish families. If they prefer to stay in an apartment, the school will help them find one.

Finances: One month's tuition costs 45,000 pesetas (approximately $345); room and full board in a family home costs 55,000 pesetas (approximately $425) per month.

Contact: F. Marín Fernández, Director (address above).

CENTRO DE IDIOMAS
Belisario Dominguez No. 1908
Mazatlán, Sinaloa
Mexico
Telephone: (52) 69-822053
Fax: (52) 69-855606

The sponsor: Founded in 1973, the Centro offers Spanish conversation courses year-round for foreigners and also has a year-round enrollment of approximately 300 Mexicans who study English.

The program: Mazatlán, the site of the Centro, is located on the Pacific coast, across from the tip of the Baja Peninsula. It is a popular vacation spot because of its beaches and semitropical climate. Courses begin every Monday of the year except Easter and Christmas weeks. Courses are at all levels, and enrollment is limited to six students per class. Beginning students are advised to allow at least two months to achieve an intermediate level of competence.

Supervision: Students between the ages of 16 and 20 are placed with homestay families that have children of similar ages. Students under 16 may study in tutorial classes by special arrangement with an instructor from the Centro or with a family member during a homestay.

Living arrangements: Homestays with "upper-middle-class families" can be arranged; if the students prefer, they may stay in a hotel or an apartment. The Centro will provide information.

Finances: The fee for one month of study with four hours of classroom work per day, two activities per week (such as visits to local places of interest), and shared room and board in a local home is $1,085.

Deadline: No set deadline, but if a homestay is desired, 30 days advance notice is necessary.

Contact: Dixie Davis, Director (address above).

CENTRO DE IDIOMAS DEL SURESTE (CIS)
Calle 14 #106 Col. Mexico
Mérida 97128 Yucatán
Mexico
Telephone: (52) 99-261155
Fax: (52) 99-269020

The sponsor: CIS is a Spanish-language school that has been in operation for more than 20 years. It is accredited by the Dirección General de Educación Pública del Estado de Yucatán (Yucatán State Department of Education).

The program: CIS's Spanish-language programs, which last a minimum of two weeks, start every Monday year-round. Students are encouraged to speak only Spanish in their classes and in the homes of their host families. Classes are conducted three hours per day, five days per week. Beginner, intermediate, and advanced levels of study are offered. Class size ranges from one to three students. Additional classroom study of two hours a day is available to students for an additional fee. Instructors are college-educated native speakers. The school is located in Mérida, the largest city on the Yucatán Peninsula and the gateway to the Mayan archaeological ruins.

Orientation: Pre-arrival information is sent to students regarding their homestay location. Free airport pickup is available. Upon arrival, a local orientation is given by school staff.

Supervision: Leaders are responsible for students' conduct at all times and are expected to accompany their group during activities.

Services for persons with disabilities: CIS accepts people with disabilities, but suggests that people with severe disabilities be accompanied. Several classrooms are accessible to students in wheelchairs. Many public areas in Mérida do not have facilities for disabled people.

Requirements: Participants must be at least 12 years old.

Living arrangements: For the language program, students are usually placed in local homes. Participants on the Yucatán field trip stay with local families (meals included) or in a student-class hotel (meals not included).

Finances: The two-week language program costs $315; each additional week costs $105. Two hours of extra daily study cost an additional $75 per week. Homestays, which include a room and all meals, cost $105 per week.

Deadline: Applications and payment must be received 30 days prior to arrival.

Contact: Chloe Conaway (address above).

CENTRO DI CULTURA ITALIANA IN CASENTINO (CCIC)
Piazza Amerighi, 1
52014 Poppi (Arezzo)
Italy
Telephone: (39) 575-52774

The sponsor: CCIC is an Italian-language school for foreigners founded in 1980 in collaboration with the municipal administration of Poppi, a medieval town in northeast Tuscany.

The program: CCIC offers intensive courses two or four weeks from April through October. All instruction is given in Italian, even at beginning levels. Language classes also include excursions and other extracurricular activities.

Supervision: The maximum student-teacher ratio is 8 to 1.

Services for persons with disabilities: Disabled or elderly persons are given priority for ground-floor accommodations.

Living arrangements: Students live in double or single rooms in two- to four-room apartments which the school reserves in the historic center of town, or in renovated cottages in the countryside. Accommodations have cooking facilities; however, students dine together in the school garden or a local restaurant at least a few nights a week.

Finances: The following costs include tuition, lodging, and four restaurant meals per week. For a double room, the two-week course costs 1,475,000 lire (approximately $870); the four-week course costs 2,680,000 lire (approximately $1,575); every additional week costs 675,000 lire (approximately $400). For a single room, the two-week course costs 1,665,000 lire (approximately $980); the four-week course costs 3,060,000 lire (approximately $1,800); every further week costs 755,000 lire (approximately $440). A 20 percent reduction on all Course fees is available to students under 26 years of age.

Deadline: One month before the course begins.

Contact: Stephen Casale, CCIC New York, 1 University Place, Apartment 17-R, New York, NY 10003; (212) 228-9273.

CENTRO DI CULTURA ITALIANA
Via Pier De Crescenzi, 14/2
40131 Bologna
Italy
Telephone: (39) 51-523486

The sponsor: The Centro di Cultura Italiana Bologna, founded in 1981, is a private language and culture school whose aim is to teach a language in Italian towns far from tourist itineraries.

The program: The three schools, in Bologna, Manciano (Grosseto), and Vicchio (Firenze), all offer one- to four-week programs of language and culture study from beginner to advanced levels, and intensive programs of four hours of instruction per day. In addition to language study, the program's activities, which will be adapted to the students' interests, include instruction in history and art, the environment, current events, and politics and society.

Supervision: The student-teacher ratio varies from program to program.

Requirements: There are no age or language requirements.

Living arrangements: Students can choose to live in a single or double room in an apartment, a hotel, or with a family. The school helps students find a place to stay.

Finances: Tuition prices range from 440,000 lire (approx. $286) for a two-week course to 780,000 lire (approx. $507) for a four-week course. Accommodation costs vary depending upon the type. In Bologna, a single room in a private household costs 125,000 lire a week (approx. $81) and a double room costs 90,000 lire (approx. $58). An apartment, depending upon availability, will cost at least 300,000 lire (approx. $195) per week.

Contact: Cristina Grigatti or Ombretta Rovinetti (address above).

CENTRO LINGUISTICO ITALIANO DANTE ALIGHIERI
Via Dei Bardi, 12
Florence 50125
Italy
Telephone: (39) 55-2342984
Fax: (39) 55-2342766

The sponsor: The Centro Linguistico Italiano Dante Alighieri is a school that specializes in teaching the language and culture of Italy to foreigners. Founded in 1966, it is authorized by the Italian government and has headquarters in Florence with an additional center in Rome.

The program: Participants have a choice of group language courses (from 20 hours to 100 hours per month), cultural courses, and individual language courses. Classes run year-round, and it is possible to enroll from one to nine months. Each month, students take at least two guided tours in the city plus an outing to another famous city. The school also organizes meetings, dinners, and parties to encourage language learning in an out-of-the-classroom setting. In 1993, 1,200 people participated in the school's program.

Orientation: Beginning language students attend an orientation once they arrive in Italy.

Supervision: Arrangements can be made for full-time supervision of a group. Single participants are supervised by a host family.

Services for persons with disabilities: The Centro is able to accommodate most types of disabilities. Participants with disabilities are placed in small class groups in easily accessible classrooms.

Requirements: The minimum age is 15.

Living arrangements: Although room and board is not included in the fee, the school will help students find accommodations with a family, in a guesthouse, furnished room, residence, or an apartment. Eight weeks' notice is required for these arrangements to be made.

Finances: The costs vary depending on the course or courses chosen. A 16-hour cultural course costs $150; the 20-hour language course costs $185; a 100-hour language course costs $650; and 100 hours of individual language study costs is $6,460. Half scholarships are available for all but the individual lessons. Students are responsible for their own travel arrangements. No insurance coverage is provided.

Deadline: One month before the course is scheduled to begin.

Contact: U.S. Student Programs, Institute of International Education, 809 U.N. Plaza, New York, NY 10017, or the address above.

CENTRO PONTEVECCHIO
Piazza del Mercato Nuovo 1
50123 Florence
Italy
Telephone: (39) 55-294511

The sponsor: This school has taught Italian language and culture since 1986.

The program: Language courses are offered in monthly sessions, year-round. Culture courses include Italian cooking, literature, politics, music, and art history. Students are given the chance to enjoy the cultural life of Florence.

Supervision: One teacher for every 12 students.

Requirements: The minimum age is 16.

Living arrangements: The Centro arranges accommodations in single or double rooms in family homes, without board, or with other students with half-board or use of a kitchen.

Finances: Fees range from 690,000 lire to 1,050,000 lire (approximately $415 to $630) per month depending on length of stay, type of course, and accommodations. Price includes fees, books, membership tax, examinations, certificate, accommodations service, and some cultural and extrascholastic activities.

Deadline: One month ahead of time.

Contact: Simonetta de'Mari di Altamura, Director of Studies (address above).

CIAL-CENTRO DE LINGUAS
Av. da Republica, 41-8°
1000 Lisbon
Portugal
Telephone: (351) 1-7940448; (351) 1-7940449
Fax: (351) 1-7960783

The sponsor: The CIAL language school has offered courses in Portuguese language and culture since 1972.

The program: CIAL runs language programs for individuals and private groups year round in Lisbon, Oporto, and Faro. Upon arrival, each student is tested and placed according to language proficiency. Students can enroll in programs that meet either three or six hours each day (it takes two to four weeks to complete each level). The program includes short excursions and other group activities. Students can also enroll in optional courses such as Portuguese literature, art history, teachers' training course (EPLE), and Portuguese for special purposes, such as for banking, insurance, and other professional fields.

Orientation: An orientation session is held upon arrival.

Supervision: The maximum number of students per teacher is six.

Services for persons with disabilities: CIAL attempts to integrate disabled persons in all programs.

Requirements: The minimum age is 16.

Living arrangements: CIAL will place students either with a Portuguese family in Lisbon or at a hotel, depending upon preference.

Finances: The six-hour-per-day course costs 70,000 escudos (approximately $420) for one week and 260,000 escudos (approximately $1,560) for four weeks. The three-hour-per-day course costs 40,000 escudos (approximately $240) for one week; 140,000 escudos (approximately $840) for four weeks. Groups receive discounted rates. Accommodations with a Portuguese family, including daily breakfast, cost 21,000 escudos (approximately $126) for one week and 64,000 escudos (approximately $385) for four weeks. Some scholarship aid is available.

Deadline: Students should apply at least two weeks before the course begins.

Contact: Renato Borges de Sousa, Director, or Alexandra Borges de Sousa, Director of Studies (address above).

COLLEGIUM PALATINUM
Chateau de Pourtales
161, rue Melanie
F-67000 Strasbourg
France
Telephone: (33) 88-310107
Fax: (33) 88-310814

The sponsor: The Collegium Palatinum is a commercial language institute founded in 1958 belonging to Schiller International University. Schiller is an independent university operating on the American system of higher education and accredited by the Association of Independent Colleges and Schools.

The program: Collegium Palatinum offers three different language programs: German in Heidelberg, Germany; French in Leysin, Switzerland;

and Spanish in Madrid, Spain. Eight-week intensive courses are offered year-round. Four-week summer courses are offered during the months of July and August.

Supervision: The teacher-student ratio varies from program to program.

Requirements: The minimum age for the Spanish program is 18; for the French and German programs, 17.

Living arrangements: Students in Leysin live in single or double rooms in a student residence. In Heidelberg, they have a choice between a student residence and local host families. In Madrid, they stay with local host families, or in pensiones and private apartments.

Finances: Course fees vary from program to program. Fees include intensive language instruction for 24 hours per week and activity programs. Room and board cost extra. Fees for four-week classes range from $800 to $1,100; eight-week classes range from $1,600 to $1,700.

Deadline: For Heidelberg and Leysin, four months in advance; for Madrid, one month.

Contact: Schiller International University, U.S. Information Office, 453 Edgewater Drive, Dunedin, FL 34698; (813) 736-5082.

CUAUHNAHUAC
Instituto Colectivo de Lengua y Cultura
Apartado. Postal 5-26
Cuernavaca 62051 Morelos
Mexico
Telephone: (52) 73-123673
Fax: (52) 73-182693

The sponsor: The Instituto, founded in 1972, teaches Spanish to people from all over the world—students, teachers, professionals, and diplomats.

The program: New classes begin every Monday. Students may study for any length of time in classes of two to four. The routine involves six hours of classroom work each day; a typical beginner can expect, after four weeks, to be able to survive in Spanish—to pronounce coherently and converse at a basic level.

Supervision: Host family parents supervise the students. Minors have curfew hours in the evening.

Services for persons with disabilities: Classes are held in rooms that are accessible to disabled persons.

Requirements: Minimum age is 12.

Living arrangements: Students live with a local family as paying guests.

Finances: The four-week class costs $600. A double room costs $16 per day; a single costs $30. The registration fee is $70.

Contact: Contact the address above or the Cuauhnahuac U.S. representative, Marcia Snell, at 519 Park Drive, Kenilworth, IL 60043; (800) 245-9335.

DE FRANCE-SUMMER PROGRAM IN PARIS
P.O. Box 788
Wallingford, CT 06492
Telephone: (203) 269-8355

The sponsor: De France was established in 1957 with the guiding principle that the study of French should not be limited to language and literature, but also should include the experience of living in France.

The program: De France is based in Paris, where students live in private homes and attend three-hour daily courses (French institutions, French cinema and theater, and history of French art) taught entirely in French at the Institut Superieur d'Electronique, located near the Luxembourg Gardens. Although there is no formal instruction in grammar and literature, students are expected to use and develop the language skills they have learned before and during the program. The courses are offered at four levels of proficiency. The rest of the time is spent sight-seeing, attending plays, or taking day trips. The program lasts from June 25 to August 6; four weeks in Paris are followed by a two-week holiday in the provinces with a vacationing French family.

Supervision: Students are supervised by De France teachers, staff, and the director during the day and on field trips, and by their host families in the evening.

Services for persons with disabilities: Each participant's case is handled individually. Activities often involve extensive walking.

Requirements: The program is open to a maximum of 50 students. Students should be in ninth or tenth grade and have studied the French language for two years.

Living arrangements: Students stay with host families.

Finances: The tuition for the summer session is $4,900, which includes airfare, classes, activities, room and board, and all other group expenses. Guidebooks, movies, laundry, dry cleaning, and pocket money are not included.

Contact: J. P. Cosnard des Closets, Director (address above).

DEUTSCH IN GRAZ (DIG)
Zinzendorfgasse 30
A-8010 Graz
Austria
Telephone: (43) 316-383747
Fax: (43) 316-383747

The sponsor: A nonprofit organization, DIG has offered courses in German as a foreign language since 1979.

The program: DIG has special language courses designed to suit the needs of young people. In addition to language training, the courses offer sports activities and an extensive leisure program. Courses last three weeks and take place in July and August.

Supervision: There is a maximum of 12 students per teacher. The sponsors advise that "students must comply with the Austrian law concerning the protection of children and young people. Children under 16, for example, are allowed out without supervision until 10 P.M. If parents express the wish that their children should not remain unsupervised, there is a supervised evening program from Monday to Friday."

Services for persons with disabilities: DIG will accommodate persons with disabilities.

Requirements: The minimum age is 15.

Living arrangements: Students can choose between homestay or boarding school accommodations.

Finances: The three-week program for students 15 to 17 years old costs 7,800 Austrian shillings (approximately $700) including language courses, materials, outdoor activities, and evening supervision. Courses for students 10 to 14 years old cost 16,400 Austrian shillings (approximately $1475) including accommodations and full board.

Deadline: Four weeks before course begins.

DEUTSCH-INSTITUT TIROL (DIT)
Am Sandhugel 2
A-6370 Kitzbuhel
Austria
Telephone: (43) 5356-71274
Fax: (43) 5356-72363

The sponsor: DIT is a commercial German-language school located in the Kitzbuhel Alps. It is a member of the Federation Europeen des Ecoles (FEDE) and of Campus Austria (recognized organization of Austrian Language schools).

The program: This school, located in the small, picturesque town of Kitzbuhel in the Tyrol, offers courses in German taught exclusively by native German speakers. Courses run throughout the year and may be as short as one week or as long as the student wishes. Language learning goes on in and out of the classroom at DIT; during after-class activities (in the company of at least one teacher), any language except German is taboo. Since Kitzbuhel and its surroundings are world famous for skiing, DIT offers a combination plan that features German lessons in the morning and skiing in the afternoon.

Supervision: Students are supervised by the director, teachers, and the owner of their residence.

Requirements: Courses are geared to students age 16 and over; however, arrangements can be made for students age 12 to 15.

Living arrangements: Accommodations at DIT are in shared or single rooms with or without a shower and breakfast. Dinner can be arranged.

Finances: For 6,000 Austrian schillings per week (approximately $540), students receive instruction, a double room with shower, breakfast, and activities. Other options are available.

Contact: Hans Ebenhoh, Director (address above).

DID DEUTSCH-INSTITUT
Haupstrasse 26
63811 Stockstadt am Main
Germany
Telephone: (49) 602-741770

The sponsor: Established in 1970 to cater to the specific needs of young people, the DID Deutsch-Institut offers German language programs in Germany, or "Deutsch in Deutschland" (DID).

The program: DID offers programs in most major cities including Frankfurt, Munich, Berlin, Hanover, and Wiesbaden, with year-long courses, summer courses, and special classes in German for beginners.

Supervision: All DID institutes have staff to supervise program participants.

Requirements: Participants must be at least 12 years old; previous German instruction is not required.

Living arrangements: All participants can choose between family or hotel accommodations. Homestays can be in single or double rooms.

Finances: Course fees range from 800 Deutsche marks to 2,500 Deutsche marks ($515 to $1600 dollars), depending on duration and location of course.

Contact: Hubert F. Koetter, Managing Director (address above).

ESCUELA INTERNACIONAL
Paseo de Carmelitas, 57
37002 Salamanca
Spain
Telephone: (34) 923-267334

The sponsor: Escuela Internacional is a private language academy created by "a team of young and enthusiastic teachers."

The program: Escuela Internacional offers five types of courses: monthly intensive Spanish classes offered year-round; beginning Spanish classes from October to the end of May; month-long summer courses; three-month courses offered in fall, winter, and spring; and Spanish culture courses.

Requirements: For all programs, the minimum age is 16. Students must be in at least the tenth grade.

Living arrangements: Students live with local families, in shared apartments with other students, or in hotels.

Finances: Intensive courses cost 47,000 pesetas (approximately $360) for four weeks; beginners' courses cost 365,000 pesetas (approximately $2,810); summer courses cost 59,000 pesetas (approximately $455); and the three-month courses cost 132,000 pesetas (approximately $1,015). Homestays cost an extra 65,000 pesetas per month (approximately $500). The Spanish culture fee is 44,000 pesetas (approximately $340) for a four-week term with 15 lessons per week. Information packets, welcome and farewell parties, certificate of attendance, city tours, and some social activities are included in the fees.

Deadline: One month prior to starting dates.

Contact: Midori Ishizaka, Director of Admissions (above address).

EURO ACADEMY
77A George Street
Croydon CR0 1LD
England
Telephone: (44) 81-686-2363
Fax: (44) 81-681-8850

The sponsor: This commercial agency has organized language courses and homestays throughout Europe since 1971.

The program: Euro Academy offers homestays and language courses year-round. Programs take place in Spain, France, Germany, Italy, Austria, and Portugal. Twelve-week language courses are available in

Berlin, Germany, and Salamanca or Madrid, Spain. Photography and painting courses are available in Florence, Italy. The organization accommodates both individuals and groups, and also sponsors youth music tours for orchestras and choirs.

Orientation: Students are given an assessment test upon arrival.

Supervision: Local coordinators are available to assist participants.

Requirements: For most programs, participants should be between 12 and 18 years old.

Living arrangements: All participants live with local families.

Finances: Prices vary from program to program. For example: three weeks of study in Dinan, France, costs 895 British pounds (approximately $1,340); three weeks of language study in Seville, Spain, costs 495 British pounds (approximately $740); three weeks in Berlin, Germany, costs 595 British pounds (approximately $890). All fees include room and board with a local family, tuition, and activities.

Deadline: Fourteen days before departure.

Contact: Monique Malone (address above).

FRENCH AMERICAN STUDY CENTER (FASC)
Boite Postale 176
14104 Lisieux
France
Telephone: (33) 31312201

The sponsor: For more than sixteen years this language school, located in a small town in Normandy (one-and-a-half hours from Paris and fifteen minutes from Deauville), has specialized in teaching French to English speakers.

The program: In the Intensive Program, lasting 1 to 10 weeks, participants live with a local family and "take a pledge to speak in French." In the three-week Vacation Learning program, participants live at the school. FASC also offers a winter program at Menton on the French Riviera and special individual or group programs, which can be set up at any time during the year.

Orientation: Students receive orientation materials in the mail.

Supervision: The student-teacher ratio is 10 to 1. Special supervision is given to teenagers.

Requirements: French is offered at all levels. Participants must be at least 14 years old. Interested students must send an application along with two letters of recommendation.

Living arrangements: FASC offers homestays or accommodations in its 23-room residence.

Finances: Fees range from $580 to $780 per week, including tuition, room, and board. Groups can receive discounts of 25 to 35 percent.

Deadline: One month before the program begins.

Contact: Ph. C. Almeras, Director (address above).

GRAN CANARIA SCHOOL OF LANGUAGES
Ruiz de Alda 12-3
E-35007 Las Palmas
Spain
Telephone: (34) 28-267971
Fax: (34) 28-278980

The sponsor: Since 1964, students from all over the world have come to study Spanish at one of the three schools operated by this organization, two in Las Palmas and one in Playa del Inglés. The schools are on the island of Gran Canaria, one of the Canary Islands, located in the Atlantic Ocean off the coast of Morocco.

The program: Classes begin every Monday of the year; however, classes for absolute beginners start the first Monday of every month. A complete course usually lasts 12 weeks, but students can enroll for as few as two weeks. Classes are held 20 hours per week, leaving time to enjoy the Canary Islands.

Requirements: Minimum age is 16.

Living arrangements: Students have two choices: local homes or a two-story house next to the beach.

Finances: Tuition for one week plus excursions, theater trips, and social activities, is $70 for classes of 6 to 13 students. Private lessons (20 hours per week) cost $410. Lodging costs $100 per week for a double room and half-board.

**IFK DEUTSCHKURSE SALZBURG
(IFK GERMAN COURSES SALZBURG)
Franz-Josef-Strasse 19/2
A-5020 Salzburg
Austria
Telephone: (43) 662-8765950
Fax: (43) 662-87659575**

The sponsor: IFK is a language school in operation since 1948 that serves approximately 500 students per year. The school offers German language courses in the city of Salzburg and at Fuschl am See, a small holiday resort 20 kilometers from Salzburg.

The program: In Salzburg, IFK offers two choices: three-week summer courses or ten-week term courses beginning in January, March/April, or October. At Fuschl am See, IFK offers three-week "German and sports" courses in the spring and summer. The sports course consists of sailing, windsurfing, canoeing, tennis, mountain biking, and hiking.

Requirements: The minimum age for participation is 16.

Living arrangements: In Salzburg, rooms are available in private homes year-round or in student residences in summer only. At Fuschl am See, rooms are available in private homes.

Finances: There is an inscription fee of 1,000 Austrian shillings (approx. $90) for first enrollment. The costs for the summer courses in Salzburg vary from 13,000 to 16,900 Austrian schillings (approx. $1,170 to $1,520); the long-term courses in Salzburg cost 16,900 Austrian schillings (approx. $1,520); and the combined courses at Fuschl am See cost from (approx. $1,330 to $1,578) 14,750 to 17,500 Austrian schillings. All course fees include German language instruction, teaching materials, certificate of exam, and cultural and social activities. The Fuschl am See combined courses also include an intensive or standard sports course. Accommodations with breakfast are included in the Salzburg summer course and the combined courses at Fuschl am See but not at the Salzburg long-term courses.

Deadline: Four weeks before the beginning of the course.

Contact: IFK office (address above).

INDIANA UNIVERSITY HONORS PROGRAM IN FOREIGN LANGUAGES FOR HIGH SCHOOL STUDENTS
111 South Jordan
Bloomington, IN 47405
Telephone: (812) 855-5241

The sponsor: Since 1960, Indiana University has offered summer study programs in France, Germany, and Mexico for high-school juniors from Indiana. The school is a member of CIEE.

The program: Students can study in St-Brieuc or Brest (Brittany) in France, Krefeld (near Dusseldorf) in Germany, or San Luis Potosí (north of Mexico City) in Mexico. Programs last for seven weeks and include a homestay, five hours of language instruction per day, and field trips.

Orientation: Prior to departure, Indiana University offers a day of orientation.

Supervision: There is the director and three instructors. The host family supervises students in the evening and on the weekend.

Services for persons with disabilities: Indiana University accepts students with disabilities that do not hinder the student's participation in all activities of the program. Persons with vision problems and mobility limitations have been accommodated in the past.

Requirements: Students must be juniors in a high school in Indiana and be in the third year of study in the foreign language.

Living arrangements: Students stay with host families.

Finances: Including airfare, tuition is $3,700 for France and Germany and $2,800 for Mexico. Scholarship grants of up to one-half the tuition are available.

Deadline: September 15.

Contact: Public and private high schools in Indiana.

INSTITUTE OF CHINA STUDIES
7341 North Kolmar
Lincolnwood, IL 60646
Telephone: (708) 677-0982

The sponsor: The Institute is a nonprofit organization registered in Illinois since 1979. It began recruiting U.S. students for Fudan University's Summer Study program in 1981.

The program: Fudan University's Summer Study program consists of four- to six-week courses beginning in early July. Chinese language courses taught by English-speaking teachers are at beginning to advanced levels; special courses can be arranged. Extracurricular activities include visits to local theaters, hospitals, factories, historical attractions, communes, and other cities. Fudan University is located in Shanghai, China.

Supervision: The coordinator of the summer program at Fudan University serves as supervisor for around 500 students.

Requirements: Participants must be at least 16.

Living arrangements: Participants stay in guest rooms at the university dormitories, two persons to a room.

Finances: The four-week program costs $2,500, which includes tuition, room and board, and international flights (West Coast departure and return).

Deadline: April 1.

Contact: Harry Kiang, Director (address above).

INSTITUTE OF SPANISH STUDIES
1315 Monterey Boulevard
San Francisco, CA 94127
Telephone: (415) 586-0180; (415) 387-6817
Fax: (415) 334-3928

The sponsor: The Institute is located in Valencia, Spain, and has been operating since 1950. Its U.S. office is in San Francisco.

The program: The Institute offers two five- to six-week Summer Sessions, which are available to both high-school and college students. Participants can choose from three programs: independent study combined with post-study travel; study followed by 11 days of travel; or the study session only. Courses include language study, the history of Spain, and Spanish art. Approximately 200 students participate each year.

Requirements: Participants must be at least 15 years old unless they are accompanied by an adult or are part of an escorted group. No previous knowledge of Spanish is required.

Living arrangements: Students live in private homes or a residence hall.

Finances: Costs vary from $989 (tuition only) to $4,278, depending on whether the post-session tour of Spain and the transatlantic airfare are included.

Deadline: Six weeks before start of the program.

Contact: Vilma Bellone, Registrar (address above).

INSTITUTO IDEAL
Apartado Postal 22-B
Cuernavaca
62190 Morelos
Mexico
Telephone: (52) 73-170455
Fax: (52) 73-175710

The sponsor: IDEAL is a nonprofit educational organization.

The program: IDEAL offers a total immersion program for learning the Spanish language that puts equal emphasis on language and culture. Students can begin on any Monday throughout the year.

Orientation: A brief orientation is held on the first day of class in Cuernavaca.

Supervision: The student-teacher ratio is five to one, at most.

Requirements: Unaccompanied students must be at least 16 years old. Classes are offered at all levels; no previous language ability is required.

Living arrangements: It is recommended that students board with Mexican families, paying $22 per day for private room and board or $15 for shared room and board.

Finances: A $100 registration fee plus $130 per week of study is required. Fee includes five hours of instruction daily, a coffee break, some parties, movies, and activities. Costs for optional cultural excursions range from $10 to $40. Groups of 10 from organizations or schools receive a scholarship.

Deadline: No set deadline, but since mail service is slow, write or fax at least two months before you wish to begin.

Contact: Edmundo Sandoval, Director (address above).

INTER SÉJOURS
179, rue de Courcelles
75017 Paris
France
Telephone: (33) 1-47630681
Fax: (33) 1-40548941

The sponsor: Inter Séjours in a nonprofit organization, founded in 1901, that sponsors language-learning holidays throughout Europe for French students, and also sponsors programs in France for non-French speakers.

The program: Participants study languages and live with local families in Perpignan and the Pyrénées Orientales. Programs are offered year-round at all levels.

Orientation: Students attend a local orientation.

Supervision: The student-teacher ratio is 10 to 1. Students are supervised by their host families.

Requirements: Students must be 13 to 18.

Living arrangements: Students live with host families.

Finances: A two-week homestay with full board costs 3,700 French francs (approximately $695). Language classes cost 100 French francs per hour (approximately $20).

Contact: Marie-Hélene Pierrot, Director (address above).

ISOK
Jan-Tooropstraat 4
2225 XT Katwijk aan Zee
The Netherlands
Telephone: (31) 1718-13533

The sponsor: ISOK, founded in 1969, places people who want to learn Dutch with Dutch families as paying guests.

The program: ISOK combines a stay with a Dutch family with language lessons—either in a group or privately. Host families take their guests on local excursions as well, to give them a chance to practice their language. Group lessons are given in a school in Katwijk; private lessons are given in the home of ISOK's principal, J.F.H. de Zeeuw. The program operates year-round.

Supervision: The program participants are under the supervision of the principal, who does the teaching and makes the homestay placements and visits. "We place advertisements, visit would-be families, inspect rooms and homes and surroundings, and ask for references from vicars, priests, burgomasters, and so on."

Services for persons with disabilities: Participants with minor disabilities are accepted.

Requirements: There is no age limit. The only prerequisite is a willingness to learn the Dutch language.

Living arrangements: The students live with a family in Katwijk and surrounding villages and towns, a region of the Netherlands where the purest Dutch is said to be spoken.

Finances: There is a registration fee of 50 guilders (approximately $30). Room and board in a host family costs 315 guilders (approximately $180) a week. Group lessons for two hours per day are 15 guilders (approximately $9); private lessons are 25 guilders (approximately $14) per hour. Participants must arrange their own insurance and their own transportation.

Deadline: Rolling admissions, but registration should be completed three weeks before arrival.

Contact: J.F.H. de Zeeuw, Principal (address above).

K.I.S.S. DANISH LANGUAGE SCHOOL
Norregade 20
1165 Copenhagen K
Denmark
Telephone: (45) 33-114477

The sponsor: K.I.S.S. stands for Kobenhavns Intensive Sprog Skole, a language school that has been in operation since 1971. It is subsidized by the state and the municipality of Copenhagen.

The program: According to K.I.S.S., its system of language learning is "hard and intensive." It is mainly a speaking course in which pronunciation is key. "You are almost constantly speaking in class, speaking in chorus, in groups, reading aloud, repeating, and being corrected. We want to get you to speak like a Dane." Beginner classes start every month. The program runs for seven and a half months and is divided into 11 levels; the first ten are approximately two and a half weeks long. Students can take as many levels as they wish.

Supervision: There are usually 8 to 14 students in a group.

Services for persons with disabilities: K.I.S.S. has accommodated minor physical disabilities in the past. There is no elevator for wheelchairs.

Requirements: Applicants must be at least 18 years old and have a student's visa before they arrive (except for private lessons).

Living arrangements: Students make their own accommodation arrangements through local youth and student organizations.

Finances: The hourly instruction fee is 11 Danish kroner (approximately $2) with a minimum enrollment of 21 hours (2 1/2 weeks).

Deadline: No set deadline, but beginner classes usually have a waiting list of two to three months.

Contact: Steen A. Christensen, Director (address above).

LANGUAGE STUDIES ABROAD
249 State Highway 101
Suite 226
Solana Beach, CA 92075
Telephone: (800) 424-5522

The sponsor: Since 1985, Language Studies Abroad has educated students and others interested in learning another language in an international setting.

The program: The two- to four-week Language Studies Abroad programs take place year-round in Costa Rica, Mexico, Spain, Italy, France, Germany, and Quebec.

Orientation: Orientation is conducted upon arrival in the country.

Supervision: The school director, staff, and teachers are available in the event of an emergency, but participants must be independent enough to go without constant supervision.

Services for persons with disabilities: There is no set policy but individuals must be independent. Vision and mobility limitations have been accommodated in the past depending on available facilities in other countries.

Requirements: The minimum age is 15 and all language abilities can be accommodated, from beginners to advanced.

Living arrangements: Participants are placed with host families who are carefully selected through references, home visits, and interviews.

Finances: Fees start at $650 for two weeks, which includes the homestay with some or all meals and at least four hours of language classes daily.

Deadline: Three weeks prior to the beginning of a program.

Contact: Charlene Biddulph, Director (above address).

MICHIGAN STATE UNIVERSITY
High School Honors Program
Office of Overseas Study
Room 108, International Center
East Lansing, MI 48824-1035
Telephone: (517) 353-8920

The Sponsor: MSU sponsors more than 70 overseas study programs in 24 countries, primarily for college undergraduates and graduate students. The French program in Quebec, however, is specifically designed for high-school students. Michigan State University is a member of CIEE.

The program: The Honors Program in French lasts one month (late June to late July) and is held at the College de Riviere du Loup, 120 miles east of Quebec City on the south bank of the lower St. Lawrence River in the heart of a completely French-speaking region. Students attend classes five mornings a week, focusing on reading, writing, speaking, and understanding French. Afternoons are spent on activities in the surrounding villages, where the host families are located. During the stay, there are several full-day excursions—two to Quebec City, a boat trip on the St. Lawrence River, and one to the nearby lakeside resort of Pohenegamook. It is recommended that students who successfully complete this honors course of study be considered by their high schools as eligible for one-half unit of high-school credit. (Final decisions on credit rest with the students' schools.) In addition, students obtaining a grade of B+ or higher may have the option of receiving, upon payment of the appropriate fees, credit at Michigan State University.

Orientation: There are two sessions, one on MSU's campus and another when the students arrive at Riviere du Loup.

Supervision: The director of the program and program assistant are with the group for the duration of the program, and a program administrator is on call at all times. All excursions and outings are closely supervised.

Services for persons with disabilities: Arrangements can be made for participation by students with special needs.

Requirements: High-school students at least 15 years old, who have completed two years of French with a B+ average, are eligible.

Living arrangements: Students live with families in villages near the college. On weekends, activities are divided between events at the college and family activities. "Materially, life in the Province of Quebec is comparable to that of the U.S. Rather than 'culture shock,' students can look forward to an experience combining a European outlook with the comfort and convenience of American life."

Finances: The fee of $1,959 includes room and board, tuition, administrative fees, and excursions. Transportation to Riviere du Loup is not included. Some scholarship aid is available.

Deadline: April 24.

Contact: Nona Anderson, Associate Director, Office of Overseas Study (address above).

NATIONAL REGISTRATION CENTER FOR STUDY ABROAD (NRCSA)
823 North 2nd Street
P.O. Box 1393
Milwaukee, WI 53201
Telephone: (414) 278-0631
Fax: (414) 271-8884

The sponsor: NRCSA is an information and registration office for a consortium of 100 language schools in 25 countries. Approximately 20 of these schools accept students under the age of 18 individually or in groups for short-term (one week to three months) foreign-language courses. Member schools have affiliations with more than 300 U.S. universities.

The program: NRCSA offers four types of programs:

- *Mexico Discovery:* There are four to six programs each summer, each lasting from 10 to 20 days. Students tour Mexico with U.S. teachers and stay with Mexican families. All meals are included in the cost of the program.
- *Total Immersion—Spanish:* Participants study the Spanish language for two weeks while staying with a host family in Mexico or Spain. There is also a three- to six-week program in the summer in Seville, Spain.
- *Total Immersion—French:* In this summer program, participants study the French language for three weeks while living with a host family in St-Malo, La Rochelle, or Dinan; four weeks in Montreal; or for three to six weeks while living in a student residence in Cap d'Ail.
- *Total Immersion—German:* Participants study the German language for two to 12 weeks while living in a school residence in Salzburg, Austria.

Orientation: Orientation materials are mailed to participants.

Supervision: Host families, host-school faculty supervise the students. In the German program, U.S. group leaders also provide supervision.

Services for persons with disabilities: Each case is handled on an individual basis.

Requirements: Students should be at least 14 for the Mexico Discovery program. The Total Immersion programs require participants to be at least 16 years old in Spain, 15 years old in Mexico and Canada, and 14 years old in Austria and France.

Living arrangements: Homestay for the Mexico Discovery and the Total Immersion programs in Mexico, Spain, France, and Canada. School residence for the Total Immersion programs in Salzburg and Cap d'Ail.

Finances: The fees for the Mexico Discovery program range from $950 to $1,500, including airfare. Fees range from $500 to $1,750 for the Total Immersion programs, depending on destination, and airfare is additional.

Deadline: Sixty days prior to start of program.

Contact: June Domoe (address above).

OIDEAS GAEL
Gleann Cholm Gille
County Donegal
Ireland
Telephone: (353) 73-30248

The sponsor: Oideas Gael is a nonprofit organization founded in 1981 that offers Irish language courses and cultural activity holidays. Oideas Gael has centers in the Gaeltacht area of southwest Donegal in the Slieve League Peninsula, famous for its scenery, as well as Glenfin, located on the fringe of the Cruacha Gorma (Blue Stack Mountains) in the heart of the Donegal highlands.

The program: Options are available through spring and summer. Oideas Gael offers a variety of language courses directed toward spoken Irish, aiming at correct pronunciation, proper idiom, and development of vocabulary particulary relating to contemporary life. Courses in archaeology, painting, weave and design, dancing, and hill-walking, as well as a summer school in Irish language and culture, also are available.

Supervision: There is a 15-to-1 ratio of students to teachers, who are also responsible for social supervision.

Services for persons with disabilities: Oideas Gael's newly built facilities have easy wheelchair access, and the organization has accommodated persons with disabilities in past years.

Requirements: Participants must be at least 16.

Living arrangements: Bed and breakfast, hostel or homestays (booking must be made directly—ask sponsor for details), or self-catering homes (in which participants cook for themselves). Bed and breakfast with dinner/self-catering may be organized by Oideas Gael.

Finances: A course fee of 85 Irish pounds (approximately $130) covers classes, lectures, recreational and cultural events; housing costs an additional 105 Irish pounds (approximately $160) per week per person sharing a room in specially approved homes with bed, breakfast, and evening dinner; or 35 Irish pounds (approximately $50 dollars) per week per person sharing a self-catering, modern, fully equipped house. Airfare and ground transportation to and from site is not included, but transportation information is available upon registration.

Deadline: At least two weeks before scheduled course.

Contact: Liam ó Cuinneagaín, Director (address above).

SAB SPANISH CENTER AND TRAVEL AGENCY
P.O. Box 187
1ª calle 12-35 zona 1
Quezaltenango
Guatemala
Telephone: (502) 9-612042

The sponsor: SAB Spanish Center is a commercial Spanish-language school.

The program: While living in the Guatemalan city of Quezaltenango, participants can choose to study beginning to advanced Spanish on a one-to-one basis with an instructor or with a group.

Orientation: There is an orientation session on the first day of the program.

Supervision: Instructors supervise activities outside of the school.

Services for persons with disabilities: Arrangements can be made to accommodate participants with minor disabilities.

Requirements: Students should be at least 13. No previous knowledge of the Spanish language is required.

Living arrangements: Students live with Guatemalan families who "provide communication, food, laundry services, and give love and care to them."

Finances: The fees for Plan A, which offers individual tutoring, range between $100 and $200 a week, depending on how many hours of instruction the student desires. The fees for Plan B, which features one instructor to every five students, range from $110 to $170, also depending on the number of hours of instruction. The fees for both plans are lower from September to May, which is the low season. Both plans include a homestay with three meals a day. Weekend tours to areas of interest in Guatemala are available at extra cost.

Deadline: Rolling admissions.

Contact: Maria Alvarado, Director (address above).

SCUOLA LEONARDO DA VINCI
Via Brunelleschi 4
50123 Florence
Italy
Telephone: (39) 55-294247

The sponsor: This school, founded in 1977, offers foreign students a variety of courses in the language and culture of Italy.

The program: The Scuola offers four-week language courses at all levels; classes meet 20 hours per week. Classroom study is combined with guided tours of Florence and its museums. Language courses can also be arranged on a one-to-one-basis. The Scuola also offers courses in the history of art, Italian cooking, Italian wines, Italian literature, Italian cinema, ceramics, photography, restoration of paintings, and more.

Supervision: The school staff is in charge of day-to-day details; on excursions, teachers accompany the group.

Living arrangements: Students can choose to live in an apartment, with a family, or in a pensione. The Scuola will help students find a place to stay.

Finances: The fee for the four-week language course is approximately $555, not including room and board.

Deadline: One month in advance of registration.

Contact: Gianni Mannu, Director (address above).

TORRE DI BABELE
LANGUAGE STUDY LINK
Via Bixio, 74
Rome 00185
Italy
Telephone: (39) 6-7008434
Fax: (39) 6-7049715

The sponsor: This language school, founded in 1984, is accredited by the Italian Language Schools Association. The school is located in the Esquilino district, near Rome's main train station and a few minutes from the Colosseum and the basilica of San Giovanni.

The program: Torre di Babele offers two programs:

- *Italian in Rome* offers two-week language courses year-round in the school's four-story building. Courses are available at beginning to advanced levels. Students choose from four hours of group instruction daily, four hours of group instruction plus two hours of individual instruction, or nonintensive courses which provide two hours of instruction twice a week.
- *Italian at the Seaside* takes place from July to September in Pisciotta, in the province of Salerno. Classes are given for periods of two or four weeks. Courses are held in the town center,

Pisciotta-paese, which is situated among olive groves on a hill 170 meters above sea level.

Supervision: There are two teachers for each class. Classes have a maximum of 12 students, although the average class size is seven or eight.

Orientation: An orientation is held at the beginning of each course.

Services for persons with disabilities: Persons with disabilities are welcome.

Requirements: The minimum age is 16. Beginners are welcome.

Living arrangements: Students share apartments with cooking facilities. Homestays are available in Rome.

Finances: A two-week "group intensive" course in Rome or in Pisciotta costs 480,000 lire (approximately $300). Room and board are extra.

UNISCO
37, rue Cardinet
75017 Paris
France
Telephone: (33) 1-46221613
Fax: (33) 1-40539629

The sponsor: UNISCO (Organisation de Voyages Universitaires et Scolaires) is a commercial organization that has offered language-study programs in France since 1956.

The program: Programs run throughout the year, but primarily during the months from June through September. Participants study in the cities of Paris, Montargis, Gien, Chamousseau, Nantes, Angers, and Forges-les-Eaux. Language study is provided, along with scheduled sports and activities.

Supervision: Group leaders are responsible for the daily supervision of students. There is one group leader for every 12 students, and a maximum of 15 students per teacher.

Requirements: The minimum age for most programs is 14, although some accept students as young as 12.

Living arrangements: Students live in college dormitories or with local families.

Finances: Costs vary from program to program. For example, a four-week program with homestay in Giens and excursions to Paris costs 8,200 French francs (approximately $1,540); a two-week program in Paris with residence in a dormitory and excursions to Versailles and Normandy costs 5,200 French francs (approximately $975).

Contact: Dominique Auger, Managing Director (address above).

UNIVERSITY OF KANSAS
Office of Study Abroad
203 Lippincott Hall
Lawrence, KS 66045
Telephone: (913) 864-3742

The sponsor: The University of Kansas operates four programs for qualified high school students. The University of Kansas is a member of CIEE.

The program: Courses are taught by native instructors and University of Kansas faculty members and staff. Four programs offered are:

- *Summer Institute in Germany:* The Intermediate Summer Language Institute in Eutin, Germany, is situated midway between Kiel and Lubeck in the northern state of Schleswig-Holstein. Eutin (population 17,000) welcomes students as guests and offers numerous cultural and recreational opportunities, from opera festivals to water sports, in addition to German language and conversation courses.
- *Spanish Language and Culture:* The academic program begins with a two-week bus tour of Spain. Following the tour, the group settles in Barcelona for four weeks of intensive coursework where sidetrips include a visit to the Dali Museum on the Costa Brava.
- *Summer Institute in Mexico:* The Summer Language Institute in Guadalajara, Mexico, has been in existence for over twenty years

and offers students the opportunity to study Spanish for eight weeks while living in private homes.
* *French Language and Culture in Paris:* The program begins with a 10-to 12-day group tour through Normandy, Brittany, and Touraine. The next four weeks are spent on language and culture instruction in Paris.

Supervision: The University of Kansas faculty direct the KU Summer programs. The directors accompany the group.

Requirements: Two semesters of college-level foreign language instruction or the equivalent experience is necessary. Parental consent is needed for applicants under the age of 18.

Living arrangements: Students live with local families.

Finances: The Summer in Germany program costs $2,575; the Spanish Language and Culture program costs $3,100; the French Language and Culture in Paris program costs $3,100; and the Summer Institute in Mexico costs $1,980. Fees include tuition, meals, lodging, cultural events, and travel for the programs with short tours. Airfare is not included. Supplemental scholarships are available to qualified University of Kansas students.

Deadline: Rolling admissions begin December 1. Applications accepted until program is filled.

Contact: Office of Study Abroad (address above).

VENTURA ESTUDANTIL
Rua Do Catete, 311 SLS 407/8
22229-900 Rio De Janeiro
Brazil
Telephone: (55) 21 265-0248
Fax: (55) 21-205-8191

The sponsor: Founded in 1985, Ventura Estudantil is a Portuguese-language school with special programs for Americans and Canadians.

The program: Ventura Estudantil provides two- and four-week courses in Portuguese language and culture studies. Cultural excursions are planned in addition to other recreational activities.

Orientation: Printed orientation materials are sent to participants.

Supervision: The organization coordinator, the school coordinator, and the group leader supervise and oversee the general welfare of the students.

Services for persons with disabilities: Participation is encouraged as long as advance notice is given so the necessary arrangements can be made.

Requirements: Students must be between the ages of 10 and 16 and in the eighth through eleventh grades. Some familiarity with Spanish and/or Portuguese is recommended.

Living arrangements: Students live with local host families.

Finances: The fee for the four-week program is $1,500, which covers room and board, tuition, and activities.

Deadline: Rolling admissions.

Contact: Fernanda Macedo (address above).

VIENNA INTERNATIONAL UNIVERSITY COURSES
Universität
A-1010 Vienna
Austria
Telephone: (43) 1-421254

The sponsor: Since 1922, this school has taught German to foreign students from beginning level to a "perfectionist course."

The program: The school offers courses during the year, special four-week courses during July and August, and three-week courses in September. Summer courses are offered at six levels, from a beginner's course to a course for teachers of German. Tours of Vienna and the surrounding area, trips on the Danube, excursions to the alpine and lake districts of Austria and to the Neusiedler See are offered during each summer session.

Supervision: The student-teacher ratio is 16 to 1. There is no special supervision.

Requirements: Minimum age is 16.

Living arrangements: During the summer session, students may make their own arrangements or stay in a single or double room in one of seven student hostels. They are responsible for making their own meal arrangements. There are many area restaurants including student restaurants where students can dine at a discount. Cost of meals averages from $7 to $11, or less at the student restaurants.

Finances: The cost of a summer course and accommodation is 10,380 Austrian schillings (approximately $935). Excursions cost extra.

CREATIVE ARTS

*I*n this section you will find programs that focus on all types of creative arts, including the visual arts, the performing arts, and creative writing. Painting, creating video productions, acting, dancing, singing, and writing are only a few of the options available.

Most of the programs involve a short-term stay, from two weeks to a month, and include instruction at various levels, from beginning to advanced. Usually, students stay in dormitories or other housing arranged by the sponsoring organization. The program participants often represent the host country and a number of other countries; however, a few of the programs described in this section accept only American participants.

ARVON FOUNDATION
Totleigh Barton
Sheepwash
Devon EX21 5NS
England
(44) 409-23-338

The sponsor: Founded in 1968, the Arvon Foundation is a nonprofit organization that receives financial support from the Arts Council of Great Britain. It operates a residential center dedicated to the study of creative writing.

The program: Arvon, according to its literature, "has one simple aim—to provide the opportunity to live and work informally with professional writers." To do this, the Foundation operates two residences. Lumb Bank, in West Yorkshire, is an eighteenth-century mill owner's house; Totleigh Barton is an eleventh-century thatched manor house situated in the Devon countryside. Each course lasts five days. During that time, students explore and practice creative writing with two professional writers. There are 14 to 16 students per course.

Orientation: The first day includes a discussion of creativity. Each day time is set aside for students to talk with the tutors about individual work; the evenings often include workshops and readings by tutors and students.

Supervision: Students supervise themselves and each other.

Services for persons with disabilities: Ground-floor accommodations have ramps for wheelchairs. The Arvon Foundation has accommodated students with various physical disabilities in the past.

Requirements: Most of the students are 16 or over, but "we welcome any student who has an active interest in writing and is prepared to be part of a conviviality, sharing in the cooking and simple running of the houses." The Arvon courses are available to groups as well as individuals.

Living arrangements: Life at Totleigh Barton and Lumb Bank is communal. Students share in the daily work of the house.

Finances: The fee of 245 British pounds (approximately $377) includes board and tuition for the five-day stay.

Deadline: There is no formal deadline. Brochures for the coming year are available in January, and courses run from March through October.

Contact: Julia Wheadon, Senior Administrator (address above).

DORA STRATOU DANCE THEATRE
8 Scholiou Street
10558 Athens, Plaka
Greece
Telephone: (30) 1-3244395

The sponsor: The Dora Stratou Dance Theatre has dedicated itself, since its founding in 1953, to preserving Greece's "heritage of traditional dance, together with the country's music, song, costumes, and instruments for the Greeks themselves and the world at large." It is a nonprofit, government-funded organization with its own 1000-seat-theater in Athens that hosts performances daily.

The program: Daily classes in Greek folk dance and folk culture and

Ancient Greek dance for young people and adults take place in the theater, on Philopappou Hill, opposite the Acropolis. Courses are conducted in English.

Supervision: The student-teacher ratio is 10 to 1. No supervision is provided outside of class and organized activities.

Requirements: The minimum age is 16.

Living arrangements: The school will help to arrange hotel accommodations in Athens for participants. There is a youth hostel nearby.

Finances: For students, programs cost 20,000 drachmas (approximately $85 per week).

Contact: Professor Alkis Raftis, President (address above).

FRIENDSHIP AMBASSADORS FOUNDATION
31 Park Street
Montclair, NJ 07042
Telephone: (201) 744-0410
Fax: (201) 744-2764

The sponsor: The Foundation fosters global understanding through performing arts exchanges to promote goodwill throughout the world. All performing arts tours provide artistic contact among peers, people-to-people meetings, receptive audiences, diplomatic contact, and sometimes include international festival and conference participation. For nearly a quarter century, FAF has fulfilled its mission by sponsoring more than 40,000 individuals on exchanges in 25 countries throughout five continents.

The program: Friendship Ambassadors designs two- to four-week programs throughout the year, balancing performances and people-to-people contact. A typical itinerary includes three performances per week, interaction with the audience, and educational sight-seeing. Performance sites range from concert halls to community centers, school auditoriums, churches, hospitals, and amphitheaters.

Orientation: The staff of Friendship Ambassadors publishes orientation handbooks and meets with the participants, parents, and teachers before departure.

Requirements: There are no age requirements, but groups must submit a performance tape.

Living arrangements: Participants generally stay in hotels or guest houses. In some countries homestays are arranged.

Finances: Costs range from $900 to $2,500 per person and include air-fare, concert arrangements, room and board, guides, local transportation, and entrance fees. Most groups who perform and travel with Friendship Ambassadors do their own fundraising.

Deadline: No official deadlines, but groups are encouraged to begin planning more than a year in advance.

Contact: Patrick Sciarratta, Executive Director (address above).

INSTITUTO ALLENDE
Ancha de San Antonio 20
San Miguel de Allende
37700 Guanajuato
Mexico
Telephone: (52) 45-20190

The sponsor: This well-known school of arts and crafts and Spanish language was founded in 1951. It is incorporated with the University of Guanajuato but operates as an autonomous unit. The Instituto is a fully accredited member of the Asociación Nacional de Universidades e Institutos de Enseñanza Superior.

The program: The Instituto is an international college for English-speaking students that emphasizes arts, crafts, and the study of Spanish. Both credit and noncredit courses are offered year-round. The courses include painting, drawing, printmaking, sculpture, silverwork, batik, enameling, ceramics, and weaving. Four-week language courses include conversational Spanish, intensive Spanish, and something called "Total Impact" Spanish, which involves one-to-one instruction for three to six hours daily. History and art history of Mexico and intercultural communication courses are also an option. Not far from San Miguel are archaeological sites, historic towns, and craft centers, which participants visit in connection with many of the classes. Life at San Miguel is lively; there are English-language films, regularly scheduled concerts, ballets and symphonies, dances, parties, gallery openings, poetry readings, tennis, golf, and horseback riding.

Requirements: Applicants must be at least 16 and in tenth grade. Although its credit programs attract students who wish to earn undergraduate and graduate transfer credit or a master of fine arts degree, the school welcomes serious noncredit students for short-term enrollment.

Living arrangements: Students make their own accommodation arrangements. San Miguel offers a wide choice of accommodations, and students can choose from a list provided by the Instituto.

Finances: Costs for classes range from $190 for a four-week fine arts and crafts course to $220 for the four-week "Aspects of Mexico" course. Four weeks of "Total Impact" Spanish costs $550 for three hours per day to $955 for six hours per day. There's an additional $10 registration fee and a $4-per-month accident insurance fee.

Contact: Jaime Fernández, President (address above).

INTERNATIONAL SUMMER ACADEMY OF FINE ARTS
Kaigasse 2
P.O. Box 18
A-5010 Salzburg
Austria
Fax: (43) 662-849638

The sponsor: This art school, established in 1953, is supported by the town and county of Salzburg and by the Ministry of Education of Austria.

The program: From the middle of July to the middle of August—five weeks in all—participants draw and paint alongside well-known artists. Sculpture, architecture, stage design, goldsmithing, photography, video, stone sculpture, graphic arts, and modeling are also taught. "Participants must be willing to work seriously and intensively. Professors expect students to be able to work at least somewhat independently." The Summer Academy is not designed for complete beginners who have never worked with a brush or pencil.

Requirements: The minimum age is 17; some knowledge of German is helpful but not absolutely necessary. Skill in the fine arts is required.

Living arrangements: The school helps students find a place to stay either in fellow students' homes or with private families in Salzburg who are chosen by the Salzburg Tourist Office.

Finances: Tuition is 8,800 Austrian schillings (approximately $808) for the five-week session. Students must pay for their own transportation, room and board, and insurance.

Deadline: June 15.

Contact: Dr. Barbara Wally, Manager (address above).

IRISH SCHOOL OF LANDSCAPE PAINTING
The Blue Door Studio
16 Prince of Wales Terrace
Ballsbridge, Dublin 4
Ireland
Telephone: (353) 1-685548

The sponsor: Founded in 1957 by painter Kenneth Webb, this is a "holiday painting school" staffed by professional painters.

The program: The school accepts advanced and amateur painters; its emphasis is on the individual student's standard of personal achievement. One-week courses held in Connemara begin at different times during the summer; a three-day course is held in Dublin during summer and winter months. Students can stay for several weeks if they prefer. Students paint outdoors from 10 A.M. to 6 P.M., five days a week.

Supervision: The school does not provide group leaders, but tutors are available to students in case of emergency.

Services for persons with disabilities: The school welcomes many students with disabilities but cannot accommodate participants in wheelchairs.

Requirements: Participants must be at least 14 years of age.

Living arrangements: Students stay in hotels or guest houses.

Finances: The cost for the Clifden, Connemara, course is from 90 to 160 Irish pounds (approximately $36 to $243) per week. The three-day Dublin course costs 100 Irish pounds (approximately $159). Hotel rooms, including breakfast and dinner, are available to students and accompanying guests at special weekly rates.

Deadline: May 6.

Contact: Clare Cryan (address above).

LOWER ASTON HOUSE POTTERY AND PAINTING SUMMER SCHOOL
Aston Bank
Knighton-on-Teme
Tenbury Wells
Worcestershire WR15 8LW
England
Telephone: (44) 584-79404

The sponsor: Founded in 1981, the Lower Aston House Pottery and Painting Summer School is an institution for persons from all countries who are interested in the arts.

The program: The Lower Aston House offers courses in pottery and painting. Weekend courses are offered in May, June, and October; week-long courses take place in July and August. Programs are organized for maximum teacher-student interaction, with individual help and advice for students at all levels, from the beginner to the experienced amateur artist. In the pottery class, participants' best five pots are fired and glazed at the end of the stay, with a small supplemental charge for postage and packaging. Participants can also keep their pots free of charge without firing them.

Supervision: All courses are taught by an experienced staff working with small groups to allow for personal attention in an informal setting. The student-teacher ratio is 9 to 1.

Services for persons with disabilities: Persons with disabilities are welcome, but the Lower Aston School has no special facilities.

Requirements: Participants must be over 14 years of age. For the pottery class, participants should bring a smock, a pair of jeans, and an old towel. For the painting class, participants must provide most of their own painting supplies. Contact sponsor for details.

Living arrangements: Individual rooms in a family house, including "all comforts and home cooking."

Finances: For the weekend stay, the cost is 124 British pounds (approximately $190 dollars); for the weeklong stay, 287 pounds (approximately $441 dollars). This includes full room and board and instruction.

There is an additional charge of 8 British pounds ($12) for the weekend and 25 British pounds ($38) for the week if a single room is required.

Deadline: One week prior to course.

Contact: Tina Homer, Organizer (address above).

OXFORD SCHOOL OF DRAMA
Sansomes Farm Studios
Woodstock
Oxford OX7 1ER
England
Telephone: (44) 993-812883

The sponsor: The Oxford School of Drama has offered teenagers the opportunity to study and perform drama since 1981.

The program: Located in the center of Oxford, the school conducts two- and four-week acting and production courses at the introductory to advanced levels. Courses run from July to the end of August.

Supervision: The live-in staff supervise participants. There is one staff member for every 10 students.

Requirements: Participants should be 14 to 18 years old.

Living arrangements: Participants are housed in student accommodations with live-in housekeepers. The school contains communal dining and recreation areas.

Finances: The tuition is 550 British pounds (approximately $847) for two weeks and 1,000 British pounds ($1,540) for four weeks, which includes accommodations, breakfast, dinner, travel during the courses, and theater tickets.

Deadline: April 30.

Contact: Hilary Davis, Administrator (address above).

PERFORMING ARTS ABROAD
P.O. Box 844
Kalamazoo, MI 49005
Telephone: (616) 629-4901
Fax: (616) 629-4176

The sponsor: This commercial tour operator has specialized in tours for nonprofessional musicians since 1962.

The program: PAA assembles students to form music ensembles for summer performance tours of Europe (Austria, England, France, Germany, Italy, the Netherlands, and Switzerland) or the South Pacific (Australia, Hawaii, and New Zealand). Individual students in band, orchestra, or choir can hone their skills during the summer months under the direction of a highly skilled conductor while gaining cultural insights and travel experience.

Orientation: Prior to departure, students are supplied with complete tour background information and music for rehearsal. Groups assemble for rehearsals and orientation at the first destination on the itinerary.

Supervision: One or more PAA staff members escort the group, with a ratio of one escort to 10 students. The conductor of the ensemble shares this responsibility.

Services for persons with disabilities: Disabilities are handled on an individual basis. PAA has accommodated students in wheelchairs and other physical disabilities in the past.

Requirements: Acceptance is based upon a positive recommendation from the individual student's music teacher or school music director. A recommendation form is sent to the teacher by PAA upon receipt of the student's application for the program.

Living arrangements: Accommodations range from hotels and university housing to homestays, depending on the itinerary.

Finances: The 21-day European concert tour costs $2,200 per person, including round-trip airfare from New York City. The sixteen-day concert tour of the South Pacific costs $2,000, including round-trip airfare from Los Angeles or San Francisco. Tour prices include complete coordination of concert and rehearsal arrangements; all transfers as required by the itinerary; breakfast and dinner daily; sight-seeing arrangements; all taxes and tips for hotel and restaurant services; and historical, geographical, and cultural information on each destination.

Deadline: May 1.

Contact: Ted Tilbury, President (address above).

STUDIO ART CENTERS INTERNATIONAL (SACI)
Via San Gallo, 30
50129 Florence
Italy
Telephone: (39) 55-486164
Fax: (39) 55-486230

The sponsor: This American nonprofit organization was founded in 1975 to provide excellence in studio art courses and art history using the rich resources of Florence. It is accredited by Bowling Green State University for both undergraduate and graduate studies.

The program: Two-Year Diploma program, Academic Year Abroad, Summer programs; one in June and one in July, plus independent study credit at undergraduate and graduate level. Classes are taught in English. Courses of study include studio arts, art history, Italian language, painting, printmaking, sculpture, film, and video. Depending on the course of study, students also take field trips to Pisa, Ravenna, Rome, and Venice.

Orientation: An orientation period is offered at the beginning of the program, during which the dean, the program director and the staff provide the students with information and advice about Florence and the program.

Supervision: The resident dean and program director act as supervisors and counselors. There is also a graduate studies coordinator plus eight administrative staff and 20 faculty members.

Services for persons with disabilities: Some facilities can accommodate physically disabled students.

Requirements: Minimum age is 17; students should be in their senior year of high school and have "a sincere interest in visual arts." Two teacher recommendations and transcripts are required, as well as parental approval for minors.

Living arrangements: Students live in fully furnished apartments, or upon special request, with an Italian family.

Finances: The four-week late-spring/summer course costs $2,435, the academic year program costs $6,500 per term. Fees include tuition, extensive field trips, library use, evening lectures and seminars.

Deadline: Six weeks before the beginning of the course.

Contact: Institute of International Education (IIE), SACI Coordinator, 809 United Nations Plaza, New York, NY 10017-3580; Telephone: (212) 984-5548, or (800) 344-9186; Fax: (212) 984-5325.

SUMMER MUSIC SUMMER SCHOOL
22 Gresley Road
London N19 3JZ
England
Telephone: (44) 71-2725664

The sponsor: This music school, operating since 1967, is at Wellington College, Crowthorne, Berkshire, about 25 miles southwest of London. The college was built by Queen Victoria in 1853 in honor of the Duke of Wellington.

The program: The program takes place in August and offers classes in string quartets, chamber music, symphony orchestras, wind ensembles, choirs, opera, song recital, conducting, composing, brass consorts, Renaissance dance, music theater, and a workshop in writing fiction. During the evenings, there are many concerts and a barn dance.

Supervision: Staff supervises participants.

Services for persons with disabilities: Participants with minor disabilities can be accommodated. The school cannot accommodate students in wheelchairs, however.

Requirements: Minimum age is 14; beginners are welcome.

Living arrangements: Participants usually live at the school in single or double rooms. Some nearby bed-and-breakfast accommodations are available for anyone preferring to live off-campus. All meals are provided for on-campus residents; all except breakfast for those staying off-campus.

Finances: The fee of 200 British pounds (approximately $308) for students living at the school includes room and board and classes.

Deadline: One week before program begins.

Contact: Murray Gordon, Organizer (address above).

TOTNES SCHOOL OF GUITARMAKING
Collins Road
Totnes
Devon TQ9 5PJ
England
Telephone: (44) 803-865255

The sponsor: The Totnes School of Guitarmaking was established in 1981 by guitar maker Norman Reed. It is located in a small pre-Norman town in the rural southwest of England, three and a half hours by train from London.

The program: Courses last 12 weeks, during which time students use seasoned hardwoods to build the guitar (or related instrument) of their choosing. The finished instrument belongs to the student at the end of the course. "For many, this is the first guitar they have built—for some, their first woodwork ever. Yet 95 percent leave with a finished, playing instrument." The school is located in a building dating from about 1700, which also houses a professional guitar workshop and retail shop. Advice on organizing one's own workshop is part of the course. Sessions are held from September 18 to December 8, January 8 to March 29, and April 29 to July 19.

Orientation: "After dealing with formalities, the first day is devoted to selecting timber, reading from drawings, and the sharpening, care, and use of tools."

Supervision: Group instruction alternates with individual attention.

Requirements: "The only qualification for entry to the course is wanting to build an instrument."

Living arrangements: Students usually take lodgings with families in the town; the school helps make arrangements.

Finances: The fee is 2,670 British pounds (approximately $4,111) including tuition and materials.

Contact: Norman Reed (address above).

ORGANIZED TOURS

*O*ften arranged by commercial tour organizers, the travel programs in this section offer participants a variety of sight-seeing and touring options. Some focus on popular tourist spots while others go to less-visited areas. Some include lectures or discussions on specific topics, such as the art history or natural environment of a particular country. Generally, participants stay in campgrounds, hotels, pensions, and hostels; some programs include short-term homestays. Groups may travel by bus, minivan, or train.

ACADEMIC ADVENTURES IN AMERICA
67 Tanglewood Drive
Summit, NJ 07901
Telephone: (908) 273-1756

The sponsor: Founded by two educators in 1988, Academic Adventures in America is a nonprofit organization that sponsors cultural and educational exchange programs for American and international students.

The program: There are two programs offered, one in France and one in Spain:

- The *Paris and Bordeaux* region homestay program consists of visits to such famous sites as the Eiffel Tower, followed by a two-week homestay in the Bordeaux region which includes trips to St. Emilion and Arachon. The program lasts from June 30 to July 22.
- The *Madrid and Marbella* homestay program includes two hours of daily Spanish lessons, trips to Segovia, Toledo, Malaga, and Ronda. Activities such as tennis, horse riding, sailing, windsurfing, swimming, and golf are also available.

Supervision: Each group is accompanied by an AAIA tour escort who is a language teacher and has experience in AAIA programs in the United States.

Requirements: Students must be at least 14 years old and in ninth grade with two years of language study.

Living arrangements: Students live with host families who are selected by cooperating student organizations in France and Spain.

Finances: The France program costs $1,995 and the Spain program costs $2,400. Fees cover air travel, homestays (room and board) with local families, all sight-seeing, and admissions. Scholarships are also available.

Deadline: May 15.

Contact: Rose Jackson, Director (address above).

AMERICAN ZIONIST YOUTH FOUNDATION (AZYF)
110 East 59th Street
New York, NY 10022
Telephone: (212) 339-6916 or (800) 274-7723

The sponsor: Founded in 1963, the American Zionist Youth Foundation is a nonprofit organization that sponsors educational programs for Jewish American youth with the purpose of bringing them closer to Israel and Judaism.

The program: AZYF sponsors its own programs for high-school students, and publishes *The Complete Guide to Israel Programs,* which lists programs of other organizations. AZYF provides Israel-related educational programs and activities for people between the ages of 12 and 35.

Supervision: Students are accompanied by group leaders.

Requirements: Depends on the program and the organization.

Living arrangements: Participants live in dormitories, on kibbutzim, or in hotels, depending on the program.

Finances: Costs vary according to the program from $650 to $5,000.

Contact: Israel Program Center (address above).

BUTTERFIELD AND ROBINSON
70 Bond Street, Suite 300
Toronto
Ontario M5B 1X3
Canada
Telephone: (800) 678-1147

The sponsor: This commercial travel agency specializes in organizing programs designed to "promote active discovery and involvement in a foreign environment," and has been doing so since 1966.

The program: Butterfield and Robinson offers two programs:

- The *European Student Biking Challenge* travels from Paris to Prague entirely by bike in 34 days. Students cycle through France, Germany, Austria, and the Czech Republic.
- The *Passage West Student Multi Adventure* trip departs from Calgary in Alberta, Canada, and arrives in Seattle, Washington. Along the way, students can bike, hike, ride horses, climb rocks, kayak, and sail on a tall ship.

Supervision: The participant-leader ratio is 10 to 1 for the European Student Biking Challenge and 7 to 1 for the Passage West.

Services for persons with disabilities: Butterfield and Robinson is willing to accommodate students with certain disabilities.

Requirements: For the European Student Biking Challenge, students must be 17 to 22; for the Passage West, students must be 14 to 16.

Living arrangements: On the bicycle tour of Europe, students stay in family-owned inns, chalets, and *Gasthöfs* (guesthouses) in the country-side, and small hotels in the cities. On the Passage West, students stay in small hostels, inns, and cabins, and some do camping in the Canadian Rockies and along the West Coast.

Finances: Costs are $4,375 for the European Student Biking Challenge and $3,375 for the Passage West. Fees do not include airfare, but Butterfield and Robinson can arrange transportation on group flights for participants.

Deadline: No official deadline, but programs fill up in March.

Contact: Karen Clausen, Coordinator of Student Programs (address above).

CET
3210 Grace Street, NW
Washington, DC 20007
Telephone: (800) 225-4262 or (202) 333-7873

The sponsor: CET is a commercial organization specializing in academic programs and educational tours of China for students of all ages. It was founded in 1979.

The program: China in Perspective is an introduction to Chinese civilization, including history, culture, language, geography, and political and economic organization. The curriculum consists of four parts: lectures on specific topics, activities and field trips designed to complement the lectures, daily "survival Chinese" classes, and a weekly seminar summarizing the lessons of each week. The program is based at the Capital Normal University College of Foreign Languages in west central Beijing. Faculty are drawn from China and the United States. The program lasts from July 7 to August 9.

Orientation: Participants receive predeparture materials. There is an orientation upon arrival in Beijing.

Supervision: The student-teacher ratio is 10 to 1. Each group is accompanied by a U.S. director fluent in Chinese and with an M.A. in a related field.

Services for persons with disabilities: Persons with disabilities are welcome to participate.

Requirements: The minimum age is 13. There is no language requirement.

Living arrangements: Students are housed in dormitory suites of two to three rooms with hot showers.

Finances: The $3,165 fee includes international airfare from New York, tuition, housing, texts, visa fees, and activities. The fee for students departing from San Francisco is $2,950.

Deadline: May 1.

FORUM TRAVEL INTERNATIONAL
91 Gregory Lane, Suite 21
Pleasant Hill, CA 94523
Telephone: (510) 671-2900

The sponsor: A nonprofit organization, Forum International was founded in 1956 with the purpose of "creating a worldwide forum for education, research, and action on a transdisciplinary, supranational, and ecosystemic basis." Forum Travel International is its travel subsidiary.

The program: Forum International has more than 1,300 travel programs geared toward "exploring nature, culture, and people . . . with special emphasis on environmental integrity, social responsibility, human health and fitness in their widest sense, and the ecosystemic interrelation among these various factors." Programs take place year-round in 135 different countries.

Orientation: Orientations vary according to the program.

Supervision: There are 4 to 15 participants per group leader.

Requirements: The minimum age is 12.

Living arrangements: Participants stay in private homes, inns, and lodges, or camp on outdoor adventures.

Finances: Program costs range upwards from $55 per day, including room and board in most cases.

Deadline: Sixty days ahead of time.

Contact: Daniel Levine, Program Director (address above).

HABONIM DROR NORTH AMERICA
27 West 20th Street (9)
New York, NY 10011
Telephone: (212) 255-1796

The sponsor: Founded in 1935, Habonim Dror North America (HDNA) is a nonprofit organization that runs student tours to Israel.

The program: HDNA conducts a summer program called Machaneh Bonim B'Israel (MBI) to Israel for 16 year olds. It runs from late June to mid-August and travels throughout Israel after a three-day stay in Italy.

Supervision: Group leaders, which consist of American and Israeli guides, provide 24-hour supervision and assistance.

Services for persons with disabilities: Anyone is encouraged to participate.

Requirements: Participants must be 16 years old.

Living arrangements: Accommodations are in dormitory rooms or youth hostels.

Finances: The cost is $3,600 plus a $225 registration fee. Some scholarships are available.

Deadline: Mid-February.

Contact: Adam Lowy, Programs Coordinator (address above).

INTERLOCKEN
RD2, Box 165
Hillsboro Upper Village, NH 03244
Telephone: (603) 478-3166

The sponsor: A nonprofit organization, Interlocken has offered summer programs for teenagers since 1961. Both travel and residential programs stress the group experience; students "enjoy the camaraderie and strength of group living as they make new friends and grow as individuals."

The program: Interlocken's Crossroads Student Travel programs emphasize experiential learning, cross-cultural experiences, and group living. Programs focus on performing arts, cycling, photo-journalism, language and culture, environment and world change. Destinations include Western Europe, Eastern Europe, China, the Caribbean, Israel, and Egypt.

In cooperation with Global Roots Community Service, a California-based nonprofit organization, Interlocken also sponsors community service projects in Africa, Asia, and Latin America.

Supervision: "Leaders are adult professionals selected for their maturity, enthusiasm, stability, good judgment, warmth, and ability to relate closely and sensitively with teenagers." Groups vary in size depending on the character and goals of the program; most programs have 12 to 18 students with two to three adult leaders.

Services for persons with disabilities: Interlocken will accept individuals with disabilities if they are able to engage in the program as designed.

Living arrangements: Crossroads Travel programs usually include camping and homestays with local families.

Requirements: For most international programs offered by Interlocken, participants should be in the ninth through twelfth grades. However, some programs accept seventh- and eighth-graders.

Finances: International programs range in cost from $2,585 to $3,595, not including airfare. Some scholarship aid is available.

Deadline: Rolling admissions.

ISRAEL YOUTH HOSTELS ASSOCIATION (IYHA)
Youth Travel Bureau
3, Dorot Rishonim Street
P.O. Box 1075
Jerusalem 91009
Israel
Telephone: (972) 2-252706
Fax: (972) 2-250676

The sponsor: The Israel Youth Hostels Association offers affordable accommodations and special programs for youth visiting Israel.

The program: IYHA offers one- to four-week travel programs including desert safaris in the Sinai and the Negev, Eilat-Red Sea Holidays, nature tours, and a trip to Egypt.

Requirements: Programs are offered for all ages.

Living arrangements: Students stay in youth hostels.

Finances: Contact the organization for current costs.

Deadline: No set deadline.

LEARNING ADVENTURE PROGRAMS, INC.
11 Davis Court
Concord, MA 01742
Telephone: (508) 462-3345

The sponsor: Founded in 1993, Learning Adventure Programs (LAP) are specifically designed for high-school students who want to learn more about the world through study, travel, and recreation.

The program: The Discover Britain 1995 program will examine British history and its prominent figures from King Arthur to Winston Churchill as the group travels through the countryside and cities of Britain. Discussion groups and museum tours during the trip will provide both the background and the context for the group's developing understanding of England and its past. Interspersed with visits to castles, museums, and country houses will be outdoor activities such as hiking and rock climbing, which will allow ample opportunity to enjoy the English landscape.

Supervision: Each group will be guided by two LAP leaders, for a ratio of six students to every leader. Leaders are chosen for their qualities of maturity and enthusiasm for teaching and learning, as well as for their appropriate academic background.

Requirements: Participants must be at least 15 years old and completing tenth, eleventh, or twelfth grade with an interest in learning about another culture.

Living arrangements: Accommodations will be in hotels, guest houses, and apartments. Meals are provided by the program or prepared by program staff and participants.

Finances: The program tuition is $5,950, which includes round-trip airfare from Boston to London, all accommodations and regular meals, ground transportation, activity and entrance fees, and other scheduled events and entertainment.

Deadline: Rolling admissions.

Contact: Meg Klingelhofer, Co-Director (address above).

LEGACY INTERNATIONAL
Route 4 Box 265
Bedford, VA 24523
Telephone: (703) 297-5982

The sponsor: Established in 1979, Legacy International is a nonprofit educational organization that promotes mutual understanding through student exchanges which include travel, homestays, and community projects.

The program: Legacy International has two outbound programs for American students, the Costa Rican Adventure and Discover NIS (Newly Independent States of the former Soviet Union).

- The Costa Rican Adventure, which includes sight-seeing, a homestay, and volunteer work, is more like an internship than a group travel program because the small size of the group (no more than six people) allows the participants to customize the programs according to their interests.
- The Discover NIS program takes place in Uzbekistan, where students cooperate with native students on tourism development projects, meeting community leaders, and visiting cultural and historical sites.

Orientation: A preliminary orientation conducted by Legacy International faculty is held in Washington, D.C., prior to departure. Discussions are held and training manuals and cultural profiles are given to the students. An in-country orientation is also held upon the students' arrival.

Supervision: The program coordinators are selected through an application and interview process that examines language ability, prior experience in the host country, and experience with young people. These coordinators arrange plans and oversee the program.

Services for persons with disabilities: Persons with disablilities are evaluated by the same standards as those without disabilities. On a trip to Uzbekistan there may be difficulty accommodating physically challenged people.

Requirements: Participants must be between 15 and 19 years of age, in the tenth grade to the first year of college. The Costa Rican Adventure requires two years of Spanish.

Living arrangements: In Costa Rica and France, participants live with host families. In Uzbekistan, hostels and hotels are provided.

Finances: The Costa Rican Adventure costs $2,700. The cost for the Discover NIS (Uzbekistan) program is $3,500. Fees include room, board, instruction, materials, and health insurance. Airfare is not included. Scholarships are available only for the Uzbekistan program.

Deadline: Rolling admissions.

Contact: Mary Helmig, Co-director Summer Program (address above).

MUSIKER STUDENT TOURS
1326 Old Northern Boulevard
Roslyn, NY 11576
Telephone: (516) 621-0718; (800) 645-6611 outside New York
Fax: (516) 625-3438

The sponsor: Musiker Student Tours is a family-owned company established in 1966.

The program: Musiker Tours offers a range of programs that emphasize sight-seeing and recreational and cultural activities. The five-week Action Europe tour visits Italy, Switzerland, France, Belgium, and England. All tours include visits to museums, historic sites, and theater, plus such activities as cruises, waterskiing, summer snow-skiing, mountain biking, whitewater rafting, and tennis. Musiker also offers tours in Canada.

Supervision: Most staff members are tour alumni who have trained for five years. The student-leader ratio is eight to one. Leaders are on duty at all times.

Services for persons with disabilities: Students with disabilities are invited to inquire. Students in wheelchairs may have a difficult time traveling.

Requirements: Participants should be between 14 and 18 years old.

Living arrangements: On the Action Europe tour, students stay in hotels.

Finances: The Action Europe tour costs $5,500, including three meals daily, all activities, excursions, admissions, and recreational activities. Airfare is extra.

Deadline: Rolling admissions.

**NORTH AMERICAN FEDERATION OF TEMPLE YOUTH
    (NFTY)**
Union of American Hebrew Congregations–Youth Division
NFTY in Israel Office
P.O. Box 443, Bowen Road
Warwick, NY 10990
Telephone: (914) 987-6300

The sponsor: NFTY is the youth division of the Union of American Hebrew Congregations, the national reform movement in Judaism. For more than 20 years, NFTY has sponsored long- and short-term programs in Israel for high-school and college students.

The program: NFTY offers two summer programs and one semester program:

- *Israel Academy* is primarily a travel program that explores ancient and modern Israel and includes a camping trip in the desert. Living and working in a kibbutz for two weeks is one of the features of the five-and-a-half-week tour.
- *Israel Safari* is similar to the Academy tour, but instead of the kibbutz experience, participants spend time at an Israeli field school exploring the geology, geography, flora, and fauna of the country.
- *The Eisendrath International Exchange Program* is an academic semester offered both in the fall and the spring. The program provides an in-depth look at historical and contemporary Israel, while enabling students to continue their normal high-school curriculum with full credit. Students spend part of the semester living with an Israeli family, and part of the time working on a kibbutz.

Recent high-school graduates might also consider other NFTY programs, some of which are suitable for the year between high school and college. Ask for details on the College Israel Academy and College and Kibbutz academic-year programs.

Orientation: A brief orientation takes place at the airport before departure.

Supervision: Group leaders have prior experience working with young people and are responsible for daily supervision, including general counseling and leading group discussions.

Services for persons with disabilities: Persons with disabilities are welcome; however, students in wheelchairs might have great difficulty participating.

Requirements: The Eisendrath Exchange Program requires participants to have completed tenth grade for the fall session. The spring session of the Eisendrath Exchange Program and other programs require participants to have completed ninth grade. There is no language requirement.

Living arrangements: These vary with the program. Participants stay in hotels, hostels, and/or kibbutzim. Participants in the semester-long program stay with families who live in a city, development town, youth village, or kibbutz.

Finances: Costs for the summer programs range from $3,995 to $4,095; the semester program costs $7,500. Fee includes round-trip airfare from New York, room and board, and all touring costs. While the participant is in Israel, insurance is provided through that country's national health network; information on other insurance is provided.

Deadline: May 1.

Contact: Paul Reichenbach, Director, Israel Programs (address above).

NSTS—STUDENT AND YOUTH TRAVEL
220 St. Paul Street
Valletta VLT 07
Malta
Telephone: (356) 244983
Fax: (356) 230330

The sponsor: NSTS is the student/youth travel organization of Malta, a country of islands in the Mediterranean, south of Italy. NSTS promotes educational and cultural development through travel by providing low-cost accommodation, transportation, entertainment, sports, and a variety of special programs to young people. NSTS is a member of the International Student Travel Confederation (see page 56).

The program: Besides offering a full range of travel services and historical and cultural day excursions in Malta, NSTS organizes a number of special programs:

- *An Appreciation of Baroque Art:* This two-week course is designed to give students an appreciation of Baroque painting and architecture through a series of lectures and visits to places of interest throughout Malta.
- *Archaeology in Malta:* Participants spend two weeks attending lectures on methodology, Maltese history, the megalithic temples, and historical archaeology; taking trips to places of historical and archaeological interest; and doing survey work, clearance work, or actual excavations.
- *Sports Encounters:* This program allows amateur sports clubs and school teams to meet their Maltese counterparts in specially organized tournaments. Sports range from basketball to tennis and water polo. Cultural programs can be combined with the basic or custom-designed sports programs.
- *Painting:* A practical holiday course that offers participants the opportunity to paint Maltese landscapes while receiving instruction on techniques of watercolor, oil painting, and sketching. Materials for the course are provided.

Supervision: Participants in all programs are attended by trained personnel.

Services for persons with disabilities: NSTS will try to make the necessary arrangements for participants with disabilities.

Requirements: The minimum age is 14.

Living arrangements: These vary from student residences to family homestays.

Finances: Fees vary with the program.

Deadline: Six weeks prior to beginning of program.

ON TOUR
217 Wolseley North
Montreal West, Quebec H4X 1W1
Telephone: (514) 488-8920; (800) 767-0227 in the United States

The sponsor: On Tour is a student travel program that allows older students to combine independence and adventure with the benefits of hassle-free group travel. Participants are free to explore on their own or join the group fun as they please. On Tour is a division of Westcoast Connection, a student travel program founded in 1982.

The program: The European Experience travels through Holland, Belgium, France (Paris, Versailles, Provence, the Riviera, and the Alps) and Switzerland. The French Escape program includes the Loire Valley, Paris, Versailles, Provence, the Riviera, the Alps, and Switzerland. Also available are the Dutch Getaway (Holland only), or Holland and Belgium. The group bikes half-days on about 60 percent of the days. Trips are vehicle-supported (A car or van follows the bicycling participants, in case they need rest or repair.) and include some travel by boat and train.

Supervision: There is one leader for every five to six students.

Services for persons with disabilities: Each case is handled individually.

Requirements: Participants should be between 17 and 22.

Living arrangements: All programs combine private campsites with two- and three-star hotels.

Finances: The European Experience costs $3,795; the French Escape costs $3,295; the Dutch Getaway is $1,395; and the Holland-Belgium trip costs $1,995. Fees include accommodations, ground transportation, breakfast and lunch daily and one group dinner per week, two snacks on many days, and all activities and admissions. Airfare is not included.

Deadline: No set deadline, but early registration is encouraged.

ORGANISATION FUR INTERNATIONALE KONTAKTE (OIK)
Alte Bahnhofstrasse 26
D-53173 Bonn-Bad Godesberg
Germany
Telephone: (228) 356076-79
Fax: (228) 364368

The sponsor: The Organisation fur Internationale Kontakte, a nonprofit organization, was founded in 1975 with the goal of promoting international understanding between the people of Germany and groups from around the world.

The program: OIK provides the following opportunities for groups only:

- *Homestay Programs:* Homestays are arranged with German families supplemented with social gatherings, school visits, and discussions. Courses in German language, art and/or history also are available. Homestays can also be designed for musical groups with planned performances and young sports teams, such as a soccer group, with scheduled games.
- *Study Tours* for high-school students provide for exploration and examination of the art, culture, and architecture of Germany and neighboring countries.
- *Sports Tours* allow soccer, basketball, volleyball, ice hockey and other sports groups to meet and compete against their German counterparts in specially organized tournaments.
- *Music Tours* for bands, choirs, orchestras, jazz groups, and folk dance groups include rehearsals, concerts, and sightseeing. Since 1981, OIK has organized its own annual international music festivals and invites any interested group to participate. Groups stay with German families.

Orientation: Printed information in addition to videotapes are supplied as an introduction.

Supervision: Groups must bring their own leader. Once in Europe, the groups are provided with an escort.

Services for persons with disabilities: Participation by persons with disabilities is encouraged, depending on the program chosen by the group. Students in wheelchairs have been accommodated in the past.

Requirements: Only groups can be placed in the programs.

Living arrangements: Accommodations include hotels, youth hostels, or homestays.

Finances: Fees vary according to the chosen tour and itinerary. Room and board is included in the fee. DM535 (approx. $343) to DM2960 (approx. $1,900)

Deadline: Varies according to program.

PHENIX INTERNATIONAL CAMPUSES
7651 North Carolyn Drive
Castle Rock, CO 80104
Telephone: (303) 688-9397

The sponsor: Phenix International, a nonprofit organization founded in 1970, offers travel-study programs that include homestays, language assistance, cultural classes, and sight-seeing.

The program: Phenix offers spring and summer travel/homestay programs. Spring programs include:

- France: Homestay in Paris plus travel to Mont-Saint-Michel and the Normandy beaches.
- Germany: Homestay in Munich plus travel to surrounding areas.
- Spain: Homestay in Seville or Leon plus sight-seeing in Madrid.
- Mexico: Sight-seeing in Mexico City and Puerto Vallarta.

Summer programs include:

- *Adventures in Germany:* A three-week journey beginning with sight-seeing in Munich, followed by a homestay in Schwandorf, Bavaria, and excursions to Nurnberg, Regensburg, and Amberg. The program concludes with several days of sight-seeing in Salzburg, Austria.
- *España es su Casa:* This three-week tour program begins with sight-seeing in Lisbon, Portugal, followed by travel to Vigo, Spain, for a day on the beach; homestay in Leon; and sight-seeing in Madrid and Toledo.
- *Adventures in Spain:* A three-week tour that begins with sight-seeing in Madrid, Toledo, and Segovia, followed by travel to Granada and a homestay in Seville.
- *Treasures of France:* This three-week tour includes four days in Paris and a homestay in Bourges. Excursions are planned near Bourges and the Riviera. (In alternate years, the homestay is in Hyeres on the Mediterranean.)
- *Modern and Historic Mexico:* A 17-day tour that includes four days in Mexico City and Teotihuacan, plus a homestay in Puebla. Two days are spent at the beach in Puerto Vallarta.
- *Russia Today:* This three-week program includes travel to St. Petersburg and Moscow, plus a homestay in the Black Sea resort

of Sochi. Meetings with local young people and language lessons are also available.

Orientation: Orientations are held monthly between January and June for students living in the Denver area. These meetings cover specific information about the countries to be visited, cultural simulations, language practice, and general trip preparation. Students from outside Colorado receive orientation materials by mail.

Supervision: For every eight students, there is one teacher-chaperone. In addition, an American educator with overseas and student-travel experience is in charge of the entire group and acts as a link to the overseas representative.

Services for persons with disabilities: Phenix will make individual arrangements to the fullest extent possible, as long as the best interests of the group can be served.

Requirements: Participants must be between 13 and 19 years old. One year of language study is required for language programs. Applicants must have references from a teacher and a school counselor.

Living arrangements: These include homestays, hotels, and youth hostels.

Finances: Program fees range from $1,189 to $2,789, depending on the destination and the length of the trip. The fee includes round-trip airfare from Denver or the gateway city nearest you, all travel, sight-seeing, room and full board.

Deadline: No set deadline, but early application is recommended.

Contact: Nellie B. Jackson, Manager (address above).

PORTUGUESE YOUTH HOSTEL ASSOCIATION
(Associação de Utentes das Pousadas de Juventude)
Tourism Department
Av. Duque D'Avila Nº 137
1000 Lisbon
Portugal
Telephone: (351) 1-3559081
Fax: (351) 1-3528621

The sponsor: The Portuguese Youth Hostel Association is a nonprofit organization that operates 18 youth hostels in various parts of Portugal. It also sponsors a variety of tours for young people.

The program: There are a variety of tours for individuals or groups, most of which last about a week and focus on a particular region of Portugal. An 18-day trip through all of Portugal is also offered. Other program options emphasize particular activities such as canoeing, mountaineering, windsurfing, and diving, or arts and crafts, including instruction in tapestry, basket-weaving, and pottery.

Supervision: Youth hostel wardens are responsible for the well-being of the hostel and hostelers staying there. There are tour guides for the day-stops throughout the tour programs.

Requirements: Most of the outdoor activities and arts and crafts programs have minimum ages: 16 for the canoeing, mountaineering, and tapestry and 18 for the others.

Living arrangements: Accommodations are in Portuguese youth hostels.

Finances: Consult the organization for current costs.

PUTNEY STUDENT TRAVEL (PST)
International Road
Putney, VT 05346
Telephone: (802) 387-5885

The sponsor: PST, a commercial agency, has been organizing "nontouristy" educational travel programs since 1952.

The program: Most PST programs last five to six weeks. They include trips to Australia, Canada, the Caribbean, China, Costa Rica, Ecuador, England, France, Holland, Hungary, New Zealand, Scandinavia, Spain, countries of the former Soviet Union, and the United States. According to the sponsor, "Our travel plans are special. They emphasize doing— having fun, getting off the beaten track, making friends, and being involved with people—rather than just touring or sight-seeing." The emphasis is on the active: participants might sail with Breton fishermen, explore the steppes of Russia, or hike through Denmark. Special language-learning trips to Spain and France emphasize speaking the languages in natural, everyday living situations.

Supervision: Leaders are college graduates completely fluent in the language, with experience living abroad and working with teenagers. There is one leader for every eight students.

Services for persons with disabilities: While its programs tend to be physically demanding, PST can accommodate people with limited disabilities (for example, visual and hearing impairments, learning disabilities, minor physical disabilities).

Requirements: Students from 13 to 18, eighth through twelfth grade, are eligible. Groups are formed according to age of participants. "Students should recognize that participation in PST is challenging. They are expected to make a positive contribution to the success of the program and the morale of the group, and to maintain high standards of personal behavior."

Living arrangements: Participants stay in small inns, chalets, student centers, and hostels—places where they have a chance to meet people from other countries.

Finances: Fees, which are all-inclusive, range from $3,290 to $6,090.

Deadline: No set deadline, but programs usually fill up by early spring.

Contact: Jeffrey Shumlin, Director (address above).

SCOTTISH YOUTH HOSTELS ASSOCIATION (SYHA)
7 Glebe Crescent
Stirling FK8 2JA
Scotland
Telephone: (44) 786-51181

The sponsor: SYHA, founded in 1931, is an organization that offers young people budget accommodations at more than 80 locations throughout Scotland.

The program: The organization offers a number of all-inclusive Breakaway Holiday packages, which offer a choice of hill-walking, canoeing, sailing, windsurfing, and pony trekking vacations. Other programs give participants the freedom to explore Scotland at their own pace. The Scottish Wayfarer and Explore Scotland passes give 7 or 14 days' unlimited travel within the pass area by coach, rail, and boat. Overnight accommodation vouchers, a SYHA handbook, timetables, and a touring map are included.

Supervision: Supervision is provided by qualified instructors on the Breakaway Holiday packages, and hostels are staffed by wardens at all times.

Services for persons with disabilities: SYHA has no specific programs, but most of the wardens are willing to help disabled individuals or groups. Some hostels cannot accommodate wheelchairs.

Requirements: On Breakaway Holidays, participants must be 14 (12 for pony trekking).

Living arrangements: Participants stay in youth hostels.

Finances: Breakaway Holiday costs begin at 48 British pounds (approximately $74) for a week. Included in the costs are activity fees, accommodations, and in some cases, meals.

Deadline: Full payment is required six weeks prior to holiday dates.

WEISSMAN TEEN TOURS
517 Almena Avenue
Ardsley, NY 10502
Telephone: (914) 693-7575; (800) 942-8005 outside New York

The sponsor: Weissman Teen Tours has offered a five-week package tour of Europe since 1974.

The program: On the 35-day summer program, participants travel through Belgium, England, France, Holland, Italy, and Switzerland by plane, bus, railroad, and hydrofoil. Activities include a full range of guided sight-seeing programs, London theater performances, a medieval banquet, a moonlight gondola ride in Venice, a cruise on the river Seine, skiing in Zermatt, tennis, swimming, and more.

Supervision: Ronee and Eugene Weissman, the founders and operators of Weissman Teen Tours, accompany each group. There is also one group leader for every eight students. Group leaders must have foreign language ability, experience working with teenagers, and prior travel experience. Their responsibilities involve daily supervision, including nightly curfew checks and acting as "a friend and adviser" to tour members.

Requirements: Participants must be 15 to 18 years old. Students entering their junior and senior year in high school or their first year of college are eligible.

Living arrangements: Accommodations are in centrally located four- and five-star hotels and resorts.

Finances: The 1994 tour cost $6,395, including full room and board, and all activities, but not airfare.

Deadline: Varies according to their irregular schedule.

Contact: Ronee Weissman, Vice President (address above).

WESTCOAST CONNECTION TRAVEL CAMP
217 Wolseley North
Montreal West, Quebec H4X 1W1
Canada
Telephone: (514) 488-8920; (800) 767-0227 in the United States

The sponsor: Westcoast Connection Travel Camp is a teen travel program "that combines the excitement and fascination of discovering and exploring Europe with the fun and camaraderie of summer camp." It was founded in 1982.

The program: The European Discovery program takes participants on a five-week bus tour of France, Italy, Switzerland, Belgium, Holland, and England. Also offered are two cycling tours: The European Experience, combining Holland, Belgium, France (Paris, Versailles, Provence, the Riviera, and the Alps) and Switzerland; and the French Escape through the Loire Valley, Paris, Versailles, Provence, the Riviera, the Alps, and Switzerland. On the cycling trips, the group bikes approximately half-days on about 60% of the days. Trips are vehicle supported and include some travel by boat and train. Additionally, there is a four-week outdoor adventure in the Canadian Rockies. The Canadian Mountain Magic combines rafting, rock climbing, glacier skiing, mountain biking, hiking, in-line skating, and tennis with some touring.

Supervision: There is one leader for every five to six students on European Discovery and one for every four on the cycling tours or outdoor adventure.

Services for persons with disabilities: Each case is handled individually.

Requirements: Participants should be in grades 9 to 12.

Living arrangements: All programs combine private campsites with two- and three-star hotels.

Finances: The European Discovery program costs $4,795; the European Experience costs $3,795; the French Escape costs $3,295; Canadian Mountain Magic is $2,995. Fees include accommodations, ground transportation, three meals a day and two snacks on most days, and all activities and admissions. Airfare is not included.

Deadline: No set deadline, but early registration is encouraged.

WORK/VOLUNTEER

*A*t first, work may not sound like much fun on a trip abroad. Some of the most exciting opportunities for teens abroad, however, include working as a volunteer or a trainee. Working with scientists to study volcanoes in Iceland, participating in an archaelogical dig in Israel, doing an internship for a law firm in England, or helping with immunization in Ecuador are only a few of the possibilities that the organizations in this section offer. Some of these "jobs" offer some form of payment, which can make the experience even more rewarding. If you're in it for the money, though, you'll be disappointed: Payment rarely, if ever, approaches the cost of your airfare and program fees. Another option is to join a volunteer service project with an international group of young people. Most overseas work programs open to teenagers are short-term, lasting from a few weeks to a few months.

AMERICAN ASSOCIATION OF OVERSEAS STUDIES (AAOS)
158 West 81st Street, Box 112
New York, NY 10024
Telephone: (212) 724-0804, or (800) EDU-BRIT outside New York

The sponsor: The American Association of Overseas Studies (AAOS), a division of Janet Kollek and Associates, is a commercial agency established in 1984.

The program: AAOS provides academic study and internship opportunities in Paris and London that give young people hands-on experience in film, law, business, government, journalism, and medicine. AAOS also offers a French-language immersion program in Montpellier. Programs take place during the summer.

Supervision: Group leaders supervise internships, lead tours, and are available for discussions. There is one leader for every five participants.

Requirements: The minimum age is 14.

Living arrangements: Participants live in school dormitories.

Finances: The London and Paris academic study-internship programs cost $4,872 for four weeks, including tuition, room and board, excursions, and activities. Film projects cost $5,072. Internships only (without academic study) cost $2,295. The Montpellier French immersion program costs $4,195 for four weeks.

Deadline: Rolling admissions.

Contact: Janet Kollek Evans, Director, AAOS, 51 Drayton Gardens, London, SW10 9RX, England.

AMERICAN FARM SCHOOL
Office of Trustees
1133 Broadway, Suite 1625
New York, NY 10010
Telephone: (212) 463-8434

The sponsor: For almost 90 years, the American Farm School has trained young men and women in Greece to become master farmers and village leaders. More than 225 participants enroll each year to learn the latest applicable farming techniques on the school's 375-acre campus farm.

The program: The "Greek Summer" program offers American high-school students the opportunity to live in a rural Greek village with a family and work on a volunteer project while getting to know the Greek culture. The program runs from mid-June to the end of July. Students spend six weeks in the Greek village and at the Farm School. The projects usually involve construction of a road or sidewalk in a village, building a playground, raising pigs and chickens, and tending vegetable gardens. The project includes a nine-day excursion through Greece and ends with a hike up Mount Olympus.

Supervision: There are five counselors and one director for 44 students at the work sites. Homestay families supervise the students in the evening.

Requirements: Participants must be students from 15 to 18 in tenth through twelfth grades.

Living arrangements: Students live with a Greek family in the village an hour or two from the Farm School.

Finances: The tuition is $2,150, plus a $500 tax-deductible contribution to the school. Airfare is additional. Scholarships are available.

Deadline: No set deadline, but applications preferred by February 15.

Contact: Patricia Mulhern, Program Coordinator (address above).

AMIGOS DE LAS AMÉRICAS
5618 Star Lane
Houston, TX 77057
Telephone: (800) 231-7796; (713) 782-5290
Fax: (713) 782-9267

The sponsor: Amigos de las Américas is a nonprofit voluntary service organization that works on public health projects in Mexico, the Caribbean, and Central and South America. Since its founding in 1965, more than 17,000 volunteers have served. The head office of Amigos is in Houston, where the projects and the 20 local training chapters are coordinated.

The program: Young people spend from four to eight weeks in a village of Central America or the Caribbean, helping to implement a variety of health programs. Some of the specific projects have included dental hygiene instruction in Costa Rica, community sanitation and latrine construction in Mexico, yellow fever immunization in Paraguay, and rabies vaccination in Ecuador. The long-term goal of every Amigos program is three-fold: "leadership development opportunities for North American youth, improved community health in Latin America, and better cross-cultural understanding on both continents."

Orientation: Participants receive approximately 72 hours of training over a three- to six-month period, focusing on public health issues, Latin American history and culture, Spanish language, and human relations. Some high schools and colleges will give academic credit for the Amigos training and experience.

Supervision: There are 8 to 10 volunteers per field staff member. Field staff visit volunteer teams weekly "to ensure that they are happy, healthy, and working well with the community."

Requirements: Participants must be at least 16 years old and have a basic knowledge of Spanish, and complete the lengthy training period described above before beginning their assignment. For those who live near an Amigos chapter, training is done locally. Those who are too far from a chapter to make this practical are called "correspondent volunteers" and are trained through correspondence with the Houston office.

Living arrangements: Volunteers live either with families in the host villages or in a public building, such as a clinic, hospital, or school.

Finances: In 1994 total costs were as follows: Mexico, $2,355; Central America and the Caribbean, $2,455; South America, $2,615, and Brazil, $2,595. Fees include international airfare, training materials, supplies, and room and board. Individual Amigos chapters help with fund-raising. Correspondent volunteers are given a fund-raising kit. Some scholarship aid is available.

Deadline: March 1.

Contact: The address above or your local chapter (call the toll-free number above for the chapter nearest you).

AUSTRALIAN TRUST FOR CONSERVATION VOLUNTEERS
Box 423
1 Ballarat
Victoria 3353
Australia
Telephone: (53) 331-483

The sponsor: Australian Trust for Conservation Volunteers, a nonprofit organization, was founded in 1982 and is accredited by the World Conservation Union.

The program: Volunteers spend six to eight weeks planting trees, doing erosion control work, and constructing fences. Assignments are made year-round and may be in New South Wales, Victoria, or South Australia. The ACTV Echidna Package is a working holiday enabling volunteers to experience Australia inexpensively while being involved in practical conservation tasks.

Supervision: A team leader who supervises the group.

Requirements: Participants must be English speakers between 16 and 60 years old.

Living arrangements: Accommodations include private homes, caravans, campsites, and shearer's quarters.

Finances: The fee for the program is AU $740 (approximately $548) which covers the costs of food, accommodation, and travel while on the working holiday. Airfare is not included.

Deadline: None.

Contact: Colin Jackson (address above).

BRATHAY EXPLORATION GROUP
Brathay Hall
Ambleside
Cumbria LA22 0HP
England
Telephone: (44) 5394-33942

The sponsor: Since 1947, Brathay Exploration Group, a nonprofit voluntary organization, has conducted expeditions, training courses, and other outdoor events around the world. Its goals are to impart understanding of other cultures while teaching new skills to enhance personal and social development.

The program: Brathay currently runs trips to South China, Siberia via Lithuania, Iceland, Nepal, the French Alps, Norway's Jotunheim National Park, the mountains of Snowdonia in North Wales, the Scottish Islands, leader training in Scotland, and mountain first aid courses in England. All programs except for the first aid and leader training courses contain scientific research work as part of the trip. Wherever possible, contact with the other cultures involved is encouraged, as is use of the foreign language.

Supervision: All expeditions are conducted by seasoned leaders who have been evaluated and approved according to their skills and experience. Group leaders are responsible for daily supervision of the participants.

Services for persons with disabilities: All people are eligible to join depending on the nature of the trip. Special needs will be considered on an individual basis.

Requirements: The minimum age is 15. While no foreign language ability is necessary, language experience in the chosen country is helpful.

Living arrangements: Groups normally camp.

Finances: Prices vary from 200 British pounds (approximately $308 dollars) to 2,000 British pounds (approximately $3,080 dollars) depending on the excursion. The fee usually includes all food, accommodation, insurance, and travel in the expedition area. Some scholarship help is available.

Contact: Ron Barrow, Administrator (address above).

CHANTIERS D'ÉTUDES MÉDIÉVALES
4 rue du Tonnelet Rouge
67000 Strasbourg
France
Telephone: (33) 88-371720

The sponsor: Since 1964, this association has organized workcamps for young people interested in the study and restoration of monuments and sites dating to the Middle Ages.

The program: Groups work on excavation sites with archaeologists, historians, architects, and ceramics experts from the Center of Medieval Archaeology in Strasbourg. Participants sign up for 15-day sessions during the summer in Ottrott or Petit-Koenigsbourg.

Requirements: The minimum age is 16, and some knowledge of French is required. Participants under 18 need to have parents' approval.

Living arrangements: Volunteers stay in barracks, houses, or schools.

Finances: Fees are 545 French francs (approximately $102) for participants under eighteen and 450 French francs (approximately $84) for participants above the age of 18.

Deadline: June 15.

CHRISTIAN WELFARE AND SOCIAL RELIEF (CWASRO)
39 Soldier Street
P.O. Box 981
Freetown
Sierra Leone
Telephone: (232) 224096

The sponsor: Founded in 1980, CWASRO is a nonprofit relief organization engaged in educational and vocational activities and youth exchange.

The program: CWASRO offers workcamps throughout rural areas in Sierra Leone. Volunteers serve from three weeks to three months during the summer and fall. Services include construction, education, and social work.

Orientation: The volunteer's first week is spent in orientation.

Supervision: Group leaders speak English and make sure that volunteers have clean clothes, food, and lodgings.

Services for persons with disabilities: Persons with disabilities are housed in area hostels. Disabilities that have been accommodated in the past include a student with one hand and another on crutches.

Requirements: CWASRO accepts volunteers from 11 to 45 years old.

Living arrangements: Volunteers live in camps, hostels, or local homes.

Finances: The fee is $600 plus $50 for orientation, including room and board.

Deadline: Applications must be received by the end of June.

Contact: Rudolph David Hill, Director (address above).

CIEE INTERNATIONAL WORKCAMPS
205 East 42nd Street
New York, NY 10017
Telephone: (212) 661-1414

The sponsor: CIEE is a member of UNESCO's Coordinating Committee on International Voluntary Service (CCIVS), whose purpose is to promote international cooperation through the exchange of volunteers. As a U.S. cooperator in this international exchange, CIEE coordinates the applications and placements of American youth on projects sponsored by CCIVS members throughout Europe and in several African and Asian countries.

The program: Workcamps last from two to four weeks and generally involve working on a community service project alongside young people from other parts of the world. While working, volunteers have a chance to learn something about the native culture, practice the language of the country, and interact with their counterparts from other countries. Actual projects vary from country to country. Here are a few examples of some that took place recently: in the French Alps, participants created a nature path in the outskirts of a small village; in Hiddenhausen, Germany, young people collected and repaired tools to send to self-help projects in the Third World; and in Uncastillo, Spain, volunteers excavated a fifteenth-century castle.

Supervision: Each workcamp has one or more group leaders who are past participants of workcamps. Group leaders facilitate work and living arrangements; they are not meant to act as chaperones or guardians.

Services for persons with disabilities: Participants with disabilities are placed in workcamps according to their disability and the nature of the workcamp's project.

Requirements: Volunteers must be mature and responsible. Age requirements vary depending on the country, but the minimum age is usually 18. Prospective participants should be aware that most individuals will be between 20 and 30 years of age, with some participants over 30. The atmosphere of the camp is one of self-government in which all participants are expected to be responsible for themselves and also to contribute to group life. Volunteers on workcamps in North Africa and Spain should have a working knowledge of the language.

Living arrangements: Accommodations vary, from tents and hostels, to schools and churches.

Finances: There is a $165 application fee. Room and board are provided for the duration of the project. Volunteers are responsible for their own transportation to and from the project site.

Deadline: There is no deadline, but participants are encouraged to apply by the end of April for summer workcamps.

Contact: CIEE, International Voluntary Service above).

CLUB DU VIEUX MANOIR
10, rue de la Cossonnerie
75001 Paris
France
Telephone: (33) 1-45088040

The sponsor: The Club is involved in the restoration of historical sites— gardens, fortresses, and churches—throughout France. Founded in 1953, it offers volunteers a chance to work and learn restoration techniques at the same time.

The program: Volunteers participate in restoration projects that usually take place during spring vacation or during the summer. "The volunteer with an inquisitive mind learns something new every day and gains manual experience as he or she receives instruction in archaeology, architecture, handicrafts, and history." Although it is possible to participate for as few as five days, a stay of 15 to 30 days on a site is necessary to gain familiarity with the kind of work that is being done.

Supervision: Group leaders are responsible for the supervision of the volunteers. Those under the age of 18 may leave the site during their stay only when accompanied by a group leader.

Services for persons with disabilities: The Club requires a certificate of good health and an aptitude for workcamp activities.

Requirements: The minimum age is 14. Applicants must be in good health.

Living arrangements: Accommodations are rustic—shelter is provided during the winter, but when the weather is warm, camps are set up in the open air. The campsite washing and cooking facilities are organized by the volunteers because the monuments are not suitable for permanent accommodations. Participants must bring a sleeping bag and blanket.

Finances: Room and board costs 65 French francs (approximately $12) per day and all travel costs are the responsibility of the participant. Insurance, required upon registration, costs 80 French francs (approximately $15).

ifteen to thirty days before you want to begin.

ct: Rosalind Guillemin, Site Director (address above). Enclose a
-addressed envelope and international postal reply coupon.

FOUNDATION FOR FIELD RESEARCH (FFR)
P.O. Box 771
St. George's
Grenada (West Indies)
Telephone: (809) 440-8854

The sponsor: Founded in 1982, this nonprofit organization sponsors research expeditions by finding volunteers to assist scientists in the field.
The Foundation supports expeditions that need and can make use of
nonspecialists' help. Citizens subsidize research expeditions by volunteering their help and labor to a scientist in the field, and by contributing
a tax-deductible share of the project's cost.

The program: Four times a year the Foundation publishes *Explorer
News,* which describes the projects that need volunteers. Some of the recent projects included Primate Census in Liberia, a two-week expedition
involving the observation of monkeys in a tropical rain forest in Africa;
Prehistoric People of Pearls in Grenada, a two-month expedition to ex-
cavate a 2,000-year-old prehistoric site; Quetzal Quest, a 10-day project
to search for nests of the quetzal in Chiapas, Mexico; and Saving the
Caguama, a one-week project to patrol sea turtle nesting beaches in the
Sea of Cortez off Baja California in Mexico. The staff of FFR wants to
be sure that participants understand what is involved: "Joining a Foundation expedition is an educational and exciting experience, but we are
not a tour company. Once in the field, be prepared to work. If you have
always dreamed of being an archaeologist, marine biologist, or natural-
ist, then this is your chance. When you join an archaeological excavation, you will actually dig and screen; when you join a marine biological
expedition, you will actually dive and collect specimens; when you join
the study of an endangered animal, you will actually search for and observe that animal."

Supervision: Each group is headed by a scientist whose research design
has been approved by the Foundation. A field manager also accompa-
nies each expedition. The ratio of participants to leaders is between 5
and 15 to 1.

Requirements: Participants must be at least 14 years old. "Volunteers generally have not had previous experience but join to learn by doing, to meet new friends, and to have an adventure."

Living arrangements: These vary with the project. Groups often camp; at times, they stay in dormitories or local pensiones.

Finances: Each volunteer is asked to make a tax-deductible contribution as a share of the project's cost. Programs include lodging, meals prepared by a cook, ground transportation, field gear, research equipment, and a preparatory booklet. Some samples: the Primate Census in Liberia costs $1,485, and includes bearers who carry your equipment; Saving the Caguama costs $725, and includes van transportation from San Diego, California. Some scholarship help is available.

Contact: Tom Banks or Annie Cody (address above).

GLOBAL WORKS, INC.
RD #2, Box 356B
Huntingdon, PA 16652
Telephone: (814) 667-2411

The sponsor: Since 1989, Global Works, Inc., a grassroots nonprofit organization, has transported groups of service volunteers to other countries.

The program: Global Works directs environmental service travel programs, running four-week trips to Puerto Rico, Costa Rica, Russia, Fiji, the Pacific Northwest, and, for 1995, the Czech Republic. In the past, projects have included rebuilding habitats, wildlife research, rain forest replanting, and recycling programs. Additional features include the indigenous culture and language, travel, adventure activities, and historical visits.

Supervision: Experienced on-site leaders provide daily supervision of the participants and emergency assistance.

Requirements: Participants must be 14 to 17 years of age, and foreign language experience is helpful, although not necessary.

Living arrangements: Volunteers live in camps, hostels, or local homes.

Finances: Fees, which do not include airfare, range from $1,995 to $2,800, depending on the program destination.

Deadline: Programs are usually full by March 1.

Contact: Gay Rodgers, Office Manager (address above).

GENCTUR TOURISM AND TRAVEL AGENCY
Yerebatan Cad. 15/3
Sultanahmet
Istanbul 34410
Turkey

The sponsor: Genctur is a commercial agency founded in 1979 that organizes workcamps, study tours, homestays, group travel, exchanges, and language courses in Turkey.

The program: Genctur sponsors a Teenage Voluntary Workcamp. The 1993 program took place in Milas, a small town in the south of Turkey, but destinations vary each year. This program is for ages 15 through 17 and is offered for two weeks in summer. In 1993, work included cleaning the surroundings of a castle, making paths, carrying branches, and collecting stones. The program includes a sight-seeing tour in return for voluntary work. Also offered is Junior Camp—Active Holiday, which takes place for two weeks during June and July; in 1993 the site was Gelibolu by the Marmara Sea. This program is for ages 11 through 15. The program is much like an American summer camp with language courses (Turkish, French, and German) as well as special activities. Participants also take a one-day excursion picnic to the national park.

Supervision: Most of the staff are professional teachers, although Genctur also employs sport specialists and activity instructors. There is a ratio of 10 participants to every staff member. Two teachers are native English speakers.

Services for persons with disabilities: Campsites are not always accessible for persons with disabilities.

Requirements: For the voluntary workcamp, participants must be able to do four to five hours of light work per day.

Living arrangements: Participants in the workcamp program stay in boarding school dormitories. In the junior camp, participants sleep in wooden huts with an average of two to three persons per room.

Finances: A $90 fee for the voluntary work camp includes room and full board plus the sight-seeing tour. A $310 fee for the junior camp includes full board, transport once at the camp, activities, and a sight-seeing tour. Fees do not include airfare to Turkey or ground transportation to the camp.

Deadline: Contact Genctur for deadlines. The deadline for the junior camp program is two weeks before the camp starts.

Contact: Zafer Yilmaz, Workcamps Coordinator (address above).

INTERNATIONAL EXCHANGE CENTER (IEC)
2 Republic Square
LV-1010 Riga
Latvia
Telephone: (7) 3712-327216

The sponsor: IEC is a nonprofit organization that promotes personal contact between people of Latvia and other countries.

The program: IEC offers a children's summer camp program from June through August and a year-round au pair program. Children's summer camps, mostly on the Baltic Sea, invite older teenagers to serve as counselors.

Orientation: Orientations are held at the campsite before the program begins.

Supervision: There is generally one group leader for every five to seven participants.

Requirements: The minimum age for camp counselor and au pair positions is 17. A basic knowledge of Latvian or Russian is desirable.

Living arrangements: Participants live in cabins or dormitories. Au pair participants have a private room.

Finances: Camp counselors and workcamp participants pay $95, which includes room and board, as well as pocket money in the local currency.

Deadline: For the summer camp, two months before program starts. For the au pair program, three months before the desired starting date.

Contact: Edward Geller, Chairman (address above).

INTERSPEAK LTD
The Coach House
Blackwood Estate
Blackwood Lanark
Lanarkshire ML11 0JG
Scotland
Telephone: (44) 555-894219
Fax: (44) 555-894954

The sponsor: Established in 1981, Interspeak Ltd is a commercial agency sponsored by the Central Bureau for Educational Visits and Exchanges.

The program: Interspeak Ltd provides young people with European work opportunities from January through December. Participants are linked with companies throughout England, France, Germany, Ireland, Scotland, and Spain.

Supervision: Students are watched over at home by their host families and at work by the participating companies. They can also obtain assistance from the regional offices of Interspeak in England; Limoges, France; Madrid, Spain; and Frankfurt, Germany.

Services for persons with disabilities: Persons with disabilities are accepted provided "they are able to do the job required and are completely mobile."

Requirements: Prospective employees must be at least 17 years old and be comfortable speaking the language of the country of employ, although fluency is not necessary. Other desirable skills include word processing, typing, and computer knowledge.

Living arrangements: Accommodations are in homestays where the participant will have his or her own room. Breakfast, evening, and weekend meals are supplied by the host family. The regional office in the host country selects the host family through an application and review process.

Finances: Fees are 250 British pounds (approximately $385 dollars) in Great Britain plus 90 British pounds (approximately $138 dollars) for accommodations. Fees are slightly lower in France, Germany, Ireland, and Spain.

Deadline: There is no set deadline, but it is best to apply early in the year.

ISRAEL ANTIQUITIES AUTHORITY
P.O. Box 586
Jerusalem 91004
Israel
Telephone: (972) 2-292607
Fax: (972) 2-292628

The sponsor: Founded shortly after the establishment of the state of Israel, this government agency oversees all archaeological digs in that
country.

The program: Volunteers are needed for archaeological digs throughout
Israel. This organization does not place volunteers; instead, it distributes
a listing of possibilities each January. Archaeological excavations take
place in Israel throughout the year, but the main season begins in June
and continues through September. "Most archaeologists enlist volunteer
help on their digs, as volunteers tend to be highly motivated to work,
learn, and gain rich experience, although the work itself is usually difficult and tedious." Some recent examples include a month-long dig at Tel
Gerisa, a large harbor city on the Yarkon River from the Bronze and Iron
Age; Akhziv, a Phoenician cemetery on the coast; and Tel Nizzana, the
remains of a large town in the Negev dating from the Hellenistic,
Roman, Byzantine, and early Arab period. In addition to the work involved on the digs, most expeditions include the opportunity to attend
informal lectures and discussions about the site. The Authority also
sponsors day-long digs.

Requirements: Most digs require volunteers to be 18 years old, but
some will accept 17-year-olds. "Volunteers should be in good physical
condition and able to work long hours in very hot and dry weather." The
work includes digging, shoveling, hauling baskets, cleaning pottery
shards, and more. The minimum period of participation is one to two
weeks.

Living arrangements: Accommodations range from sleeping bags in a
field to rooms in a hostel or kibbutz near the site. A fee for room and
board is often (but not always) required. Excavations conducted in a city
often require the volunteer to find his or her own accommodation.

Finances: Each excavation has its own fee. At times, room and board
are provided; some digs provide pocket money, while others require the
volunteers to pay their own way.

Contact: Applicants should write to the address listed above for the department's listings. Once they have found a site that interests them, they must contact the director of the project itself.

MALTA YOUTH HOSTELS ASSOCIATION (MYHA)
17, Triq Tal-Borg
Pawla PLA 06
Malta
Telephone: (356) 693957

The sponsor: The Malta Youth Hostels Association is a member of the coordinating committee for International Voluntary Service (CCIVS).

The program: MYHA runs a workcamp program in which volunteers administer, maintain, and repair youth hostels or work on hostel-related projects throughout Malta. Volunteers work a minimum of three hours a day, seven days a week.

Requirements: The minimum age is 16.

Living arrangements: Volunteers live in youth hostels.

Finances: Volunteers receive free accommodations and daily self-prepared breakfast.

Deadline: Three months before the desired starting date. Sessions begin on the first and fifteenth of each month.

Contact: The W.S. Organizer (address above). Enclose three international postal reply coupons.

MOBILITY INTERNATIONAL USA (MIUSA)
P.O. Box 10767
Eugene, OR 97440
Telephone: (503) 343-1284 (voice and TDD)
Fax: (503) 343-6812

The sponsor: MIUSA is the U.S. branch of Mobility International, a nonprofit organization founded in London in 1973 to integrate people with disabilities into international educational exchange programs and travel. Mobility International now has offices in more than 30 countries. (For more detailed information on MIUSA and its publications, see page 30).

The program: MIUSA's programs include organizing international educational exchange programs in which disabled and nondisabled people work together in the United States and overseas. MIUSA programs have taken place in Bulgaria, China, Costa Rica, East Asia, England, Germany, Italy, Mexico, and the former Soviet Union. Themes of the exchange vary, but the goals are to increase international understanding through people-to-people contact, and to improve the lives of disabled people around the world by sharing information and strategies for independent living. The exchange experiences last three to four weeks and usually include a community service component and a stay with a family in the host country. MIUSA also offers an international leadership program.

Supervision: The leader-participant ratio is usually one to five.

Services for persons with disabilities: Persons with and without disabilities are encouraged to apply for all programs. Students who need language interpretation are also accommodated.

Requirements: Applicants should have an interest in disability rights, independent living, and international understanding. Specific requirements vary depending on the program.

Living arrangements: Accommodations vary according to the program, but might include youth hostels, homestay families, tents, or hotels.

Finances: Fees for participation vary according to the program. Some scholarships for persons needing to use attendants or sign language interpreters may be available.

Deadline: Varies depending on the project.

Contact: Susan Sygall, Director (address above).

R.E.M.P. ART.
1, rue des Guillemites
75004 Paris
France
Telephone: (33) 1-42719655
Fax: (33) 1-42717300

The sponsor: The name stands for Réhabilitation et l'Entretien des Monuments et du Patrimoine Artistique (Restoration and Preservation of Historical Monuments). Its 150 member associations are dedicated to restoring old buildings and monuments throughout France.

The program: R.E.M.P. ART. publishes a catalog each year of its members' projects—workcamps that last a weekend, two weeks, or longer. All projects involve the restoration of historic buildings, including churches, castles, old villages, and industrial sites.

Supervision: Each workcamp has its own leader at the site.

Requirements: For some workcamps, 14- to 17-year-olds are eligible; others require applicants to be at least 16 or 18.

Living arrangements: These vary, but camping is common.

Finances: Applicants pay a fee of approximately $40. The charge for room and board is about $6 to $8 a day.

SERVICE ADVENTURES, INC. (SAI)
P.O. Box 480065
Denver, CO 80248
Telephone: (303) 892-5743

The sponsor: Service Adventures, Inc. "was formed to help implement the vision of a healthy and sustainable future" by providing American students and professionals with life-enriching experiences and adventures that have a positive impact on the people and natural environment of Central Asia and Russia.

The program: SAI combines scientific research and natural resource education with wilderness adventure, intercultural exchange, and service opportunity. Future project locations, which vary from year to year, are being proposed in Brazil, Mexico, and Vietnam, in addition to the existing programs in Russia and Uzbekistan. Currently, teams of U.S. high-school students and specialists join Central Asian and Russian teams to participate in results-oriented projects such as the development of Vodlozero National Park in Karelia, known for its enormous lakes surrounded by spruce and fir forests, in northwest Russia. Students are paired with American and Russian educators and scientists. Research and service options for this project include examination and development of a system of low-impact campsites; water quality studies; construction of tables, signs, and latrines; plant community studies; determination and discussion of sites that merit special protection under the laws of the Russian Federation; and the development of environmental education programs.

Orientation: The orientation procedure varies in length and depth depending on the high school that is hosting the program.

Supervision: Supervision is provided by the program director, the specialists, and the scientists. The group leaders are responsible for monitoring the daily activities and the well-being of the students. In the event of an emergency, the staff at the Vodlozero National Park will administer assistance.

Services for persons with disabilities: SAI has accommodated persons with learning disabilities in the past.

Requirements: Participants must be between the ages of 15 and 19 and between ninth and twelfth grades. Previous exposure to Russian language is helpful but not required.

Living arrangements: When the program is in cities, accommodations are provided in hotels. Most of the time, however, participants camp and backpack.

Finances: The fee ranges from $1,500 to $1800 and includes ground transportation, food, and lodging. The fee does not include airfare, although flights can be booked at discounted group rates. Need-based financial aid is sometimes granted.

Deadline: Applications must be received by the end of April.

Contact: Judi Justus, Program Director (address above).

UNIVERSITY RESEARCH EXPEDITIONS PROGRAM (UREP)
University of California, Berkeley
Berkeley, CA 94720
Telephone: (510) 642-6586

The sponsor: University Research Expeditions Program (UREP)'s goal is to preserve endangered natural resources by constructing partnerships among participants, researchers, and the host country populace. UREP is a nonprofit, tax-exempt organization through its affiliation with the University of California (501C3).

The program: UREP has programs exist worldwide in the areas of archaeology, arts and culture, natural resource conservation, environmental studies, and earth sciences. In Europe, UREP groups are restoring an ancient Irish monastery and a prehistoric hunting ground in Germany. In Africa, UREP is investigating cultural topics such as the formation of national identities and indigenous music traditions. In Costa Rica and Ecuador, UREP representatives are striving to forestall destruction of the rain forests through cooperation with local communities.

Orientation: There is an orientation during the first two days of the expedition.

Supervision: The University of California academic at the research site supervises the participants.

Services for persons with disabilities: Persons with disabilities are accepted depending on the circumstances of the program. In the past, persons in wheelchairs have participated and led the expedition.

Requirements: Participants must be 16 or older.

Living arrangements: Accommodations are usually in small hotels or, when hotels are unavailable, in local people's homes.

Finances: Fees, which range between $1,000 and $2,000, are tax-deductible due to the nonprofit educational status of UREP. The fee includes meals, lodging, ground transportation, and camping and field gear. Airfare is not included.

Deadline: No deadline. Applications are accepted until the program fills up.

VOLUNTEERS FOR PEACE (VFP)
43 Tiffany Road
Belmont, VT 05730
Telephone: (802) 259-2759

The sponsor: VFP, founded in 1981, coordinates volunteer placement in International workcamps throughout the United States, Europe, North Africa, Central America, and countries of the former Soviet Union.

The program: In its *International Workcamp Directory,* which is available for $10 (deductible from the placement fee), VFP lists workcamps that include reconstructing an open-air museum in the Czech Republic, enlarging a park in Denmark, and restoring a three-masted ship in Finland. Workcamps take place from July to September, usually for two to three weeks at a time. Write or call for a free copy of VFP's newsletter.

Supervision: All workcamps have leaders who supervise participants. The ratio is usually 12 participants to one leader.

Services for persons with disabilities: VFP places volunteers with disabilities throughout western Europe. Each camp has its own policy regarding acceptance of the disabled.

Requirements: The minimum age for placement is 16.

Living arrangements: Volunteers live together in a variety of communal settings—tents, dorms, houses, and so on.

Finances: The placement fee is $150, which includes room and board for a two- to three-week program.

Deadline: No set deadline, but it is best to apply before May 20 to get first choice of workcamp.

Contact: Peter Coldwell, Director (address above).

WORLD HORIZONS INTERNATIONAL
P.O. Box 662
Bethlehem, CT 06751
Telephone: (203) 266-5874

The sponsor: Founded in 1987, World Horizons is a nonprofit community service organization that sends high-school students to locations throughout the Caribbean, Central America, rural Alaska, Western Samoa, and Ireland.

The program: Coed groups of about 10 young people from the United States live and work together with teenagers from the host country for the month of July. This intercultural program combines group projects with individual internships in areas of the students' special interests. Group interactions might include a light construction project, such as refurbishing a school, medical clinic, or day care center, or establishing a day camp for local children. "With each project, whether it be group or individual, the student will engage in an experience of intercultural work, learning, and living that will last well beyond the summer."

Orientation: A one-day orientation is held prior to departure.

Supervision: Group leaders are responsible for the well-being of the students at all times. The ratio of students to leaders is 10 to 1.

Services for persons with disabilities: Persons with disabilities are accepted whenever possible.

Living arrangements: Students live together in a house, dorm, or community building provided by the local host organization.

Requirements: Participants must be 15 to 18 years old and in ninth through twelfth grades. Knowledge of Spanish is required for service in Spanish-speaking countries.

Finances: The 1994 fee was $3,200, including airfare from New York, room and board, and all incidental expenses.

Contact: Judy Manning, Executive Director (address above).

WWOOF
Working for Organic Growers
19 Bradford Road
Lewes
Sussex BN7 1RB
England
Telephone: (44) 273-476286

The sponsor: WWOOF is a nonprofit exchange system in which volunteers work in return for food and lodging. WWOOF supplies hands-on experience with organic farming, which is labor-intensive and rejects the use of artificial fertilizers and pesticides.

The program: WWOOF conducts volunteer farm work and homestay programs throughout the United Kingdom and has agreements with similar organizations in Australia, Canada, Germany, Ireland, New Zealand, and the United States. Listings of sites needing help are published in the organization's newsletter, which is sent to members every two months. The newsletter also provides information on prolonged stays, developments, events, training, and job openings in organic farming.

Supervision: The host farmer provides assistance in the event of an emergency.

Services for persons with disabilities: Some disabilities can be accommodated, depending on the site and the host farmer.

Requirements: Participants must be at least 16 years old.

Living arrangements: Accommodations vary depending on availability, but usually a bedroom is provided. If there are no bedrooms, arrangements are made for participants to camp.

Finances: The membership fee is 10 British pounds (approximately $15). Farm placement service fee, if required, is 15 British pounds (approximately $23).

Deadline: No set deadline.

Contact: WWOOF (address above).

OUTDOOR ACTIVITIES

*C*anoe trips in the Canadian wilderness, summer camps in Europe, biking tours in Africa, and scuba diving in the Caribbean are a few of the programs offered by the organizations described in this section. All of the programs are short-term, lasting from a week to an entire summer. Some programs combine an outdoor activity with sight-seeing, leadership training, or language instruction.

ACTIONSAIL/ACTIONDIVE
P.O. Box 5507
Sarasota, FL 34277
Telephone: (813) 924-6789
Fax: (813) 924-6075

The sponsor: Actionsail/Actiondive is a nonprofit organization that has operated sailing and diving adventure programs for teenagers since 1970.

The program: Accredited by the American Sailing Association and the Professional Association of Diving Instructors, Actionsail offers sail training aboard 50-foot sailing yachts in the Caribbean and the Mediterranean seas. Courses are offered from mid-June through mid-August.

Supervision: Leaders are certified instructors in sailing and diving, and supervise full-time on yachts. The ratio of students to leaders is four to one.

Requirements: Participants should be between 13 and 18 years old. No experience is necessary.

Living arrangements: Participants live aboard the sailing yachts.

Finances: Program costs vary from $2,475 to $2,985, not including airfare.

Deadline: No set deadline, however, the program usually fills early in May.

Contact: James Stoll, Director (address above).

BARU ADVENTURES
1718 M Street NW #187
Washington, DC 20036-4503
Telephone: (800) 297-2278

The sponsor: Founded in 1993, the mission of Baru Adventures is "to expand the horizons of its students through immersion in another culture, participation in ecologically-oriented activities, and adventure."

The program: During the summer, Baru Adventures offers a four- to five-week cultural immersion in Costa Rica: "Accompanied by a U.S.-based teacher or counselor, a second leader familiar with Costa Rica, and high-school students from Costa Rica, your group begins the experience by spending approximately one week in the San Jose area getting to know one another, the local customs, and the language. With a foundation of new friendships and diverse backgrounds, the group then moves onto the more remote Southern zone for the remaining three to four weeks of environmental study, community integration, and adventure."

Orientation: Orientation, which consists of language training, group dynamics, and photography class, is held in Costa Rica for the first three days.

Supervision: Three leaders travel with the group of 15. There is also a country coordinator.

Requirements: Participants must be high-school students between the ages of 14 and 18.

Living arrangements: Accommodations include small bed-and-breakfasts, tent camping, and homestays with families in rural communities of Costa Rica.

Finances: Prices range from $1,150 to $2,880, which includes room and board. Programs during the school year include airfare; programs during the summer do not. Some scholarships are available on the basis of financial need.

Deadline: 60 days prior to start of program.

Contact: Miles V. Smith, President and Program Director (address above).

THE BIKING EXPEDITION
P.O. Box 547
Henniker, NH 03242
Telephone: (603) 428-7500; (800) 245-4649

The sponsor: Accredited by the Better Business Bureau, the Biking Expedition is a commercial organization that has planned summer bicycle trips for young people since 1973.

The program: The Biking Expedition offers trips throughout Canada from the middle of June until the end of August. Each trip is open to two and occasionally three school-year levels to maintain a high level of group compatibility. Trips are also rated according to skill level: introductory, moderate, and challenging.

Orientation: Participants spend two days in Henniker checking out equipment, learning safety fundamentals, packing gear, and reviewing the itinerary.

Supervision: Leaders travel with the group and are responsible for everything along the way, including supervising the students in buying and preparing meals and making travel plans. The ratio of participants to leaders is usually six to one.

Requirements: Applicants must be 13 to 18 years of age. They also must be "capable of keeping up physically and being a contributing member of a small group."

Living arrangements: Accommodations are a combination of camping and hosteling.

Finances: Fees range from $1,300 to $4,000, including food, lodging, airfare, and all program features.

Deadline: April 10.

Contact: Steve Silverstein or Allyson Krzyzaniak, Directors (above address).

BRITISH SCHOOLS EXPLORING SOCIETY
Royal Geographical Society
1 Kensington Gore
London SW7 2AR
England
Telephone: (44) 71-584-0710
Fax: (44) 71-581-7995

The sponsor: The British Schools Exploring Society is an educational charity that provides students with the opportunity to take part in expeditions to "remote and harsh environments." The Society was founded in 1932 by the late Surgeon Commander G. Murray Levick, a member of Robert Falcon Scott's 1910 Antarctic expedition.

The program: The Society offers two basic programs, a six-week expedition during summer vacation and a three- to four-month "gap" program designed for those who plan to take time off between secondary school and the next step in their education. Expeditions travel to arctic and subarctic regions of Greenland, Iceland, Norway, North America, and Russia. Expeditions also travel to Southern Africa, the Himalayas, India, the South Pacific, and Australia. Participants contribute to scientific fieldwork, such as studying glacial and volcanic activity and the animal and plant life. While these programs are designed for U.K. students, limited numbers of overseas "guests" are accepted.

Orientation: Participants receive a handbook and have a two-day residential briefing in the United Kingdom.

Supervision: Expeditions are led by outdoor skills experts and scientists. There are usually six participants to each leader.

Services for persons with disabilities: Persons with disabilities are welcome as long as they have full walking mobility.

Requirements: The minimum age is 16.5 years and the maximum is 20 on the expedition start date. Applicants must be enrolled in a full-time educational program. An interview is a required part of the application process. Some knowledge of camping and hill-walking is important. Also important are enthusiasm, determination, common sense, the ability to work as a member of a team, physical fitness, and a sense of humor. "As all expeditions need a broad cross section of abilities among their members, there will be places for the academically inclined and the artistic as well as those with an adventurous and enquiring nature."

Living arrangements: Participants live in three-person tents.

Finances: Participants are expected to raise their own funds as a contribution to the expedition. The Society provides assistance in this effort. Contributions range from 1,550 British pounds to 2,700 British pounds (approximately $2,387 to $4,158), depending on the program. Because the Society is a charitable organization, the contribution is less than the actual cost of each expedition. Assistance is given to those who cannot meet the suggested contribution. "No one who has shown the appropriate commitment and effort to raise the contribution, but was unable to meet it in full, has been denied a place." The contribution covers insurance, travel from the United Kingdom, food and group equipment, but not personal clothing and equipment.

Deadline: For standard expeditions, October 31; for "gap year" programs, one year before departure date.

Contact: Peter F. Steer, Executive Director (address above).

CAMP AROWHON
72 Lyndhurst Avenue
Toronto, Ontario M5R 227
Canada
Telephone: (416) 975-9060
Fax: (416) 975-0130

The sponsor: This coed camp has been operating for 60 years; it is accredited by the American Camping Association and the Ontario Camping Association.

The program: The camp is located in Algonquin Park in Ontario. The season runs from June 29 to August 23; campers sign up for four to eight weeks, with a two-week junior camp also available. Approximately 110 boys and 110 girls attend the camp each session. Campers come from the United States, Canada, and Europe. According to the staff, close attention is given in order to both nurture and challenge the campers. The camp features sailing, windsurfing, canoeing, kayaking on its own lake in the Algonquin Park wilderness, as well as tennis, archery, horseback riding, and drama and crafts classes. Camp Arowhon also has a Counselor in Training (CIT) program for 16-year-old campers to promote leadership.

Supervision: There is one counselor for every three campers.

Requirements: Campers must be from 7 to 16 years old.

Living arrangements: Campers live in cabins spread along the shore of Teepee Lake, with six campers and two counselors to a cabin. All cabins have indoor bathrooms.

Finances: An eight-week session costs 3,800 Canadian dollars (approximately $2,758), one month is 2,450 Canadian dollars (approximately $1,778). CIT fees are 2,325 Canadian dollars and 2,950 Canadian dollars (approximately $1,714 and $2,175), respectively.

Deadline: No set deadline; however, the fees rise by 200 Canadian dollars for applications filed after February 1.

Contact: Joanne Kates, Director (address above).

CANOE QUEBEC KAPITACHOUANE
Kapitachuan Club, P.Q.
via Senneterre, P.Q. J0Y 2MO
Canada

The sponsor: Canoe Quebec/Kapitachouane was founded in 1948 on the belief that one of the most valuable experiences young people can have is to be on their own in the wilderness, and that a canoe trip is the best way for them to test themselves.

The program: The camp is small and teaches the fundamentals of camping and canoeing, stressing cooperation, responsibility, and leadership. The canoe trips take place on the lakes, rivers, and portages which were traveled for centuries by the canoes of the Algonquin and Cree Indians, and the French and English fur traders. Trips usually go through a chain of lakes to the headwaters of a long river, then down the river, returning to base camp by another lake and river route. There are rapids to be run or lined, falls to portage, and tiny "moose" ponds or vast expanses of open lake to cross. Moose, bear, beaver, and other wild animals are often seen, sometimes at close range.

Orientation: A short training program is held on the first two days of the program at the base camp.

Supervision: An experienced trip leader, who has been on at least four week-long trips with the director, and an assistant lead the trip. All trip leaders and assistants have advanced first aid certificates and CPR training.

Requirements: Participants must be good swimmers between 14 and 18 years old and the ninth to twelfth grades.

Living arrangements: Campers stay in cabins in the base camp and tents during the canoe trip. Meals are similar to those campers would enjoy at home.

Finances: The cost of the two-week trip is $600, which includes everything except the cost of train transportation from Montreal to the camp. Some scholarship opportunities are available.

Deadline: June 10.

Contact: Roderick Beebe, Jr., 67 East Street, Washington, CT 06793; Telephone: (203) 868-7898.

**CENTRALE DES AUBERGES DE JEUNESSE
   LUXEMBOURGEOISES**
18, place d'Armes
Boite Postale 374
L-2013 Luxembourg
Telephone: (352) 225588
Fax: (352) 463987

The sponsor: This nonprofit organization is the youth hostel association of Luxembourg and is affiliated with Hostelling International. It has been in operation since 1934 and is also a member of the International Student Travel Confederation (ISTC).

The program: Besides operating a network of 13 youth hostels, the Luxembourg Youth Hostel association offers the following do-it-your-self tours:

- *Cycling Tour of Luxembourg:* This tour, which provides accommodations and full board in youth hostels for seven nights, along with a rented bicycle, a topographical map of the country, a handbook, and a tourist guidebook, starts any day of the week from March 1 to October 31.
- *Individual Hiking Tour:* This tour begins in Luxembourg City

and provides seven nights in a hostel, full board, a map, a handbook, and a guidebook. Hikers need sturdy shoes and all-weather clothes.

- *Stopover in Luxembourg:* This is a two-day program specially designed for those who, on their way to other destinations, must cross Luxembourg and would like to see the main tourist attractions of the Capital of the Grand-Duchy of Luxembourg.
- *Multisport in Luxembourg:* This one week program covers instruction and equipment rental for tennis, golf, horsebackriding, canoeing, and mountain biking.

Requirements: All participants must have a youth hostel card (which can be purchased in Luxembourg) and be at least 16 years old (18 for the Multisport program).

Living arrangements: All accommodations are in youth hostels.

Finances: Fees range from 2,500 Luxembourg francs (approximately $80) to 17,600 Luxembourg francs (approximately $568).

Deadline: Usually two weeks before program begins.

CHILDREN'S INTERNATIONAL SUMMER VILLAGES (CISV)
MEA House, Ellison Place
Newcastle-upon-Tyne NE1 8XS
England
Telephone: (44) 91-2324998

The sponsor: CISV is a nonprofit organization founded in 1946 by Dr. Doris Allen, a psychologist at the University of Cincinnati who believed that youth from different nations could use the experience of living together to help create a peaceful world. In 1951 CISV had 55 participants from nine countries; by 1994 it had 103,833 participants from 93 countries.

The program: CISV offers four program possibilities which are conducted in 60 countries:

- *The Village Program* is a four-week international summer camp in which delegations of two boys and two girls (all 11 years old) from twelve countries participate with adult leaders and six junior counselors in a multilingual camp that combines traditional camp activities with cross-cultural communication and cooperative living.

- *The Interchange Program* is a family-centered exchange between two CISV chapters. A delegation of five boys and five girls plus an adult reciprocally host partners from another country for two to four weeks; a short multinational camp stay is usually included.
- *Seminar Camps* are three-week programs conducted for 30 young people 17 to 18 years of age by an international staff of five adults, with a focus on fostering peace, international relations, and cooperative living.
- *Summer Camps* include a three-week theme camp for 13- and 14-year-olds and *Youth Meetings,* a one-week regional theme camp during major school holidays for youths, age 11 and up.

Supervision: Adults traveling with student delegations are responsible for supervision of participants en route to the CISV activity, during the program, and returning home. They are joined by CISV staff.

Services for persons with disabilities: CISV accepts candidates with disabilities and tries to locate barrier-free facilities; but this is difficult in many countries that have no legal obligation to upgrade facilities to accommodate the disabled. American Sign Language is used in the Village program.

Requirements: The Village Program is for 11-year-olds; the Interchange and Summer Camp programs are for students 12 to 15 years old; and the Seminar is for 17- and 18-year-olds. Tolerance and a genuine interest in peace and global cooperation are important to CISV participation.

Living arrangements: The three camp programs involve communal living in a boarding school or camp setting. Interchange participants live with host families.

Finances: An administrative fee of approximately $250 is charged for the Village, Interchange, and Associated Organization Exchange Programs; a fee of 146 British pounds (approximately $224) for the Seminar Camp includes room and board.

Deadline: January 15.

Contact: CISV USA, c/o Sally Stein, Executive Director, 833 North Dorset Road, Troy, OH 45373-1268; (513) 335-4640.

CLIVE POWELL MOUNTAIN BIKES
The Mount, East Street
Rhayader, Powys
Wales LD6 5DN
Telephone: (44) (597) 810585
Fax: (44) (597) 810585

The sponsor: Clive Powell Mountain Bikes is a commercial agency that has led summer mountain bike excursions since 1984.

The program: Clive Powell offers trips every weekend from April through September, called "Dirty Weekends," and the "Wild Wales Week," in July. Trips are open to all skill levels of cyclists, from beginner to expert.

Supervision: Clive Powell, director of the program, personally leads and supervises the groups.

Requirements: Applicants should be in good health and physically fit. It is suggested that you cycle regularly before arrival.

Living arrangements: Participants stay in guest houses or a bed-and-breakfast.

Finances: The Dirty Weekend costs 96 British pounds (approximately $147) and the Wild Wales Week costs 249 British pounds (approximately $383). Bike rentals are extra.

Deadline: None.

Contact: Clive Powell, Director (address above).

CYCLISTS' TOURING CLUB
69 Meadrow, Godalming
Surrey GU7 3HS
England
Telephone: (44) 483-417217

The sponsor: Promoting cycling as a method of transport and travel since 1878, the Cyclists' Touring Club (CTC) is Britain's largest national association for cyclists.

The program: CTC leads bicycle tours worldwide all year long. The extensive choices include everything from trips in the British Isles to trips in Nepal and South America. Cyclists of all levels of ability and experience are encouraged to participate. Trips vary in length from as short as three days to as long as 21 days. "Sag-Wagon" service, a van that follows the riders to provide assistance, is available on some trips.

Orientation: Advice and information is mailed to all participants after they first contact CTC. An orientation meeting is held after participants arrive in the country.

Supervision: Tours are all led and guided by CTC tour leaders, who must have good references, a suitable attitude, and experience. Usually leaders act as deputy leaders before leading their own tours.

Requirements: Depends on the tour.

Living arrangements: Varies according to the tour. Possibilities include hotels, hostels, lodges, and apartments.

Finances: Fees differ widely depending on the chosen tour, from 150 to 900 British pounds (approx. $231 to $1,386).

Deadline: The CTC Tours Guide is published every December for the following year. Due to the popularity of the tours, early reservations are recommended.

Contact: CTC Tours Guide, Touring Department (address above).

DICK PHILLIPS
Whitehall House
Nenthead, Alston
Cumbria CA9 3PS
England
Telephone: (44) 434-381440

The sponsor: The mission of Dick Phillips Specialist Icelandic Travel Service, a commercial agency founded in 1960, is "to assist walkers, cyclists, mountaineers and kindred travellers . . . to get the most from their visits to Iceland, without adding to their expenses." Another guiding principle is refraining from any practice that would change Iceland's beauty and natural character.

The program: Dick Phillips has a tour for anyone with an interest in Iceland, encompassing photography, hiking, cycling, motor coach, sailing, and ocean liner tours to Iceland. Diverse features of Iceland include volcanoes, hot springs, farmland, rivers, fjords, coastal townships, mountains, ice caps, and black sand deserts. Tours are conducted from May through September.

Supervision: The tour leader provides supervision and emergency assistance.

Requirements: Participants must be at least 16 years old.

Living arrangements: Most tours house participants in simple mountain huts.

Finances: Prices vary according to particulars of the trip. 418 British pounds to 1,148 British pounds (approx. $643 to $1,767).

Deadline: No deadline.

Contact: Dick Phillips, Director (address above).

GLENCOE OUTDOOR CENTRE
Glencoe
Argyll PA39 4HS
Scotland
Telephone: (44) 8552-350

The sponsor: Situated in the North West Highlands of Scotland and set among the mountain scenery of Glencoe, the Glencoe Outdoor Centre is a residential holiday and outdoor activity training center that has welcomed individuals and groups of all ages since 1988. The aim of the Centre is to offer fun and challenging activities in a relaxed Christian atmosphere.

The program: The Glencoe Outdoor Centre offers two-, five-, and seven-day programs through the entire year. In the winter, there are skiing and winter skills courses. In the summer, programs are conducted that feature sailing, kayaking, windsurfing, rock climbing, hiking, orienteering, and environmental studies.

Supervision: The Outdoor Centre staff provides supervision and emergency assistance.

Requirements: Participants must be at least 12 years old. Certain programs require the participants to be 14 or 15 years old.

Living arrangements: There are seven bedrooms, each sleeping from two to eight people in comfortable bunkbeds (maximum 36 to a room), and separate mens' and womens' showers and washrooms.

Finances: Prices vary according to the program and its length. For example, the two-day Skiing package and the two-day Multi-Activity both cost 80 British pounds ($123) and the seven-day package for both costs 205 British pounds ($315).

Contact: Chris Williams, Director (address above).

**HOSTELLING INTERNATIONAL
    AMERICAN YOUTH HOSTELS (HI-AYH)**
733 15th Street, NW
Suite 840
Washington, DC 20013-7613
Telephone: (202) 783-6161
Fax: (202) 783-6171

The sponsor: Founded in 1934, now has more than 125,000 members and 39 local councils throughout the United States. Its mission is to "help all people, especially the young, gain a greater understanding of the world and its people through hostelling." Toward this end HI-AYH provides access to a worldwide network of hostels—more than 5,000 in 70 countries, including more than 150 in the United States. This non-profit organization is a member of CIEE.

The program: HI-AYH sponsors a number of tours in the United States, Canada, and Europe. Although most people think "bicycle" when they think of HI-AYH, the organization sponsors hiking, backpacking, and other trips in addition to bike tours. Possibilities include the Loire Valley Chateaux, one or two weeks of cycling through France's Loire Valley. Another is the Peaks of Swizerland—From the Jungfrau to the Matterhorn, an eight-day backpacking trip on two of Switzerland's most famous mountains. Trips take place in the summer.

Supervision: International trips usually have 10 to 20 participants and are conducted by experienced leaders from the youth hostel association in that country.

Requirements: Trips are offered for all ages, with many designed for ages 15 and older. All trips are geared to people in good physical condition. HI-AYH membership is required ($10 for ages 17 and younger; $25 for ages 18 to 54).

Living arrangements: Accommodations are usually in Hostelling International hostels. Some trips include camping. Hostels are dormitory-style, with separate facilities for males and females. Most are equipped with self-service kitchens where the group will prepare many of its own meals. Some hostels have cafeterias and may provide breakfast. All have common rooms for relaxing and socializing. Guests may be asked to perform a small chore to contribute to the hostel's upkeep. No two hostels are alike, from a castle in Scotland to a chalet in Switzerland.

Finances: European trips cost $400 to $900 (land cost only, airfare not included). Fees include accommodations, group-prepared meals, local transportation, a group activities budget, administrative and leadership costs. Insurance is the responsibility of the participant.

Deadline: All applications must be accompanied by a $200 deposit; any balance must be paid 60 days before the trip departure.

Contact: HI-AYH Travel Department (address above). A free catalog describing all trips offered in the United States and abroad will be sent upon request.

INTERNATIONAL BICYCLE FUND
4887 Columbia Drive South #C
Seattle, WA 98108-1919
Telephone: (206) 628-9314

The sponsor: The International Bicycle Fund, a nonprofit organization, was founded in 1984 by David Mozer, a former Peace Corps volunteer in Liberia. Mozer is an African studies specialist and an avid cyclist.

The program: Bicycle Africa offers the adventurous and curious a chance to experience the diverse cultures of Africa. Participants need not be experienced long-distance cyclists, since the cycling level is "moderate." Bicycle Africa has tours from 15 to 30 days in west, central, southern, and east Africa. Tours include the following:

- *West Africa People to People:* "The tropical zone of West Africa provides a lush setting for meeting a fascinating people: some are traditional, some are 'modern,' and many seem to be caught in between." On this program, participants have the opportunity to meet traditional villagers, chiefs, government officials, and missionaries. Itineraries vary among Cîte d'Ivoire, Ghana, Togo, Benin, Senegal, Gambia, Mali, and Burkina Faso.

- *East Africa—From Anthropology to Zoology:* "East Africa provides visitors with a rich mix of geological wonders, colorful indigenous tribes, renowned wildlife, tantalizing environmental diversity, motivated rural economic development, modern urban centers, and specimens of the oldest known human fossils." Participants bicycle across steppes and scenic plateaus, past lakes, waterfalls, and snowcapped mountains; in the game parks, vans are used for transportation.
- *Cameroon—Country of Contrast:* "One of the world's best-kept secrets is the diversity, beauty, and friendliness of the Cameroons." The program itinerary skirts the coast, passes the base of 14,000-foot Mount Cameroon, climbs through mountains and verdant highlands, crosses waterless plains, and ends amid the geological wonders and wildlife areas of the north.
- *Zimbabwe Sojourn:* In addition to its political history, Zimbabwe is noteworthy for its environmental awareness, land reform, material and musical culture, and its two-thousand-year-old wall paintings of the hunter-gatherer San people. The program takes participants to Victoria Falls, on raft trips on the Zambezi River, on bike rides among the kopjes, to rock art and stone sculptures, the Great Zimbabwe Ruins, wildlife, museums, and more.

Supervision: Each tour group (usually 10 people or fewer) is accompanied by a guide who must have extensive knowledge of the program country, firsthand knowledge of the route to be traveled, and bicycle and leadership skills. Participants should be mature and independent, as they are responsible for themselves much of the time.

Services for persons with disabilities: Bicycle Africa provides motor transportation at participant's expense. Participants should be able to travel independently.

Requirements: No minimum age. Applicants should be healthy and in good physical condition.

Living arrangements: Accommodations include hotels, guesthouses, hostels, and homestays.

Finances: The program fees range from $900 to $1,290 and include room and board (two meals a day). International airfare is not included.

Deadline: Rolling admissions.

Contact: David Mozer, Director (address above).

INTERNATIONAL PEACE WALK
4521 Campus Drive, Suite 211
Irvine, CA 92715-2699
Telephone: (714) 856-0200

The sponsor: International Peace Walk was founded in 1986 with the belief that conflict can be resolved peacefully by joining opposing peoples in organized peace walks.

The program: International Peace Walk has two-week walks planned in Cuba, Russia/Ukraine, and Vietnam. The walks take a leisurely pace lasting about three hours a day. All groups participate in study programs, newsgathering, and delivering humanitarian aid.

Orientation: Participants receive a handbook and a one-day orientation for most projects.

Supervision: Leaders are selected from experienced IPW staff. The number of leaders varies depending on group size, which can be as large as 500.

Services for persons with disabilities: Special accommodations and meals are provided for persons with disabilities, who are encouraged to participate.

Requirements: Anyone can participate, regardless of foreign language ability.

Living arrangements: Participants stay in various accommodations from hotels to tents.

Finances: Fees vary by project; the average fee is $1,000 plus airfare. The fee includes meals, hotels, guides, program and health insurance, and airfare to the host country from the departure point. The fee does not cover transportation to the departure point, visas (typically $50), or personal items. Some need-based scholarships are available by application.

Deadline: Two weeks before the trip.

Contact: Allan Affeldt, President (address above).

INTERNATIONAL SUMMER CAMP VERBIER
Incoming Travel Service
Av. Ouchy 15
1006 Lausanne
Switzerland
Telephone: (41) 21-6165675

The sponsor: This international summer camp is organized by Incoming Travel Service, a Swiss travel agency established in 1988.

The program: The summer camp is held in Verbier, a ski resort situated 130 kilometers from Geneva at an altitude of 1,500 meters. The camp is divided into two sections, one for 7- to 12-year-olds and another for 13- to 18-year-olds. Campers participate in scheduled activities such as sports, language classes, and excursions.

Supervision: There is one group leader for every five participants.

Services for persons with disabilities: Participants with minor disabilities are accepted.

Requirements: The minimum age is 7, maximum is 18.

Living arrangements: Younger participants live in a lodge house. Older participants live in nearby hotels, three to five per room.

Finances: A two-week session costs 2,450 Swiss francs (approximately $1,873), including room and board, sports, language courses, and all activities.

Contact: Philippe Stettler (address above).

JUGI TOURS
Schaffhauserstrasse 14
Postfach
CH-8042 Zurich
Switzerland
Telephone: (31) 301-23-26
Fax: (31) 301-66-71

The sponsor: Jugi Tours is the travel division of the Swiss Youth Hostels.

The program: From late June to mid-October, Jugi Tours offers a number of walking, mountaineering, and cycling tours in and around Swiss valleys and mountains. Participants spend one to two weeks with "an international group of young people in a friendly and relaxed atmosphere." The programs include the following:

- *Rambling Weeks:* The ramblers are based at a youth hostel with a picturesque setting, such as Zermatt or Grindelwald. Group leaders arrange half- and full-day walks according to the interests and physical condition of participants. According to the sponsor, "Zermatt offers a great variety of beautiful walking tours at the foot of the Matterhorn. Even today the village has kept its traditional character with its wooden chalets and romantic lanes."
- *Mountaineering Courses:* These courses are offered at beginning and advanced levels in several locations in the Swiss Alps. Experienced Swiss mountain guides introduce participants to rock climbing, ice and glacier techniques, and rope handling.
- *Cycling Tours:* A two-week bicycle tour through central Switzerland is designed for young people who prefer a more easygoing pace.

Supervision: Group leaders are selected by Jugi Tours staff and must be experienced hikers. Most speak three or more languages. There is approximately one group leader for every 20 participants. Leaders are not expected to chaperone the young people, but they lead the tours, accept the group's suggestions, and work to provide "an unforgettable holiday" for the participants.

Services for persons with disabilities: Jugi Tours can accommodate some disabilities.

Requirements: Minimum age is 16. Knowledge of German is helpful, since that is the "official" language of the tours; most leaders also speak English.

Living arrangements: Participants stay in youth hostels with dormitory-style rooms.

Finances: Most programs last for seven days and cost from 275 to 770

Swiss francs (approximately $210 to $588). Youth hostel accommodations, breakfast and dinner, and local transportation to program sites are included.

Deadline: No set deadline, but early booking is encouraged.

Contact: Ursula Muhlemann (address above).

NATIONAL OUTDOOR LEADERSHIP SCHOOL (NOLS)
288 Main Street, Box AA
Lander, WY 82520
Telephone: (307) 332-6973

The sponsor: Founded in 1965, the National Outdoor Leadership School (NOLS) operates as a nonprofit licensed private school and offers college credit through the University of Utah.

The program: NOLS courses are educational wilderness expeditions that include up to 20 people and generally last from two to five weeks; a semester course includes a series of expeditions spanning as many as 14 weeks. "The NOLS program is designed to teach you to be safe, competent, and comfortable in the wilderness. Our objective is to give you the skills to enjoy and conserve the wilderness so that by the end of the course you can lead groups of family or friends on a rewarding and safe wilderness expedition." Many NOLS programs take place in the United States (Alaska, Washington, and Wyoming), but some are international—the Semester in Kenya, the Semester in Patagonia, short-term courses, and a spring and fall semester in Baja California, Mexico.

The 65-day Semester in Kenya includes a three-week mountaineering expedition on Mount Kenya, backpacking through the Nguruman Escarpment and the Loita Hills, exploration of the Great Rift Valley, safari, and sailing on the Indian Ocean. Passing through various ecological habitats, from the veldt and rock and snow to coral reefs, participants study biology, geology, and ecology. "This is a tough expedition. Your pack will weigh 60 pounds, sometimes 70. On Mount Kenya, it often rains or snows. While you're backpacking through Masai country, it may be 90 degrees in the shade, if you can find any. Vehicles tend to break down in remote places, and you may have to push them out of the mud."

The 75-day Semester in Patagonia combines mountaineering, kayaking, and hiking. The Semester in Patagonia sometimes includes rock climbing or other activities as well. "Because this is NOLS's newest course, the exact format is being adjusted to include the widest variety of outdoor opportunities the time can allow. Flexibility in our schedule and in our activities gives us the best ability to explore and learn."

In Baja, the semester courses include kayaking, sailing, natural history, technical climbing, fishing, skin diving, and Mexican culture. The three-week courses involve sea kayaking and sailing expeditions along the Baja California coastline.

Supervision: NOLS instructors have completed an intensive five-week training course and either hold advanced first aid cards or are registered emergency medical technicians.

Services for persons with disabilities: A disability may interfere with an individual's ability to take part in a particular program safely. Call the NOLS Admissions Office for further details.

Requirements: The minimum age is 17 for the semester courses and mountaineering courses, 16 for wilderness hiking courses, 14 to 15 for adventure courses. Final acceptance of all students is contingent upon NOLS approval of a medical review.

Living arrangements: NOLS participants camp, sometimes under difficult conditions. All courses are wilderness expeditions.

Finances: The semesters in Kenya and Patagonia cost $7,200; the Baja semester costs $6,700; the short-term Baja course costs $2,025. Tuition does not include equipment, optional college credit, or travel to and from the starting point of the course. Participants must make their own travel arrangements. Scholarships are available for particularly needy persons.

Deadline: No specific deadline, but the semester courses often fill six months prior to the starting date, and summer courses can fill four months prior.

Contact: Admissions Office (address above).

NORTHERN LIGHTS ALPINE RECREATION (NLAR)
Box 399
Invermere
British Columbia V0A 1K0
Canada
Telephone: (604) 342-6042

The sponsor: Since 1970, Northern Lights Alpine Recreation has been providing unique mountain trips in southeastern British Columbia.

The program: "With an exceptional diversity of over 40,000 square kilometers of the southern Canadian Rockies and Purcell Range at our disposal, terrain of every level of difficulty is available. Your trip in the mountains may range from a simple summer hike or a winter's day tour on skis/snowshoes to a multiweek mountaineering expedition climbing striking peaks on a major ice field." Suitable for individuals or groups, the trips are customized to the needs and experience of the participants.

Supervision: The guides provide supervision and emergency assistance. If necessary, local law enforcement agencies can also be called upon to provide assistance.

Services for persons with disabilities: If possible, NLAR will work with individuals to arrange a suitable trip based on their skills, abilities, and desires.

Requirements: Participants must be interviewed regarding skills, experience, and interests, and must be at least 14 years old.

Living arrangements: Accommodations are in hotels at the start and the finish of the program. During the program, participants camp.

Finances: The fees vary for the programs, depending on what course is chosen. An eight-day program can cost $500.

Contact: Kirk or Katie Mauthner, Co-Directors (address above).

OUTWARD BOUND
Chestnut Field
Regent Place
Rugby Warwickshire CV21 2PJ
England
Telephone: (44) 788-560423
Fax: (44) 788-541069

The sponsor: Since 1941, Outward Bound has conducted personal development courses for people of all ages. These provide an opportunity for people to "learn about their attitudes, their potential, and their relationships with each other." There are five Outward Bound schools in the United Kingdom.

The program: The goal of the Outward Bound movement is to offer participants an opportunity for personal growth and self-discovery through a series of courses offered year-round. The basic three-week course is given at all of the U.K. centers. In the first week, participants learn basic techniques of navigation, search and rescue, rock climbing, canoeing, and expedition planning. The climax of the course is an extended expedition of three to four days as a virtually self-sufficient unit. More extensive expeditions take place in Scotland, Wales, and the Lake District. Examples include trekking through the mountains of Snowdownia, canoeing through the Scottish lochs, and sailing around the islands off Scotland's coastline.

Supervision: According to Outward Bound, leaders are "some of the most experienced mountaineers and sailors in the U.K." There is at least one leader for every 10 participants.

Services for persons with disabilities: Disabilities accommodated by Outward Bound in the past include blindness, Down's syndrome, cerebral palsy, and Tourette's syndrome. Special programs for persons with disabilities are also available.

Requirements: Outward Bound programs are generally available to anyone age 14 and over. There is no fitness standard—"all Outward Bound asks is that you are prepared to have a go."

Living arrangements: Participants stay in dorms, except when camping.

Finances: Course costs range from 199 to 525 British pounds (approximately $306 to $808), depending on location and length of program. The fee includes room and board, instruction, and equipment.

Deadline: No set deadline.

Contact: Contact the address above for a course catalog.

RHIWIAU RIDING CENTRE
Llanfairfechan
Gwynedd LL330 EH
Wales
Telephone: (44) 248-680094

The sponsor: Rhiwiau is a family-owned horseback riding center where "we have a relaxed and informal atmosphere and try to make your holiday fun, exciting, and instructive."

The program: The Centre accommodates up to 25 people at a time. The program includes instruction in jumping, two- and three-hour rides through the woods, and training in stable management. Guests can expect to do 18 to 20 hours of riding per week. Minibus trips, swimming, or visits to the Anglesey Sea Zoo can be arranged for nonriding time. Programs begin every Saturday throughout the year.

Supervision: Family and staff members supervise guests. Students under 18 are not allowed out at night without supervision.

Services for persons with disabilities: Minor physical and mental disabilities can be accommodated. Facilities are not wheelchair-accessible.

Living arrangements: Accommodations are "motel style." Mrs. Hill, the owner, prepares the meals.

Finances: The fee for young people under 16 is 200 British pounds ($308); over 16, 220 British pounds ($338). There is a 10-percent reduction for groups of 10 or more. Prices include room and board, riding, evening activities, and local field trips. Insurance is not included.

ROCK LEA ACTIVITY CENTRE
Station Road
Hathersage, Via Sheffield
Peak National Park
Derbyshire S30 1DD
England
Telephone: (44) 433-650345
Fax: (44) 433-650342

The sponsor: Rock Lea conducts active vacations including everything from walking to windsurfing. A founding member of the British Activity Holidays Association, Rock Lea is also accredited by the English Tourist Board.

The program: Rock Lea offers a Multi-Sports Activity Week year-round which consists of waterskiing, rock climbing, caving, mountain biking, orienteering, windsurfing, canoeing, sailing, bog trotting, gorge walking, and a mystery tour. Shorter weekend trips are also available.

Orientation: Predeparture information is provided by mail.

Supervision: Senior staff is on duty 24 hours a day. Full-time, permanent staff lead all groups and have teaching, sports coaching, and first aid qualifications.

Services for persons with disabilities: Rock Lea Activity Centre can accommodate some disabilities.

Requirements: Participants must be at least 16 years old and speak English.

Living arrangements: Participants stay in Rock Lea, the Victoran mansion that is also the home of the owners of the Centre, which features single-sex rooms with bunk beds. Meals are served at the house as well. Local hotels and a bed-and-breakfast next door are available if needed.

Finances: The Multi-Sports Activity Week varies in cost from 389 British pounds to 499 British pounds, depending on activities and time of year.

Deadline: No set deadline, but a reservation two months in advance is suggested.

Contact: Iain Jennings, Director (address above).

SAIL CARIBBEAN
79-B Church Street
Northport, NY 11768
Telephone: (516) 754-2202

The sponsor: Sail Caribbean, in operation since 1979, specializes in sailing programs for young people. As a training facility for the American Sailing Association, it also offers participants national certification in sailing.

The program: Sail Caribbean sails a fleet of chartered yachts through the Virgin and Leeward islands for two to six weeks in the summer. The goal of the program is learning to sail, and instruction is given throughout the trip. The program is based on cooperative living in a coed environment. Each group, under the guidance of a skipper, is responsible for the operation of the yacht, its cleaning and maintenance, and the daily preparation of meals. Full scuba certification is also available, along with instruction in marine biology and oceanography.

- *Virgin Islands Program:* Participants sail around the more than fifty islands and cays of the U.S. Virgin Islands. Besides learning to sail, windsurf, snorkel, and water-ski, crew members attend a Fourth of July celebration in St. John featuring steel bands and local foods, take a Land Rover trip along the mountain roads of Tortola; and visit Bluebeard's Castle overlooking the waterfront of St. Thomas. This program includes three to four hours of sailing per day and is appropriate for the novice sailor.
- *The Leeward Islands Programs:* These excursions focus on a more diverse group of larger islands. The emphasis is on ocean sailing and navigation. Participants certified in scuba diving are able to take scheduled trips to deeper waters.

Supervision: Group leaders have extensive sailing and supervisory experience. They are responsible for the operation of the yacht, sailing instruction, and coordinating the activities and living arrangements of the crew. There is one instructor for every four participants.

Requirements: Participants must be between 13 and 19 years old, seventh-graders through high-school seniors. No prior sailing experience is required.

Living arrangements: Participants live on 50-foot yachts, ten per boat.

Finances: Program fees range from $1,500 to $5,500 and include accommodations, full board, equipment rentals, and instruction.

Deadline: May.

Contact: Michael Liese, Owner/Director (address above).

SEA QUEST EXPEDITIONS/ZOETIC RESEARCH
P.O. Box 2424P
Friday Harbor, WA 98250
Telephone: (206) 378-5767

The sponsor: Sea Quest Expeditions is a nonprofit organization founded in 1989 that specializes in outdoor environmental education and scientific research, focusing on sea kayak travel and whale research.

The program: Five-day and seven-day trips in the Gulf of California/Baja Peninsula are offered in February, March, and April. The area is known as the "Blue Triangle" for the large number of blue whales and other large species that live in the area. In addition to whale sightings while kayaking, the trips feature snorkeling, hiking, and photography. Travel/study credit also can be arranged.

Supervision: All leaders have a comprehensive knowledge of natural history and outdoor education experience. Each trip is accompanied by a field biologist. The ratio of participants to leaders is usually four to one.

Services for persons with disabilities: To be eligible for the program, persons with disabilities must be able to travel by sea kayak or boat.

Requirements: Participants must be at least 16 years of age (unless accompanied by an adult or teacher) and able to paddle a sea kayak or travel by boat in open water.

Living arrangements: Participants stay in tents.

Finances: The cost of the trip is $699 (5 days) or $849 (7 days) which includes all gear, food, and guides but does not include airfare to and from site. Participants must supply their own sleeping bag, clothing, and personal items.

Deadline: Reservations can be made with a 50-percent deposit; however, the full amount is due not less than 60 days before the trip departs.

Contact: Mark Lewis, Executive Director (address above).

SKI CLUB OF GREAT BRITAIN
118 Eaton Square
London SW1 9AF
England
Telephone: (44) 71-245-1033

The sponsor: Founded in 1903, Ski Club of Great Britain is the world's largest club for recreational skiers.

The program: Ski Club of Great Britain organizes skiing parties to Austria, France, Italy, Switzerland, and North America. Skiing is organized by age group and skill level and always takes place with an instructor or leader. Technique improvement is encouraged in all groups.

Supervision: The ratio of skiers to leaders is 8 or 12 to one. Each skiing party is closely supervised.

Requirements: Participants must be at least 11 years old.

Living arrangements: Participants live in half-board accommodations, whenever possible with private facilities.

Finances: Costs are around 625 British pounds (approximately $962) and include accommodations (half-board) and travel between London and program site. Ski and boot rental is approximately 50 British pounds extra (approximately $77).

Deadline: A nonrefundable deposit of 80 British pounds (approximately $123) per person is required for booking. Participants who book within eight weeks of the departure date must include payment for the total cost of the trip with the booking form.

SONS OF NORWAY INTERNATIONAL
1455 West Lake Street
Minneapolis, MN 55408
Telephone: (800) 945-8851; (612) 827-3611
Fax: (612) 827-0658

The sponsor: Camp Norway is sponsored by Sons of Norway International, a nonprofit organization dedicated to preserving Norwegian heritage.

The program: Camp Norway offers a program of Norwegian language courses, discussions on cultural and social issues, field trips such as hiking or a picnic at a *seter* (mountain farm), and other sports and cultural activities. The camp takes place from June 30 to July 30 in Sandane with an optional Bergen-to-Oslo trip. Four semester credits are offered in conjunction with Augsburg College. High-school credit can also be earned.

Supervision: The ratio of students to teachers is 7 to 1.

Requirements: The minimum age for participants is 16. Students must have a B average or better.

Living arrangements: Students live in bungalows.

Finances: The fee for Sons of Norway members is $2,245; for nonmembers, $2,345. Fees include travel from Oslo to Sandane, one overnight stay en route, full room and board, instruction, all field trips, and activities. Scholarships are available through the Sons of Norway.

Deadline: Scholarship applications must be received by March 1. Application to Camp Norway should be made prior to applying for scholarships. Otherwise, the application deadline is June 15.

STICHTING NEDERLANDSE JEUGDHERBERG CENTRALE (NJHC)
Prof Tulpstraat 2
1018 HA Amsterdam
The Netherlands
Telephone: (31) 20-5513155

The sponsor: This national youth hostel association operates 38 youth hostels throughout the Netherlands and a travel agency, Future Line Travel, that caters to young people and budget travelers.

The program: NJHC offers several programs for active holidays, including bike tours through the Netherlands with stays at youth hostels and watersport programs with or without instruction.

Supervision: Participants in all watersport and instruction programs are supervised during their stay. Other holiday packages do not offer special supervision. All NJHC youth hostels do, however, have a trained managing staff.

Services for persons with disabilities: Several NJHC youth hostels offer special accommodations for disabled persons.

Requirements: Staying at Dutch youth hostels requires a valid International Youth Hostel membership. (See page 58.)

Living arrangements: Students stay at Dutch hostels.

Finances: Contact the organization for current costs.

Deadline: Bookings are accepted from March to October, but full payment must be received four weeks before the trip is scheduled to begin.

Contact: Information Service (address above).

STRACOMER RIDING CENTRE
Bundoran, County Donegal
Ireland
Telephone: (353) 72-41685
Fax: (353) 72-41002

The sponsor: Stracomer is situated on the edge of six miles of beach and 600 acres of sand dunes off the Atlantic Ocean. The Centre is approved by the British Horse Society.

The program: The Centre specializes in riding lessons for the beginning to advanced rider. Courses are taught April to September.

Supervision: There is one instructor for every seven students. Staff members (including instructors) supervise students while at the Centre.

Services for persons with disabilities: Disabled persons are welcome to apply. Staff is qualified to handle most physical disabilities.

Requirements: Participants should be between the ages of 10 and 16.

Living arrangements: Students stay in owner's home at the school or other homes in the area.

Finances: Write to the Centre for current costs.

Contact: Terry Fergus-Browne, Owner-Director (address above).

STUDENT HOSTELING PROGRAM (SHP)
Ashfield Road
Conway, MA 01341
Telephone: (413) 369-4275; (800) 343-6132

The sponsor: SHP has offered bicycling trips to teenagers for 25 years.

The program: Bicycle trips are available in Austria, Canada, England, France, Holland, Ireland, Italy, and Spain, as well as in the United States. They range in length from 1 to 9 weeks and vary in difficulty from easy to challenging. An example of one of SHP's European trips is a 28-day tour of England that involves touring the English countryside and visiting castles, beaches, and cathedrals.

Orientation: At a two-day orientation in Conway, participants get to know their group members and their leaders and work out any "bugs" in their bicycles.

Supervision: Each group of 8 to 11 participants has a senior and an assistant leader. Senior leaders are at least 21 years old and have "formidable experience with teenagers."

Services for persons with disabilities: SHP accepts any disability that does not impair participant's ability to cycle in a safe manner.

Requirements: Students ages 12 to 18 are eligible. "Our trips demand self-discipline and a reasonable level of maturity. You will be expected to respect the rights and lifestyles of other people you meet during the trip. You'll be expected to do your share of work and day-to-day chores."

Living arrangements: Participants stay in campgrounds, youth and student hostels, inns, bed-and-breakfasts, dorms, pensiones, and occasionally a hotel or motel.

Finances: Program costs range from $760 for an eight-day tour of Vermont to $4,700 for a 45-day trip from Vienna to Paris. Fees include transportation, room and board, and all necessary equipment. Participants provide their own 10- to 21-speed bikes, but rentals are possible.

Contact: Ted Lefkowitz, Director (address above).

TIGLIN THE NATIONAL ADVENTURE CENTRE
Ashford
County Wicklow
Ireland
Telephone: (353) 404-40169

The sponsor: Tiglin the National Adventure Centre (TNAC) is operated by the Association for Adventure Sports (AFAS), the Irish coordinating organization for adventure sports. TNAC was established in 1971 to meet AFAS's goal of providing increased access to adventure sports while instituting high skill level and safety guidelines. TNAC is located in the heart of the Devil's Glen forest which is an hour's drive from Dublin.

The program: Tiglin provides courses in mountaineering, hiking, rock climbing, canoeing, kayaking, orienteering, and first aid. Some programs are conducted at the residential center in Wicklow while others take place throughout Ireland or abroad. Courses are available for novices, intermediates, and experts; instructor training is also available. Special programs for disabled persons are offered as well. Courses take place between May and October.

Supervision: TNAC staff provide daily supervision and are supplemented by local rescue services in the event of an emergency.

Services for persons with disabilities: Disabled persons are encouraged to participate. In the past, both physical and mental disabilities have been accommodated.

Requirements: Participants must be at least 10 years old.

Living arrangements: Participants stay in dormitories.

Finances: The fees vary widely depending on location and activities of the program. Contact TNAC for up-to-date fees.

Deadline: Applications should be received at least one full week before the course begins.

Contact: Tiglin the National Adventure Centre (address above).

T.M. INTERNATIONAL SCHOOL OF HORSEMANSHIP
Sunrising Riding Centre
Henwood Nr. Liskeard
Cornwall, PL14 5BP
England
Telephone: (44) 579-62895

The sponsor: T.M. International is a residential riding school that provides both riding holidays and training for those wishing to take British Horse Society exams.

The program: The Riding Centre provides instruction at all levels. Programs last from a week to nine months, September to June.

Supervision: There is one group leader for every six students.

Services for persons with disabilities: Ground-floor accommodations are available for people with minor physical disabilities.

Requirements: Students must be at least 16 years old.

Living arrangements: Dormitory-style accommodations.

Finances: Courses cost 70 British pounds (about $107) per week, including room, full board, riding lessons, and lectures on horse care and stable management. Prices for holidays start at about $350 per week.

Deadline: There is no formal deadline, but it is advisable to apply as early as possible.

Contact: Captain E.W.R. Moore, Principal (address above).

UNDERWATER SAFARIS LTD
25C Barnes Place
Colombo 7
Sri Lanka
Telephone: (94) 1-694012
Fax: (94) 1-698730

The sponsor: Underwater Safaris Ltd was founded in 1969 and is accredited by the PADI Dive Centre.

The program: Underwater Safaris Ltd offers scuba diving courses from December through April in Colombo and Hikkadowa vicinities in Sri Lanka.

Services for persons with disabilities: Underwater Safaris Ltd makes every effort to accommodate persons with disabilities.

Requirements: Participants must be at least 17 years old and be able to swim.

Finances: The cost is $450 for PADI Open Water Diver which includes manual tables, log book, lectures, pool classes, and four boat dives (equipment hire).

Deadline: Rolling admissions.

Contact: Valerie Fuller Ekanayake, Consultant/Instructor (address above).

VILLAGE CAMPS
CH-1296 Coppet
Switzerland
Telephone: (41) 22-776-2059
Fax: (41) 22-776-2060

The sponsor: Village Camps was founded in 1972 with the purpose of "education through recreation." The program aims to bring children of different nationalities and languages together so they may better appreciate each other's background and culture.

The program: Village Camps offers two-week educational and sports programs for youth ages eight to nineteen. Included are English, French, and German language institutes in England, Switzerland, and Austria; a computer and leadership training course in Switzerland; golf and tennis in England; and canoeing, caving, and outdoor adventure in the south of France. In addition to these specialty camps, participants can choose from a variety of multiactivity programs in Austria, England, and Switzerland.

The program in Switzerland is the only camp outside of North America to be accredited by the American Camping Association.

Supervision: Adult group leaders are responsible for daily supervision of students. The ratio of students to counselors is five to one.

Requirements: Students should be between 8 and 19 years old, depending on the program.

Living arrangements: Students live in shared rooms in a group hotel.

Finances: Fees range from 1,450 to 2,300 Swiss francs (approximately $1,108 to $1,758). Individual scholarships are sometimes available.

Contact: Roger Ratner, Director (address above).

WEST OF IRELAND CAMPS
Loughanelteen
County Sligo
Republic of Ireland
Telephone/Fax: (353) 71-43528

The sponsor: The Camp, which is based in the United Kingdom but located in the west of Ireland, has been in operation since 1919.

The program: Set in "the breathtaking beauty and tranquility" of the west Irish county of Sligo, this camp offers sailing, windsurfing, canoeing, horseback riding, hill walking, fishing, and archery in July and August. "The background of these holidays is a sane and balanced Christian influence."

Supervision: Many of the leaders are former campers; all are volunteers who pay their own way. There is one leader for every two campers.

Requirements: Campers may be 8 to 16 years old.

Living arrangements: Campers live in chalet tents and eat together in a dining hall.

Finances: Each two-week camping period costs approximately 310 Irish pounds (approximately $471).

Deadline: Applications should be made as early as possible.

Contact: Keith McNair (address above).

HOMESTAYS

W hile many of the programs in other sections of this book involve homestays, those in this section offer a homestay as the central feature of the program. Participants spend a week or more living with a host family and taking part in its daily activities. Usually teenagers on a homestay experience have the opportunity to improve foreign language skills in day-to-day conversation and to do some traveling, either on their own or with their host family. They also learn firsthand what it's like to live in another country and establish a personal relationship that crosses international borders.

Most language institutes offer their students the opportunity to live with host families as paying guests. Rather than list each of these programs here, we suggest you look through the Language Institutes section of this book if you're interested in that type of arrangement.

ACCUEIL FRANCE FAMILLE
5, rue Francois Coppee
75015 Paris
France
Telephone: (33) 1-45542239

The sponsor: This nonprofit organization specializes in homestays with French families.

The program: Participants live with families throughout France for a minimum of one week. According to the sponsor, "These families are willing to let you share their way of life and you should be prepared to adapt accordingly."

Requirements: The minimum age is 16 (18 for Paris homestays). A basic knowledge of French is advisable.

Living arrangements: Participants live in private rooms in comfortable homes. They are matched with appropriate families by filling out a questionnaire. The staff "will do everything in our power to send you to your chosen region of France, but we are principally concerned in placing you with a family whose tastes and interests correspond to your own."

Finances: A week-long homestay with full board costs 2,250 French francs (approximately $420).

ANGLA AGENCY
70 Southsea Avenue
Leigh-on-Sea
Essex SS9 2BJ
England
Telephone: (44) (07) 02471648

The sponsor: The Angla Agency, a commercial agency established in 1983, administers homestay programs throughout Britain as well as in Europe and the United States.

The program: The International En Famille Holidays participants stay with local families on a weekly basis year-round. The Angla Agency staff also organize trips, visits, recreation, and studies.

Supervision: The family with whom the students are staying provide supervision.

Requirements: Participants must be at least 14 years old if unaccompanied. There is no age limit if the participant is accompanied by an adult family member.

Living arrangements: The accommodations are single or shared bedrooms in a family home which is selected through a process of recommendation, verified references, and visitation.

Finances: The cost per week is 150 British pounds ($230). In the Southend Essex area, organized trips are included.

Deadline: Reservations are done on a first-come, first-served basis.

Contact: Jill Corbett (address above).

278 / *The Programs*

ANIMATIONS LOISIRS JEUNES
58 bis, rue Sala
69002 Lyons
France
Telephone: (33) 72409642
Fax: (33) 78375756

The sponsor: This nonprofit exchange organization, approved by the Ministère de la Jeunesse et des Sports (the French ministry of youth and sports), offers homestays for young people visiting France. It has been in operation since 1971.

The program: Participants live with French families for up to four weeks.

Supervision: Participants are supervised by the host family.

Requirements: Students must be between 12 and 18 years old.

Living arrangements: Participants may choose between half and full board.

Finances: One week with full board costs 1,315 French francs (approximately $245). Half board costs 1,205 French francs (approximately $225). Airfare is not included.

Contact: M. Clarence Beckert, Director of International Exchanges (address above).

AQUITAINE SERVICE LINGUISTIQUE (ASL)
6, rue Louis Pasteur
33127 Martignas
France
Telephone: (33) 56214096
Fax: (33) 56780401

The sponsor: This nonprofit organization has been organizing homestays for visitors to France since 1978. ASL also places French students in England, Ireland, Germany, Spain, Italy, and the United States.

The program: Participants live with French families on a weekly basis year-round. Host families are located in the regions of Bordeaux and

Charente. Homestays in Charente (the region surrounding Cognac) include the option of scheduled French instruction in the home.

Supervision: Participants are supervised by their host families. Representatives of ASL are available for assistance.

Services for persons with disabilities: ASL does not restrict participation by persons with disabilities as long as families can be found to accommodate them.

Requirements: The minimum age is seven.

Living arrangements: Host families are expected to treat participants as members of the household. "Students will take their meals with their families and will be taken on outings and will be given every opportunity of meeting French people of their own age."

Finances: Family accommodation with full board costs 1,490 French francs (approximately $280) per week. Ten hours of French lessons per week cost 700 French francs (approximately $130).

ARES
Druzsteunicka 20
736 01 Havírov
Czechoslovakia
Telephone: (42) 69231412
Fax: (42) 699425312

The sponsor: ARES is a commercial Czech homestay organization founded in 1991.

The program: Homestays, usually in apartments with university students, last from two days to eight weeks during the summer months. Participants should be aware that their hosts are eager to practice English. ARES offers another program in which foreign visitors are offered employment as language instructors in children's summer camps.

Requirements: The minimum age is 17; maximum is 35.

Living arrangements: Most participants live with university students, typically in three-room apartments. Homestays with families are also possible. Breakfast and dinner can be arranged.

Finances: ARES charges a $10 fee for arranging the homestay. Participants pay their hosts approximately $4 per day. Breakfast and dinner cost an extra $3 per day. The salary for English instructors is approximately $200 per month, plus free room and board.

Deadline: May 31.

Contact: Martin Gres (address above).

AVALON STUDENT TRAVEL
11 Marlborough Place
Brighton, BN1 1UB
Sussex
England
Telephone: (44) 273-553417
Fax: (44) 273-559321

The sponsor: A South East Tourist Board member, Avalon Student Travel has organized homestays and language courses for numerous international student travel groups and thousands of individual students over the past 15 years.

The program: Avalon has hundreds of families on their agency list in the Brighton area and quite a few families in villages and small towns in the Sussex countryside. The Brighton and Hove twin town area combines history and tradition with big-city entertainment as well as the beach.

Requirements: Participants traveling as individuals must be at least 16 years old; group members must be at least 12.

Living arrangements: Participants stay with local families in their homes which are inspected and subject to yearly reinspection.

Finances: For individuals, fees start at 70 British pounds ($105 dollars) per week. For groups, fees start at 61.30 British pounds ($90 dollars) per week.

Deadline: The deadline is one to two weeks before arrival, but it is best to reserve further in advance.

Contact: Aart Smith, Director (address above).

BELAF STUDY HOLIDAYS
Banner Lodge
Cherhill-Calne
Wiltshire SN11 8XR
England
Telephone: (44) 249-812551

The sponsor: Belaf is a commercial agency that has administered family homestay holidays with English families since 1975. Belaf is sponsored by the French Ministry of Youth.

The program: The year-round homestays are located in West London and central southern England including Hampshire, Berkshire, Wiltshire, Gloucestershire, Somerset, Avon, and Dorset. Language study classes are offered for non-English speakers. There is also a Summer Holiday au pair program in which girls help out the mother of a British family in exchange for the stay in England. School group visits can also be arranged for short stays (4 to 10 days) in England.

Supervision: The local organizers, who are also teachers, provide daily supervision and emergency assistance for the participants.

Requirements: Contact Belaf. Participants must be 17 years old for the au pair program. There are homestay programs for all ages.

Living arrangements: Homestay with families selected through references and inspection by Belaf.

Finances: Fees vary depending on the chosen program, but include room and board. Some scholarships are also available.

Deadline: No deadline, but early booking is advised.

Contact: Belaf Study Holidays (above address).

CASTLE HOLIDAY HOMES
1 New Inn Lane
Guildford
Surrey GU4 7HN
England
Telephone: (44) 483-32345

The sponsor: Castle Holiday Homes is a commercial agency founded in 1958.

The program: Castle Holiday Homes provides homestays in England specializing in short-stay school groups, sports/activity groups, language and cultural courses, travel groups, and holidays in castles. Various homestay opportunities are available in the country, the town, and the seaside. Special study tours can be arranged which, in the past, have included cooking, theater, history, archaeological, and bird watching groups.

Supervision: Local organizers are there to supervise and assist the students in any manner necessary.

Services for persons with disabilities: People in wheelchairs have been accommodated in the past although, due to the special facilities, the housing fees were higher.

Requirements: Students must be at least 14 years old.

Living arrangements: The homestay arrangements place two students per family. Other options include hotels, hostels, and guest houses.

Finances: For a student under 18, an individual stay with a host family with full board costs 112 British pounds (approximately $170 dollars) per week.

Deadline: Six weeks before arrival. Early reservations are advised to ensure the area of choice.

Contact: Castle Holiday Homes (address above).

ECI
62, avenue DeLattre de Tassigny
13100 Aix-en-Provence
France
Telephone: (33) 42-210768
Fax: (33) 42-214293

The sponsor: ECI, a nonprofit organization whose main purpose is to send French students to the United States, also arranges homestays for U.S. students in France.

The program: Students live with families in Aix-en-Provence, a city of about 130,000 inhabitants in the south of France. ECI can also arrange programs for student groups with language courses and excursions.

Supervision: Students are supervised by their host families.

Requirements: The minimum age is 15. Students must have at least two years of French language study.

Living arrangements: "Our families are carefully selected and will provide room, board, and activities."

Finances: One week at full board costs 1,400 French francs (approximately $260).

Deadline: Two weeks before intended stay.

Contact: Valerie Deltour, Director of Incoming Programs (address above).

EN FAMILLE OVERSEAS
60b Maltraver Street
Arundel
West Sussex BN18 9BG
England
Telephone: (44) 903-883266

The sponsor: For more than 40 years, En Famille has helped thousands of people to get to know a foreign country and its people by staying with a host family.

The program: En Famille has numerous host families around France as well as combination homestay and language instruction programs called language holidays.

Supervision: The French representative or the host family provide supervision.

Requirements: Participants must be at least 14 years old and have two years of French instruction.

Living arrangements: Accommodations are arranged with host families who are selected by recommendation and inspection.

Finances: Full board accommodation costs between 150 and 230 British pounds ($225 and $345 dollars) per week plus an enrollment fee of 20 British pounds ($30 dollars).

Deadline: There is no deadline, but early registration is encouraged to ensure placement.

Contact: Mrs. D. K. Crawford, Director (address above).

EUROPEAN EDUCATIONAL OPPORTUNITIES PROGRAMME
122 Canterbury Road, Lydden
Dover, Kent CT15 7ET
England
Telephone: (44) 304-830948/823631

The sponsor: The European Educational Opportunities Programme (EEOP) was founded in 1986 and is accredited by the Central Bureau for Educational Visits and Exchanges.

The program: EEOP arranges numerous international options featuring homestay programs, organized tours and volunteer service programs throughout England and mainland Europe.

Orientation: An orientation is held for group trips only, not for individuals.

Supervision: Group leaders are available for emergency assistance but not daily supervision.

Requirements: Participants must be at least 14 years old and, depending on the country of choice, some foreign language ability may be required.

Living arrangements: Participants stay with host families who are chosen through an interview process.

Finances: Fees vary depending on the program.

Deadline: Rolling admissions.

Contact: Sue Bugden, Office Manager (address above).

EUROYOUTH
409 Westborough Road
Westcliff-on-Sea
Essex SSO 9PT
England
Telephone: (44) 702-341434
Fax: (44) 702-330104

The sponsor: Euroyouth has sponsored low-cost homestays since 1962.

The program: Euroyouth is convinced that the best and cheapest way to learn a foreign language or to increase proficiency is to stay with a family in the country of your choice. Euroyouth concentrates on placing students and young people with local families in Austria, Belgium, France, Germany, Greece, Hungary, Italy, Portugal, Spain, and Turkey. The minimum stay is two weeks. Activities and sports vary, depending on the site chosen.

Supervision: Local associates provide assistance in the event of an emergency.

Requirements: The minimum age is 14 or 15 for most programs. No language experience is necessary.

Living arrangements: All participants live with host families.

Finances: Fees vary widely according to the country and program of interest.

Deadline: Six to eight weeks' advance booking is suggested, especially for France and Germany.

Contact: Euroyouth (address above).

FORMATION INTERNATIONALE VOYAGES ETUDES
   (FIVE)
9, rue Barla
06300 Nice
France
Telephone: (33) 93-267255
Fax: (33) 93-268774

The sponsor: Founded in 1980, FIVE is a nonprofit organization that offers homestay programs, language courses, excursions, and residence accommodations in Paris and the French Riviera.

The program: FIVE offers two programs for teenagers:

- *French Riviera Homestay:* Participants spend two to three weeks during the summer in Cannes, Nice, or Antibes taking French language courses and living with a French family.
- *Paris/French Riviera Excursion:* Participants spend three days touring Paris and 10 days on the French Riviera in June or July. (The excursions can be arranged at any time of the year for groups.)

Orientation: Students meet with FIVE staff in the United States two weeks before departure for the homestay program. There is no orientation for the French Riviera excursion.

Supervision: There is one group leader for every eight students.

Requirements: Participants should be between the ages of 13 and 20.

Living arrangements: Students live with a French family in the French Riviera Homestay program and stay in a hotel or homestay in the Paris/French Riviera Excursion.

Finances: The homestay program is 4,300 French francs ($806) for two weeks and 6,500 French francs ($1,218) for three weeks. Write FIVE for the current price of the Paris/French Riviera excursion.

HOST AND GUEST SERVICE
Harwood House
27 Effie Road
London SW6 1EN
England
Telephone: (44) 71-731-5340
Fax: (44) 71-736-7230

The sponsor: Host and Guest Service, established in 1957, is an agency that provides bed and breakfast accommodation in family homes in Britain and other European countries in family homes.

The program: Host and Guest Service offers more than 3,000 homes in the United Kingdom, of which 900 are in the London area. These metropolitan locations provide easy access to theatres, clubs, restaurants, and pubs in central London.

Living arrangements: Accommodation of all types is available, from cottages to mansions, typical British-style terraced houses to modern town apartments.

Finances: Fees vary from 65 British pounds (approximately $100) per week for a long-term (minimum two-week stay) student accommodation to 120 British pounds (approximately $184) per week for luxury and/or private facilities. Agency fees vary from 10 British pounds to 55 British pounds (approximately $15 to $84) per person, depending on length of stay.

Contact: Carol Rutter, Proprietor (address above).

INTERCAMBIO INTERNACIONAL DE ESTUDIANTES
1333 North 10th Street
Fargo, ND 58102
Telephone: (800) 437-4170

The sponsor: Founded in 1959 in Mexico City, Intercambio sponsors exchanges between the U.S. and countries in Central America.

The program: U.S. students spend July and August in Costa Rica or Mexico. Each participant lives with a local family and "becomes a true family member."

Supervision: Local delegates and the head of the host family supervise the participant's day-to-day activities.

Services for persons with disabilities: Intercambio, which has accommodated disabilities in the past, handles each case individually.

Requirements: Students from 11 to 16 are eligible; applicants should have a working knowledge of Spanish.

Living arrangements: Students live with families in urban or rural areas.

Finances: Fees range from $1,300 to $1,700, depending on the destination. Members of families who host Intercambio students receive a $200 to $300 deduction. The fee includes round-trip airfare, health and accident insurance, and supervision.

Deadline: Three months before departure.

INTERFON
Koroglu Cd. Kahramankadin Sok. 18/3
Gaziosmanpasa, Ankara 06700
Turkey
Telephone: (90) 312-4361964

The sponsor: Interfon is a commercial organization established in 1982 with the aim of introducing Turkish culture to young visitors.

The program: From June through September, Interfon runs its Holiday in Turkey program, in which visitors live with host families in Ankara, Antalya, Bursa, Istanbul, Izmir, Konya, and summer resort towns.

Orientation: Participants are met at the airport by an Interfon representative, who introduces them to the host family.

Supervision: Interfon representatives are in Ankara, Istanbul, and Izmir. Participants are supervised by their hosts.

Requirements: The minimum age is 16.

Living arrangements: Participants live in houses or apartments, depending on the family.

Finances: Participants pay a registration fee of $150, which includes full board and accommodation. The fee is valid for stays of one to three months. Host families are volunteers; participants are expected to teach their native language to their hosts by speaking with them.

Deadline: At least two months before you wish to arrive, send a letter to Interfon that introduces you and expresses your interest in a homestay in Turkey. A medical report indicating satisfactory health and three photographs for prospective families to view should accompany this letter.

INTERNATIONAL ASSOCIATION OF LIONS CLUBS
Youth Programs Department
300 22nd Street
Oak Brook, IL 60521-8842
Telephone: (708) 571-5466, ext. 323
Fax: (708) 571-8890

The sponsor: Lions Clubs International is the world's largest service club organization, with 41,000 clubs in 179 countries.

The program: The Lions Youth Exchange Program offers exchanges throughout the year that last from two to six weeks. Exchanges are arranged between local Lions Clubs. In most cases, youths stay in the home of a club member in another country. Lions Clubs in many countries also have International Youth Camps, which last from one to six weeks. More than 3,000 young people participate in the Lions exchange program each year.

Supervision: Youths are supervised by the host Lions Club or host district youth exchange chairman.

Services for persons with disabilities: Individuals with disabilities have been accommodated in the past, often as guests of families in which someone has a similar disability.

Requirements: Students must be between the ages of 15 and 21. Participants are interviewed and chosen by their local Lions Club. Applicants must be eager to learn about another culture and to share their own culture with their hosts.

Living arrangements: Exchangees live with host families; it is hoped that the sending community will, in turn, host a foreign visitor.

Finances: Financing for transportation and insurance vary. These costs may be paid by the participant, his or her host family, a Lions Club, or some combination of these sources. Room and board in the host country is paid by the host family. The host club may pay for special events. About $75 per week is suggested as pocket money.

Deadline: Varies, but applications should be initiated six months before departure date.

Contact: Your local Lions Club, or write to the address above.

**INTERNATIONAL CATHOLIC CORRESPONDENCE AND
   EXCHANGE SERVICE**
Veilchenweg 2
D-6634 Wallerfangen
Germany
Telephone: (49) 6831-60638

The sponsor: Since 1950, this nonprofit organization has arranged homestays for young people primarily in Germany, but also in Austria and France. It is also active in establishing written correspondences between people throughout the world.

The program: Participants are placed in the homes of local families as paying guests. Participants are expected to become "integrated members" of their host families.

Orientation: Students correspond with their hosts before arrival.

Supervision: Participants are supervised by their hosts.

Requirements: Students must be between 13 and 18 years of age and have studied German for at least two years.

Living arrangements: "We would point out that host families can by no means provide the lavish services one would expect in a hotel or pension-house. We want to provide a sensible balance, presenting the 'average family.' "

Finances: Costs range from 400 deutsche marks to 1000 deutsche marks (approximately $256 to $642) for stays of two to four weeks.

Deadline: Four weeks ahead of time.

INTERNATIONAL LANGUAGE HOMESTAYS LIMITED
2 Cecil Square
Margate, Kent CT9 1BD
England
Telephone: (44) 843-227700
Fax: (44) 843-223377

The sponsor: International Language Homestays Limited (ILHL) provides language courses in Argentina, Australia, Austria, Brazil, Canada, Costa Rica, France, Germany, Ireland, Italy, Japan, Malta, Mexico, Netherlands, Portugal, Russia, Spain, Sweden, Taiwan, and the United Kingdom. ILHL has been operating since 1989.

The program: Students live in the home of a language teacher and receive 15, 20, or 25 hours of private lessons per week. Participating in the social life of the teachers and their families complements the formal language instruction. Activities such as the theater, music, tennis, golf, and horseback riding are offered near most homestay sites.

Supervision: Supervision is provided by the teacher.

Requirements: Participants must be at least 14 years old.

Living arrangements: Participants live in the teacher's residence.

Finances: Prices range from 340 British pounds to 2,000 British pounds (approximately $523 to $3,080), which includes tuition, meals, and accommodation.

Contact: Adam Wilton, Reservations Officer (address above).

INTERNATIONAL LINKS
145 Manygate Lane
Shepperton
Middlesex TW17 9EP
England
Telephone: (44) 932-229300
Fax: (44) 932-222294

The sponsor: International Links, a commercial agency founded in 1989, believes that language students can learn not only the language but the culture and way of life of a different country by living with a foreign family.

The program: International Links offers year-round homestay programs for anyone learning the given language in France, Germany, Spain, Italy, Russia, and Japan. In addition to the study and homestay opportunities, students can choose work and group travel options such as the au pair program and the Escorted Homestay to Brittany, in which the group travels from Victoria to St. Malo and back.

Orientation: An orientation occurs in every area of each country where there is a program.

Supervision: There is always a local representative of International Links living near the areas where the students live, in case they need assistance from someone other than the host family.

Services for persons with disabilities: International Links makes every effort to accommodate disabled persons whenever possible. Vision-impaired students have participated in the past.

Requirements: Although there is no age requirement, the student must have at least one to two years of instruction in the foreign language.

Living arrangements: All the programs are homestays. Students always receive their own room and are treated as a member of the host family

Finances: A full fee schedule is available upon request. Room and board is included in the fee.

Contact: Eve Moody, Principal (address above).

LABO INTERNATIONAL EXCHANGE FOUNDATION
Suite 1850
1201 Third Avenue
Seattle, WA 98101
Telephone: (206) 554-7255
Fax: (206) 554-7211

The sponsor: The Labo International Exchange Foundation is a non-profit foundation based in Tokyo, Japan, that has hosted educational exchange programs between Japan and the United States, Australia, China, and other countries since 1972.

The program: Labo offers a variety of exchange programs in conjunction with 4-H organizations in 38 states, as well as Canada and Mexico. During the four-week Summer Homestay Program, students participate in weekly Labo club activities and attend a four-day camp in the countryside. Time is allotted for sight-seeing in Tokyo. Labo also offers the Nihongo Japanese Language Program, a three-week intensive Japanese language program immediately prior to the homestay exchange. In addition to language lessons, students go on field trips and attend lectures in English on Japanese history, society, and culture.

Supervision: All Japan programs are supervised by Labo staff members and club leaders, and by U.S. chaperons.

Services for persons with disabilities: Labo does not discriminate on the basis of disabilities.

Requirements: Students should be between the ages of 12 and 19.

Living arrangements: In the Summer Homestay Program, homestays are located throughout Japan; the host family has a child the same sex and age as the U.S. participant. In the Nihongo Japanese Language Program, all homestays are in the Tokyo area.

Finances: The fee for the Summer Homestay Program is $720 plus airfare; the fee for the Nihongo Program is $700 plus airfare. Fees include all travel, food, and lodging in Japan, health and accident insurance, overnight orientation, chaperon supervision, and a packet of $30 in yen.

Deadline: March 15.

LEX AMERICA
68 Leonard Street
Belmont, MA 02178
(617) 489-5800

The sponsor: Lex, the Institute for Language Experience, Experiment and Exchange, is a nonprofit organization that offers international homestay programs in Japan and Korea.

The program: The Lex Exchange is offered during July and August in four- and six-week programs. "The emphasis is on mutuality: not only do participants learn to see the world as the host family does, but the members of the host family also learn what it is like to be an American. Participants are not tourists; the role is much more like that of an ambassador. They discover many new things about themselves and come home changed, with a clearer sense of what it means to be a member of the family of humankind." Participants visit historic sites and participate in local festivals.

Orientation: An initial one-day orientation allows participants to meet one another and also to prepare to enter another culture. Upon arrival in their host country, participants receive the second half of their orientation and meet their host families.

Supervision: Host families are fully screened, and all have some English ability. Families host because they are interested in sharing their life with a new family member. Accompanying group leaders are responsible for participants during travel, with a ratio of 15 participants to one leader.

Services for persons with disabilities: Lex America does not discriminate on the basis of disabilities.

Requirements: Students must be 12 or older.

Living arrangements: Program emphasis is on the homestays. Participants absorb the customs and characteristics of their host culture by taking part in activities of daily life as a member of the family.

Finances: The program fee ranges from $2,500 to $3,000 and includes round-trip airfare from the U.S. West Coast, supplemental travel insurance, and all costs abroad except for personal expenses and any local transportation costs.

Deadline: May 1.

Contact: Steffi R. Samman, Program Manager (address above).

PEOPLE TO PEOPLE INTERNATIONAL
501 East Armour Boulevard
Kansas City, MO 64109
Telephone: (816) 531-4701

The sponsor: People to People began in 1956 when President Dwight D. Eisenhower invited a group of business leaders to a White House conference to establish a citizen organization dedicated to the pursuit of world peace. Thirty years later there are People to People chapters and international committees in 156 cities of the world.

The program: People to People's High School Student Ambassador Program sends approximately 6,000 students to any of 30 countries each summer. While abroad, the students attend briefings by overseas government officials and make field visits to manufacturing plants, farms, universities, and other facilities. The heart of the program is the homestay: Student Ambassadors live with families for five-day periods in several different countries. The entire trip lasts 21 to 28 days.

Orientation: Student Ambassadors attend six two-hour orientation meetings locally. For certain programs, a two-day orientation in Washington, D.C., is offered in June; it includes intensive briefings on U.S. government, business, and history.

Supervision: Student Ambassadors travel in groups of 30 to 35 with three or more leaders in each group. All leaders are certified teachers.

Requirements: Applicants must be 13 to 18 years old and enrolled in junior high or high school at the time of application. They must supply four letters of recommendation and pass a screening review conducted by a local committee of professional, business, and education leaders. "Maturity, well-rounded interests, and the ability to adapt are as important to a student's selection as academic standing."

Living arrangements: When students are not living with host families, they stay in hotels.

Finances: Fees range from $3,275 to $3,990, which includes airfare, food, lodging, and all travel and educational visits while overseas. Accident insurance is provided; health insurance is required, but is not included in the fee.

Deadline: April 1.

Contact: Paul Watson, Associate Director, People to People High School Student Ambassador Program, Dwight D. Eisenhower Building, S-110 Ferrall, Spokane, WA 99202; (509) 534-0430.

SÉJOURS INTERNATIONAUX LINGUISTIQUES ET CULTURELS (SILC)
32, Rempart de l'Est
16022 Angouleme Cedex
France
Telephone: (33) 45-958356

The sponsor: SILC is a French-based for-profit organization with wide experience in the field of student exchange programs. Since its creation in 1965, SILC has enabled over half a million young people and adults to travel abroad and live as members of a family, gaining firsthand experience of a foreign culture and language.

The program: Academic year of semester programs. Students live with a volunteer host family and attend a local French school.

Supervision: SILC has a support staff of 50 and operates by means of an efficient and extensive network of regional and local counselors throughout France, almost exclusively of the teaching profession. All participants are supervised by a local counselor. SILC also provides assistance through its 24-hour emergency on-call service.

Requirements: Students must be between 15 and 18 years old and have studied French for at least two years.

Living arrangements: Homestays. Participants live with a carefully selected volunteer host family.

Finances: Academic-year programs vary in price depending on the length of the program.

Contact: Jessica Germanaud, Academic Program Director (address above).

UNOSEL
15/19, Rue des Mathurins
75009 Paris
France
Telephone: (33) 44-51-0800

The sponsor: UNOSEL (Union Nationale des Organisations de Séjours Linguistiques), a group of professional organizations approved by the French Ministry of Tourism, administers French homestays which are approved by the Ministry of Youth and Sports.

The program: UNOSEL brings together 35 professional organizations providing homestays in different countries, 25 of which are specialized in courses in France.

Supervision: Specially qualified teachers, monitors, and program organizers superivise the participants.

Living arrangements: Participants live with local families or in establishments approved by the public authorities.

Finances: Contact UNOSEL for updated prices.

Deadline: No deadline.

Contact: Olga Gonzalez, Déléguée Generale (address above).

WEST (WORLD EDUCATIONAL STUDENT TRAVEL)
  PROGRAMS, INC.
28 Garey Drive
Chappaqua, NY 10514
Telephone: (914) 666-0500

The sponsor: Founded in 1986, WEST is an educational organization whose main function is helping students learn about other peoples through international travel and homestays.

The program: WEST offers American students the opportunity of one-month summer homestay programs in London, England; throughout France; in Bonn and Krefeld, Germany; and in Denia, Spain. Language instruction is included in the Germany and Spain programs.

Orientation: Students have an orientation upon arrival in their host country.

Supervision: Groups of 10 or more are accompanied by an American group leader.

Services for persons with disabilities: Persons with disabilities can be accommodated if a host family can be found. In the past, WEST has accepted diabetics, students in wheelchairs, and students with special dietary requirements.

Requirements: Students must be between the ages of 13 and 18 and have two years of foreign language experience.

Living arrangements: Accommodations are with a host family and vary according to the family.

Finances: Fees range between $2,145 and $2,600, which includes airfare, room and board, and excursions.

Deadline: April 15.

Contact: Vera Dickson Frumkes, National Director (address above).

WORLD LEARNING
Kipling Road, Box 676
Brattleboro, VT 05302
Telephone: (802) 257-7751; (800) 345-2929 outside Vermont

The sponsor: For more than 60 years, World Learning, formerly called the Experiment in International Living, has provided more than 100,000 young people with "the opportunity to build bridges of cross-cultural understanding and to develop lasting friendships through a broad range of international programs designed to illustrate the simple but powerful idea advanced by the founder of World Learning: people learn to live together by living together. Programs artfully combine travel, study, and a variety of activities with the cornerstone feature, an extended homestay with a host family." World Learning is a member of CIEE.

The program: World Learning sponsors a number of comprehensive summer programs in 15 different countries as diverse as France, Australia, Kenya, Thailand, and Ecuador.

- *The Homestay* lasts from two to four weeks and includes regional sight-seeing.
- *Language Study* is offered in selected countries. College credit is granted in some cases.
- *Multicountry Tours* are offered in various combinations, such as Spain, Morocco, and Portugal, or France, Italy and Switzerland.
- *Youth Service Programs* provide students an opportunity to take part in projects overseas such as working with refugees, or building a children's playground.

Orientation: Programs include predeparture orientations focusing on cross-cultural adaptation, introduction to the host country, role-playing, and discussions, so that group members can get to know one another.

Supervision: There is one leader for every group of 8 to 15 young people, and in every host country a representative is available to help. Leaders are responsible for daily supervision—their duties include "absolutely everything!"

Services for persons with disabilities: Persons with disabilities are considered on a case-by-case basis.

Requirements: The summer program age range is 15 to 20. The language requirement varies with the country.

Living arrangements: Participants live with families. This is the part of the program for which World Learning is best known, and is considered "perhaps the richest, warmest, and most satisfying part of the program." Homestay placements are arranged by World Learning national offices in the host country; host families undergo extensive interviews and must provide excellent references.

Finances: The cost of the summer program ranges from $1,600 to $5,200 and includes transportation, insurance, and all costs in the host country, with the exception of personal spending money.

Deadline: April 15.

APPENDIX
MEMBERS OF THE COUNCIL ON INTERNATIONAL EDUCATIONAL EXCHANGE

Adelphi University
Adventist Colleges Abroad
AFS International/Intercultural
    Programs
Albertson College of Idaho
Alma College
American Council on the Teaching
    of Foreign Languages
American Graduate School of
    International Management
American Heritage Association
American University
American University in Cairo
American Youth Hostels,
    Inc./Hostelling International
Antioch University
Arkansas College
Associated Colleges of the South
Associated Colleges of the Midwest
Association for International
    Practical Training
Attila Jozsef University

Auburn University
Augsburg College
Austin Community College
Australian National University
Babson College
Ball State University
Bates College
Beaver College
Beloit College
Bentley College
Boston College
Boston University
Bradley University
Brandeis University
Brethren Colleges Abroad
Brigham Young University
Brown University
Bucknell University
Butler University
California State University
California State University, Long
    Beach

California State University,
Sacramento
Canadian Universities Travel
Service Ltd.
Carleton College
Carroll College
Central Michigan University
Central University of Iowa
Central Washington University
Chapman University
College of Charleston
College of Lake County
Colorado College
Colorado State University
Cornell University
Curtin University of Technology
Dartmouth College
Davidson College
De Paul University
DePauw University
Drake University
Earlham College
Eastern Michigan University
Eberhard-Karls-Universitat
Tubingen
Eckerd College
École Centrale de Paris (École
Centrale des Arts et
Manufactures)
Elmira College
Empire State College–SUNY
Flagler College
Florida A & M University
Florida Atlantic University
Georgetown University
Gonzaga University
Goshen College
Great Lakes Colleges Association
Grinnell College
Guilford College
Gustavus Adolphus College
Hampshire College
Hartwick College
Harvard College
Hebrew University of Jerusalem
Heidelberg College
Hiram College
Hollins College
Hope College
Illinois State University
Indiana University
Institute of International Education

International Business School,
Moscow
International Christian University
International Christian Youth
Exchange
International Student Exchange
Program
Iowa State University
James Madison University
Kalamazoo College
Kent State University
Lancaster University
LaSalle University
Lehigh University
Lewis and Clark College
Lincoln University
The Lisle Fellowship
Longwood College
Louisiana State University
Loyola Marymount University
Macalester College
Marquette University
Mary Baldwin College
Marymount College, Tarrytown
Memphis State University
Metropolitan State College of
Denver
Miami University
Michigan State University
Middlebury College
Middlesex University
Millersville University
Monterey Institute of International
Studies
Moorhead State University
Morehouse College
Murdoch University
National Chengchi University
Nebraska Wesleyan University
New Mexico State University
New York University
North Carolina State University
Northeastern University
Northeast Missouri State University
Northern Arizona University
Northern Illinois University
Northern Kentucky University
Northern Michigan University
Northfield Mount Hermon School
Nottingham Trent University
Oberlin College
Obirin University

Ohio University
Ohio State University
Old Dominion University
Open Door Student Exchange
Pace University
Pennsylvania State University
Pepperdine University
Pitzer College
Polytechnicum de Lille
Pomona College
Portland State University
Prince of Songkla University
Purdue University
Ramapo College of New Jersey
Reed College
Rochester Institute of Technology
Rollins College
Rosary College
Rutgers, the State University of
  New Jersey
St. John Fisher College
St. Lawrence University
St. Olaf College
St. Peter's College
Scandinavian Seminar
School Year Abroad
Scripps College
Shoreline Community College
Skidmore College
Southern Illinois University at
  Carbondale
Southern Methodist University
Southwest Texas State University
Southwestern University
Spelman College
Springfield College
Stanford University
State University of New York
Stephens College
Stetson University
Syracuse University
Texas A&M University
Texas Christian University
Texas Tech University
Trinity College
Trinity University
Tufts University
Tulane University
Universidad Autónoma de
  Guadalajara
Universidad de Belgrano
Universidad del Salvador

Universidad Iberoamericana,
  A.C./International Division
Universidade Estacio De Sa
Université de Bordeaux II
University College London
University of Alabama
University of Alabama at
  Birmingham
University of Amsterdam
University of Arkansas at
  Fayetteville
University of Arkansas at Little
  Rock
University of British Columbia
University of California
University of Colorado at Boulder
University of Colorado at Denver
University of Connecticut
University of Copenhagen (DIS
  Program)
University of Denver
University of Essex
University of Evansville
University of Findlay
University of Florida
University of Hartford
University of Hong Kong
University of Hull
University of Idaho
University of Illinois
University of Iowa
University of Kansas
University of Kentucky
University of La Verne
University of Limburg/Center for
  European Studies
University of Louisville
University of Maine
University of Maryland
University of Massachusetts,
  Amherst
University of Michigan
University of Minnesota
University of Nebraska–Lincoln
University of Nevada, Las Vegas
University of Nevada, Reno
University of New Hampshire
University of New Orleans
University of New South Wales
University of North Carolina at
  Chapel Hill
University of North Texas

University of Notre Dame
University of Oklahoma
University of Oregon
University of the Pacific
University of Pennsylvania
University of Pittsburgh
University of Rhode Island
University of St. Thomas, St. Paul, MN
University of St. Thomas, Houston
University of South Carolina
University of South Florida
University of Southern California
University of Sussex
University of Tennessee at Knoxville
University of Texas at Austin
University of the Pacific
University of Toledo
University of Utah
University of Vermont
University of Virginia
University of Washington
University of Wisconsin at Green Bay
University of Wisconsin at Madison
University of Wisconsin at Milwaukee
University of Wisconsin at Platteville
University of Wisconsin at River Falls
University of Wollongong
University of Wyoming
University System of Georgia
Utah State University
Valparaiso University
Volunteers in Asia

Villanova University
Wake Forest University
Washington College
Washington State University
Wayne State University
Webster University
Wesleyan University
Western Michigan University
Western Washington University
Westminster College
Whitworth College
Wichita State University
Wilmington College
Wittenberg University
Wofford College
Worcester Polytechnic Institute
World Learning Inc.
YMCA of the USA
Youth for Understanding International Exchange

Associates
American Center for Students and Artists
Association of College Unions–International
Canadian Bureau for International Education
European Association for International Education
Fontainebleau Fine Arts and Music Schools Association
NAFSA: Association of International Educators
National Association for Equal Opportunity in Higher Education
United Negro College Fund

Index